# NUMERICAL SOLUTION OF

# INITIAL VALUE PROBLEMS

Prentice-Hall
Series in Automatic Computation
*George Forsythe, editor*

BAUMANN, FELICIANO, BAUER, AND SAMELSON, *Introduction to ALGOL*
CESCHINO AND KUNTZMANN, *Numerical Solution of Initial Value Problems*
DESMONDE, *Computers and Their Uses*
DESMONDE, *Real-Time Data Processing Systems: Introductory Concepts*
GOLDEN, *FORTRAN IV: Programming and Computing*
HULL, *Introduction to Computing*
MARTIN, *Programming Real-Time Computer Systems*
MOORE, *Interval Analysis*
SCHULTZ, *Digital Processing: A System Orientation*
SNYDER, *Chebyshev Methods in Numerical Approximation*
STROUD AND SECREST, *Gaussian Quadrature Formulas*
TRAUB, *Iterative Methods for the Solution of Equations*
VARGA, *Matrix Iterative Analysis*
WILKINSON, *Rounding Errors in Algebraic Processes*

PRENTICE-HALL INTERNATIONAL, INC., *London*
PRENTICE-HALL OF AUSTRALIA, PTY. LTD., *Sydney*
PRENTICE-HALL OF CANADA, LTD., *Toronto*
PRENTICE-HALL OF INDIA (PRIVATE), LTD., *New Delhi*
PRENTICE-HALL OF JAPAN, INC., *Tokyo*

# NUMERICAL SOLUTION OF
# INITIAL VALUE PROBLEMS

**F. CESCHINO**

*Civilian Ordnance Engineer*

**J. KUNTZMANN**

*Professor of the Faculty of Sciences, Grenoble*

Translated by

**D. BOYANOVITCH**

*Research Mathematician*
*Grumman Aircraft Engineering Company*

**PRENTICE-HALL, INC.**

ENGLEWOOD CLIFFS, N. J.

Current printing (last digit):

10  9  8  7  6  5  4  3  2  1


Library of Congress Catalog Card No. 66-17165


Printed in the United States of America
62733-C

# FOREWORD

In their preface the authors have indicated the scope of this work and its relations to the literature existing when their manuscript was completed. Let me supplement this by a brief comparison with outstanding monograph by Henrici [9]. Of comparable length and with similar chapter titles, the book of Henrici presents rather few particular methods for solving differential equations. Most of that book is devoted to analysis in depth of these few methods and of large general classes of methods. The numerical computations are generally chosen to illustrate such important special matters as the growth of round-off error.

The book of Ceschino and Kuntzmann, on the other hand, presents a large number of particular related methods of the classes considered, with less analysis of any one of them. There is more explicit attention to the practical considerations involved in choosing a particular method for automatic computation. There are more heuristic methods for approximating the errors in the numerical solution, and fewer precise error bounds. Moreover, the very large number of numerical examples make the nature of the methods transparent even to a reader with only a modest mathematical background. Thus generally more elementary and more practical, the present book serves to complement Henrici's excellent monograph.

I am therefore very happy that Prentice-Hall is bringing the book of Ceschino and Kuntzmann to the English-reading public in this translation by D. Boyanovitch. Acknowledgments are due to James Varah for a careful reading of the manuscript.

GEORGE E. FORSYTHE

*Computer Science Department*
*Stanford University*
*Stanford, California*

# PREFACE

The present book deals with the exposition of problems concerning the approximate numerical integration of initial value problems.

The whole theory is based on the approximate representation of derivatives and integrals by discrete expressions. We assume that this theory is known to the reader. In case of need, he can refer back to one of the previous books: Boole, Kuntzmann [4], Mineur, Richardson [1], Scarborough, Ziller.

The classical results of approximate integration of initial value problems are presented in most treatises on numerical analysis. Among others we cite: Alt; Bennett, Milne, and Bateman; Booth [2]; Buckingham; Grabbe, Ramo, and Wooldridge; Hartree [2]; Householder [1]; Kopal; Kunz; Levy and Baggott; Moulton; National Physical Laboratory; Salvàdori and Baron; von Sanden. These questions have been studied and developed in a detailed manner in Collatz [6] and Milne [6], which can be considered as the two classical works on this subject. Other works which have appeared on the subject since this manuscript was submitted are: Fox [5], Henrici [9].

Although we have collected an abundance of recent literature on this subject, we did not conceive this work as a compilation. We have tried to group the formulas and proposed methods around a central idea. We have also set up a terminology which was lacking in this field. Finally and above all, we have investigated a certain number of theoretical questions which, consequently, led us and some of our students to propose new integration formulas.

Naturally, these studies required several years, but they were completed at a time when these questions presented a renewed interest. As a matter of fact, the great speed of electronic computation could have led, as certain authors have been thinking for the last fifteen years, to nothing but very simple procedures, the theoretical point of view being relegated to secondary importance. But the increasing complexity and growing extent of these problems forced the calculators to construct more and more powerful methods and to study thoroughly in what way they can be used.

The principal tool in all our studies is Taylor's series. We neglected deliberately everything that could have led us away from it:
—the Monte Carlo method: see Bauer [2], Curtiss, Metropolis and Ulam, National Bureau of Standards, Todd[2];
—the recourse to function spaces: Altman;
—the stochastic evaluations: Blanc [1, 2], Blanc and Liniger;
—approximation by exponential sums: Brock and Murray [2, 3], Radok [1], or by means of other functions: Lanczos, Unger;
—Chaplygin's method: Artemov, Babkin [1, 2], Slugin, Voronovskaya, Vorobev, etc.
—methods which consist in utilizing another problem, for instance a boundary value problem: Fox [3], Fox and Mitchell.
So as not to get too far away from our principal subject, we have also disregarded:
—graphical methods: Gautschi [1], Ku, Quinlan, Slibar, Somerville, Inzinger, Simokawa, Franck;
—integration in the complex plane: Bocek, Mikeladze [5], Salzer [4];
—methods relating to equations which present peculiarities: Blanch, Chechik, Clenshaw, Cohn and Saltzberg, Gray and Schelkunoff, Grosswald, Grünsky, Neidhofer, Tihonov and Samarskii, Winn, Flügge, Pugachov [1, 2], Rabinovitch.[1]

In numerical calculation, perfect accord between theory and practice is rare. This is partly due to the imperfect practical realization of the infinitesimally small. Also, in conjunction with theoretical studies, a number of calculations have been carried out on electronic computors (IBM 650 and Gamma BULL) and desk calculators: the testing of methods or computations of problems in practice by various techniques. The outlines of those computations are contained in this book in the form of numerous examples based on a small number of equations (most of them very simple) which permit one to compare the advantages of different methods. These examples are intended to convince the reader of the realistic character of the proposed methods, and thus to invite him to venture and to use other methods, often even just other coefficients than those to which he is accustomed.

The authors express their gratitude to many persons of the "Service de Mathématiques Appliquées de la Faculté des Sciences de Grenoble" as well as of the "Service des Machines à calculer du Laboratoire central de l'Arme-

---

[1]This list, as well as those which one finds in the chapters of this book, does not claim to be exhaustive.

ment" who have, in one way or another, participated in the elaboration of this work. They also thank the publisher Dunod for the particular care they took with the printing of this book. Finally they would like to thank Professor John Carr III, whose invitation has allowed one of them to teach certain of the materials in this book at the University of North Carolina and to find the necessary calm for completing the preparation of this book.

F. CESCHINO

J. KUNTZMANN

# CONTENTS

# NOTATION

| | |
|---|---|
| $t$ | independent variable |
| $i, n$ | number of the step (placed as a subscript) |
| $t_0 = a$ | initial value of the variable |
| $h_i = t_i - t_{i-1}$ | length of the $i$th step |
| $h$ | length of the step if it is constant ($t_i = t_0 + ih$) |
| $(p)$ | order of the highest derivative |
| $(p - k)$ | order of the intermediary derivative. The first values are denoted by $'$, $''$ |

The differential system is written:

$$y^{(p)} = Y(y, y', \ldots, y^{(p-1)}, z, z', \ldots, z^{(p-1)}, \ldots, t),$$

$$z^{(p)} = Z(y, y', \ldots, y^{(p-1)}, z, z', \ldots, z^{(p-1)}, \ldots, t), \text{ etc.}$$

One can also write in the matrix form:

$$x^{(p)} = X(x, x', \ldots, x^{(p-1)}, t)$$

| | |
|---|---|
| $x$ | a column whose components are $y, z, \ldots$ |
| $X$ | a column whose components are $Y, Z, \ldots$ |

By convention, $x$ and $X$ will always denote columns.

| | |
|---|---|
| $y_0, z_0, \ldots$ | initial values of the unknown functions. For the derivatives one writes: |

$$y_0', z_0', \ldots, y_0^{(p-1)}, z_0^{(p-1)}, \ldots$$

| | |
|---|---|
| $x_0$ | the column of initial values. For the derivatives one writes: |

$$x_0', \ldots, x_0^{(p-1)}$$

| | |
|---|---|
| $y(t), z(t), \ldots$ | functions which constitute the exact solution of the initial value problem |

$x(t)$      exact column solution of the initial value problem

$Y(t), Z(t), \ldots$      values of the $p$th derivative along the exact solution

$X(t)$      columns of values of $x^{(p)}$ along the exact solution

$y_n, z_n$      approximate values at the abscissa $t_n$. For the derivatives one uses:

$$y'_n, z'_n, \ldots, y_n^{(p-1)}, z_n^{(p-1)}$$

$x_n$      column of approximate values at the abscissa $t_n$

$Y_n, Z_n$      values of $Y(y_n, y'_n, \ldots, y_n^{(p-1)}, \ldots, z_n^{(p-1)}, \ldots, t_n)$

$X_n$      column of values of $X(x_n, x'_n, \ldots, x_n^{(p-1)}, t_n)$

$Y_n(t), Z_n(t)$      solution of the differential system passing through the point $t_n, y_n, y'_n, \ldots, y_n^{(p-1)}, z_n, \ldots$

$X_n(t)$      column solution of the differential system passing through the point $t_n, x_n, x'_n, \ldots, x_n^{(p-1)}$

$[m]$      number of cycles of iterations (placed as a superscript). The first are denoted by *, **

$J_1$ (at times $J$)      Jacobian matrix of the system

$r$      rank of an approximate integration method

$\omega$      order of an approximate integration method

$A, B, C, \ldots,$
    $K, L, R$      letters denoting the coefficients of the various methods

$\alpha, \beta$      indices of location in the interior of a step

$\epsilon$      global error

$\tau$      local error (at one step or of quadrature)

$\nabla$      symbol of backward difference

$\Delta$      symbol of forward difference

$\delta$      symbol of central difference

# NUMERICAL SOLUTION OF

# INITIAL VALUE PROBLEMS

# 1 INTRODUCTION

## I INITIAL VALUE PROBLEMS

### 1.1 Notations relating to a first order differential equation.

We write a first order differential equation as

$$y' = Y(y, t),$$

where $t$ denotes the independent variable and $y$ the unknown function
One can, in place of $y$, use other letters such as $z$ or $u$.

### 1.2 Notations relating to a differential system in canonical form.

We write a differential system in canonical form as

$$y'_i = Y_i(y_1, y_2, \ldots, y_n, t), \qquad i = 1, \ldots, n,$$

where $t$ denotes the variable and $y_1, y_2, \ldots, y_n$ the unknown functions.

We recall that, in such a system, the only derivatives present are those of the first order. These derivatives are expressed explicitly in terms of the unknown functions and of $t$.

### 1.3 Other notations for a system in canonical form.

For systems of a little higher order, such as two or three, one frequently is interested in using a notation less cumbersome, such as

$$y' = Y(y, z, u, t),$$
$$z' = Z(y, z, u, t),$$
$$u' = U(y, z, u, t).$$

*Remark.* An equation of the first order can be considered as a system for one unknown function.

1

### 1.4 Condensed notation.

In theoretical studies, for systems in canonical form, we will use a condensed notation. With the notations of 1.3 applied to the columns

$$x(t) = \begin{Vmatrix} y(t) \\ z(t) \\ u(t) \end{Vmatrix} \quad \text{and} \quad X(x, t) = \begin{Vmatrix} Y(y, z, u, t) \\ Z(y, z, u, t) \\ U(y, z, u, t) \end{Vmatrix},$$

we can write the system in the obvious convention

$$x' = X(x, t).$$

This is exactly the same form as for a single equation.

### 1.5 Elimination of the independent variable.

Let us consider a new variable $\tau$ defined by

$$t = \tau.$$

We can write the system of 1.3 as

$$\begin{aligned} dy/d\tau &= Y(y, z, u, t), \\ dz/d\tau &= Z(y, z, u, t), \\ du/d\tau &= U(y, z, u, t), \\ dt/d\tau &= 1. \end{aligned}$$

Relative to the old system, this new system allows one additional unknown function $t$. The new independent variable $\tau$ does not enter into the second set. This transformation is of interest in the theoretical studies of numerical methods.

### 2. Initial value problems for a system in canonical form.

We call an *initial value problem* for a system in canonical form one which consists in determining for the equation or for the above system the solution defined for $t \in [a, b]$, where $b$ is finite or not, and which, in terms of the respective notations of 1.1, 1.2, 1.3, and 1.4, satisfies

$$y(a) = y_0, \qquad y_i(a) = y_{0i}, \qquad y(a) = y_0,$$
$$i = 1. \ldots, n, \qquad z(a) = z_0, \qquad x(a) = x_0.$$
$$u(a) = u_0,$$

### 3.1 Existence and uniqueness theorem for a first order equation.

Let $R$ be the rectangle

$$a \leqslant t \leqslant a + h,$$
$$y_0 - k \leqslant y \leqslant y_0 + k.$$

Let us suppose that in $R$, the function

$$Y(y, t)$$

is continuous relative to the variables and that, in addition, in $R$

$$Y'_y(y, t)$$

is bounded in absolute value.

In analysis, we show that, by means of these conditions, the problem posed in the preceding paragraph possesses a continuous and unique solution in $R$.

*Remark.* We do not assert that this solution is defined for $a \leqslant t \leqslant a + h$. Indeed, it can happen that the integral curve might just not touch the side $t = a + h$, but one of the sides $y = y_0 - k$, $y = y_0 + k$ (see Fig. 1-1).

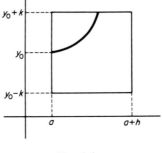

*Remark.* It would be possible to replace the condition of existence of $Y'_y$ with a less stringent condition. For this we refer to treatises on pure mathematics. It is clearly understood that we suppose the existence and continuity of all derivatives which we

**Fig. 1-1**

need. It is up to the reader to make the necessary modifications in those cases where this condition might not be satisfied.

### 3.2 Existence and uniqueness theorems for a system in canonical form.

Let us consider the case of three unknown functions and retain the notation of paragraph 1.3. Let $R$ be the cube:

$$a \leqslant t \leqslant a + h,$$
$$y_0 - k \leqslant y \leqslant y_0 + k,$$
$$z_0 - l \leqslant z \leqslant z_0 + l,$$
$$u_0 - m \leqslant u \leqslant u_0 + m.$$

Let us suppose that in $R$ the functions

$$Y(y, z, u, t), \qquad Z(y, z, u, t), \qquad U(y, z, u, t)$$

are continuous in all the variables and that, in addition, the partial derivatives

$$Y'_y \quad Y'_z \quad Y'_u$$
$$Z'_y \quad Z'_z \quad Z'_u$$
$$U'_y \quad U'_z \quad U'_u$$

are bounded in absolute value by a number $M$.

In analysis, one shows that the problem posed in paragraph 2 possesses in $R$ a unique solution. This solution is not necessarily defined in the whole interval. In effect, the integral curve might touch one of the lateral faces of the cube. It is possible to weaken the hypothesis of this theorem. We refer the reader who might be interested in this question to treatises on analysis.

### 4.1 Notations relating to a differential equation in resolved form.

For a differential equation in resolved form, we adopt an expression such as

$$y''' = Y(y, y', y'', t),$$

where $t$ denotes the independent variable and $y$ the unknown function. We recall that, in such an equation, the highest order derivative (here $y'''$) is explicitly expressed in terms of the function, the lower order derivatives, and the independent variable.

The most general expression of a differential equation in the resolved form is

$$y^{(p)} = Y(y, y', y'', \ldots, y^{(p-1)}, t).$$

### 4.2 Notations relative to a system in resolved form.

We write a system in resolved form as, for example,

$$
\begin{aligned}
y'' &= Y(y, y', z, u, u', u'', t), \\
z' &= Z(y, y', z, u, u', u'', t), \\
u''' &= U(y, y', z, u, u', u'', t),
\end{aligned}
\tag{1}
$$

where $t$ denotes the independent variable and $y, z, u$ the unknown functions.

We recall that in such a system the highest order derivatives are expressed explicitly in terms of the unknown functions, the lower order derivatives, and the independent variable.

The most general expression for such a system in resolved form is

$$
\begin{aligned}
y_j^{(p_j)} &= Y_j(\ldots, y_k, \ldots, y_k^{(p_k-1)}, \ldots, t), \\
\left.\begin{matrix} k \\ j \end{matrix}\right\} &= 1, \ldots, s,
\end{aligned}
\tag{2}
$$

where the numbers $p_1 \ldots, p_s$ are fixed in advance.

*Remarks.* (a) Each system in canonical form can be equally written in the resolved form. (b) An equation in the resolved form can be considered as a system written in the resolved form with a single unknown function.

### 4.3 The order of a system written in the resolved form.

We recall that one denotes by the *order* of a system the sum of orders of maximal derivatives of the various unknown functions. The system (1) of paragraph 4.2 is of the sixth order. We recall also that the order of the system is equal to the number of arbitrary constants appearing in the general integral.

*Remark.* For a system in canonical form, the order is equal to the number of unknown functions.

### 4.4 The elimination of the independent variable.

As in 1.5, it is possible to arrange that the independent variable does not enter explicitly in the system. For example, the system of 4.2 can be replaced by

$$d^2y/d\tau^2 = Y(y, y', z, u, u', u'', t),$$
$$dz/d\tau = Z(y, y', z, u, u', u'', t),$$
$$d^3u/d\tau^3 = U(y, y', z, u, u', u'', t),$$
$$dt/d\tau = 1.$$

*Remark.* This transformation as well as the one in 1.5 increases the order by one.

### 4.5 The equilibrated resolved form.

The resolved form which was just defined and of which an example was given in 4.2 suffers an asymmetry among the several variables whose orders of the maximal derivatives are not the same. One way to remedy this inconvenience is the following: Returning to system (1) of paragraph 4.2, let us set

$$y = v', \qquad z = w''.$$

We then have the system

$$v''' = Y(v', v'', w'', u, u', u'', t),$$
$$w''' = Z(v', v'', w'', u, u', u'', t),$$
$$u''' = U(v', v'', w'', u, u', u'', t),$$

which we can consider as being of the form

$$u''' = U(u, u', u'', v, v', v'', w, w', w'', t),$$
$$v''' = V(u, u', u'', v, v', v'', w, w', w'', t),$$
$$w''' = W(u, u', u'', v, v', v'', w, w', w'', t).$$

This is what we call an equilibrated resolved form. The use of this form will permit us to consider only systems where all the orders of the maximal derivatives are equal. For a system in the equilibrated resolved form we can use the columnar notation:

$$x''' = X(x, x', x'', t).$$

### 5. Transition from the resolved form to the canonical form.

Let us return to system (1) of 4.2. Setting

$$y' = v, \qquad u' = w, \qquad u'' = s,$$

we can write

$$
\begin{aligned}
y' &= v, \\
v' &= Y(y, v, z, u, w, s, t), \\
z' &= Z(y, v, z, u, w, s, t), \\
u' &= w, \\
w' &= s, \\
s' &= U(y, v, z, u, w, s, t).
\end{aligned}
$$

Notice that the order has not changed.

### 6. The initial value problem for a system in resolved form.

Let us return to system (1) of paragraph 4.2. We call the *initial value problem* the problem which consists of finding the solution defined for

$$t \in [a, b]$$

and satisfying

$$
\begin{aligned}
y(a) &= y_0, \qquad y'(a) = v_0, \\
z(a) &= z_0, \\
u(a) &= u_0, \qquad u'(a) = w_0, \qquad u''(a) = s_0.
\end{aligned}
$$

In other words, we fix the values for $t = a$ of the unknown functions and their derivatives up to, but not including, the maximal order.

### 7. Existence and uniqueness theorem for a system in the resolved form.

Let us take up again system (1) of paragraph 4.2. After the transformation of paragraph 5, we can state the following result: Let $R$ be the cube in the space of $x, u, y, z, v, w, t$ defined by

$$a \leqslant t \leqslant a + h,$$

$$y_0 - k \leqslant y \leqslant y_0 + k, \qquad u_0 - l \leqslant u \leqslant u_0 + l,$$

$$z_0 - m \leqslant z \leqslant z_0 + m, \qquad w_0 - n \leqslant w \leqslant w_0 + n,$$

$$v_0 - p \leqslant v \leqslant v_0 + p, \qquad s_0 - q \leqslant s \leqslant s_0 + q.$$

If, in this cube, the functions

$$Y(y, v, z, u, w, s, t), \qquad Z(y, v, z, u, w, s, t), \qquad U(y, v, z, u, w, s, t)$$

are continuous in all the variables and if the partial derivatives

$$Y'_y, \quad Y'_v, \quad Y'_z, \quad Y'_u, \quad Y'_w, \quad Y'_s,$$
$$Z'_y, \quad Z'_v, \quad Z'_z, \quad Z'_u, \quad Z'_w, \quad Z'_s,$$
$$U'_y, \quad U'_v, \quad U'_z, \quad U'_u, \quad U'_w, \quad U'_s$$

are bounded in absolute value, then the initial value problem possesses a unique solution. This solution does not necessarily exist in the whole interval

$$a \leqslant t \leqslant a + h.$$

### 8.1 Transition from the canonical form to any resolved form.

Let us consider the system in canonical form:

$$u' = U(u, y, z, t),$$
$$y' = Y(u, y, z, t),$$
$$z' = Z(u, y, z, t).$$

Differentiating the first relation, we obtain

$$u'' = f(u, y, z, u', y', z', t).$$

In general, we can eliminate $y$ and $y'$ between the four written relations. We obtain thus relations which we write

$$u'' = g(u, u', z, t),$$
$$z' = h(u, u', z, t),$$
$$y = k(u, u', z, t).$$

The first two formulas form a third order system in the resolved form. When this system has been integrated, the last relation yields $y$.

Upon differentiating again the first relation, we obtain in the general case

$$u''' = G\,(u, u', u'', t),$$
$$y = H\,(u, u', u'', t),$$
$$z = K\,(u, u', u'', t).$$

The first formula is a third order equation written in the resolved form. When this equation has been integrated, the other two relations give $y$ and $z$.

The preceding transformation carries one initial value problem into another initial value problem. Of little interest in pure analysis, it is in certain cases advantageous in approximate integration.

### 8.2 Discussion of the possibility of the transformation.

The transition from the canonical form to the resolved form may be:
—in certain exceptional cases impossible due to theoretical reasons. Such a system has a particular structure which facilitates its integration.

EXAMPLE

$$u' = U(u, t),$$
$$y' = Y(u, y, t).$$

The first equation is integrated alone; then the second one is integrated independently. It is impossible to regard $u$ as a single unknown function.

—rather frequently, not realizable in practice if one insists that the expressions used be elementary functions.

EXAMPLE

$$u' = e^u + y + \sin y,$$
$$y' = u^2 + y^2.$$

We obtain

$$u'' = e^u u' + (1 + \cos y)(u^2 + y^2).$$

It is impossible to write an elementary relation between $u, u', u''$, even one that is not resolved in $u''$.

### 9.1 System not written in the resolved form.

One system not written in the resolved form would be, for example, the following:

$$F (u, u', u'', y, y', z, z', z'', z''', t) = 0$$
$$G (u, u', u'', y, y', z, z', z'', z''', t) = 0 \qquad (1)$$
$$H (u, u', u'', y, y', z, z', z'', z''', t) = 0$$

A general notation for a system not in the resolved form would be, for example,

$$F_j(\ldots, y_i, \ldots, y_i^{(n_i)}, \ldots, t) = 0,$$
$$i, j = 1, 2, \ldots, p, \qquad (2)$$

where the numbers $n_1, \ldots, n_p$ are fixed in advance.

### 9.2 Explicit transition to the resolved form.

Resolving the system of these $p$ relations with respect to the highest order derivatives of the $p$ unknown functions, we obtain *in general*, one or several systems in the resolved form.

EXAMPLE

Let us consider the equation

$$y'^2 = 4y.$$

It decomposes into two equations written in the resolved form:

$$y' = +2\sqrt{y} \tag{1}$$
$$y' = -2\sqrt{y} \tag{2}$$

The first of these equations admits the following solutions:

$$y = 0,$$
$$y = (t - c)^2, \qquad t \geqslant c, \qquad c = \text{arbitrary constant.}$$

The second admits the solutions

$$y = 0,$$
$$y = (t - c)^2, \qquad t \leqslant c.$$

These integrals are represented in Fig. 1-2 in solid lines for (1), in dotted lines for (2).

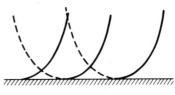

*Remarks.* (a) For $y = 0$, any $t$, there is no unique solution for (1) or (2). One can verify easily that the hypotheses of the existence and uniqueness theorem are not actually fulfilled.

**Fig. 1-2**

(b) The equation, not written in the resolved form

$$y'^2 = 4y,$$

does not possess, at any point, the existence and uniqueness property.

(c) There exist exceptional cases of systems which cannot be put into a resolved form by the above-mentioned procedure, for example:

$$y'' + z' = y,$$
$$y' = z.$$

If it is a question of a problem of physical origin, this circumstance discloses that this equation has been poorly formed.

### 9.3 Transition to the resolved form by differentiation.[1]

Let us return to system (1) of 9.1. There exists a second procedure for reducing this system to the resolved form. Let us set

$$u' = l, \qquad u'' = m,$$
$$y' = w,$$
$$z' = p, \qquad z'' = q, \qquad z''' = r.$$

Upon differentiating the three equations which form (1), we obtain the new system

[1]Abian and Brown [1, 2, 3], Weissinger [2].

$$\begin{cases} F'_u l + F'_l m + F'_m m' + F'_y w + F'_w w' + F'_z p + F'_p q + F'_q r \\ \qquad\qquad\qquad\qquad\qquad\quad + F'_r r' + F'_t = 0, \\ G'_u l + G'_l m + G'_m m' + G'_y w + G'_w w' + G'_z p + G'_p q + G'_q r \\ \qquad\qquad\qquad\qquad\qquad\quad + G'_r r' + G'_t = 0, \\ H'_u l + H'_l m + H'_m m' + H'_y w + H'_w w' + H'_z p + H'_p q + H'_q r \\ \qquad\qquad\qquad\qquad\qquad\quad + H'_r r' + H'_t = 0, \qquad (3) \\ u' = l, \\ l' = m, \\ y' = w, \\ z' = p, \\ p' = q, \\ q' = r. \end{cases}$$

We observe that, by this transformation, the order of the system has gone from 6 to 9.

The solution of system (3) with the initial condition satisfying

$$F\,(u, l, m, y, w, z, p, q, r, t) = 0,$$
$$G\,(u, l, m, y, w, z, p, q, r, t) = 0,$$
$$H\,(u, l, m, y, w, z, p, q, r, t) = 0,$$

is equivalent to that of system (1). We note again that

$$F\,(u, l, m, y, w, z, p, q, r, t) = C,$$
$$G\,(u, l, m, y, w, z, p, q, r, t) = C,$$
$$H\,(u, l, m, y, w, z, p, q, r, t) = C$$

are the first integrals of system (3).

### 9.4 Restriction to the resolved form.

In conclusion of what was said before and in particular to avoid difficulties which are entirely peculiar to approximate integration, we suppose, once and for all, that the systems under study are in the resolved form.

### 10. Examples of initial value problems in physics.[1]

A great number of physical and technical problems represent initial value problems. Let us cite, for example:

—the motion of a point or of a solid under the action of given forces.

[1]Here are some references where one will find such examples: Anderson and Johnson, Basforth and Adams, Cowell and Cromlin [1, 2], Dederick, Brouwer, Kjellberg, Muller, Sauer and Posch, Shane, Kelley and Reno, Valiron and Dodier, Lance and Rogers.

—the transient operation in mesh networks.

—the economic or biological problems relative to the evolution of a situation.

## II  METHODS OF APPROXIMATE SOLUTION

### 11.  Shortcomings of the exact methods of integration.

One knows that the equations and differential systems admitting an exact solution in terms of elementary functions are very limited in number. In the majority of cases, one has to resort to other procedures. In particular, one is obliged to do this when in the equation the known functions occur empirically and are given in the form of a table of numbers. Furthermore, even in the rare cases where there exists a formal solution, it can be far too complicated to be usable. This is shown by the following example:

$$y' = \frac{y-t}{y+t}, \qquad y(0) = 1,$$

whose solution is

$$t^2 + y^2 = \exp\left(\pi - 2 \arctan \frac{y}{t}\right).$$

In order to find a value of $y$ corresponding to a not too large value of $t$, one finds it more convenient to integrate the equation numerically than to utilize the formulas giving the exact solution.

The knowledge of a formal solution is, however, in all cases a source of valuable information on the behavior of the function and on the evaluation of errors in the approximate integration. Furthermore, it furnishes a means of verifying the calculations.

### 12.  Fundamental properties of the solution of an initial value problem.

The solution of an initial value problem possesses the following two important properties: One can determine the solution for

$$t_0 \leqslant t \leqslant t_1$$

without being obliged to determine it for $t > t_1$. The solution for $t > t_1$ depends only on the values for $t = t_1$. The methods of approximate solution will have to possess, as far as possible, these two properties.

### 13.1  The character of the methods of approximate solution.

These methods do not give the general integral but only a well-determined integral.

These methods can furnish, instead of the exact solution which we do not know or do not wish to write down, an approximate solution in the sense of numerical calculus. We thus understand that this solution is defined in a finite interval by a procedure actually executable and that we possess certain information on the error by which it is affected.

### 13.2 Relation with the existence theorems.

The fundamental ideas which serve as a base for demonstrating the existence theorems will lead us to the approximate integration methods.

We shall carry these ideas back to the following three:

—Cauchy-Lipschitz' polygonal line.
—Picard's iteration.
—Taylor's series.

We will proceed rapidly with studying these, referring for more details to special treatises of analyses, where one finds them shown with all desirable rigor, and we will interest ourselves mainly with the application of these ideas to the problem of approximate integration.

### 14.1 The Cauchy-Lipschitz polygonal line.

Let us set forth the Cauchy-Lipschitz method in the case of the equation

$$y' = Y(y, t), \qquad y(t_0) = y_0.$$

We divide the $t$ axis into the points

$$t_1, t_2, \ldots, t_n$$

close enough so that the differential quotient

$$\frac{y(t_{i+1}) - y(t_i)}{t_{i+1} - t_i}$$

differs only little from the derivative. We then consider the sequence of approximate values

$$t_i = t_0 + ih,$$
$$y_{i+1} = y_i + hY(y_i, t_i).$$

The existence and uniqueness theorem shows that, as $h$ tends to zero, the polygonal line defined by the points

$$t_i, y_i$$

tends toward a limit which is the only possible solution of the initial value problem.

In the exploitation of this idea, to obtain a really usable method of integration, we will have to use more elaborate approximations than the replacement of the derivative by the differential quotient. This will permit us an equal and even superior precision by increasing the length of the elementary interval.

In analyzing the intrinsic characteristics of these methods, we arrive at the following definition.

#### 14.2 Step methods.

We call a *step method* any method which determines an approximate value of the solution successively in each of the elementary intervals

$$(t_0, t_1), (t_1, t_2), \ldots, (t_{n-1}, t_n).$$

There can be two different cases: (a) Either the approximate solution is defined only for the discrete values $t_i$, (b) or else in addition it may be defined in different intervals $(t_i, t_{i+1})$. This family of methods consists of integration procedures which are most effective and most useful.

#### 14.3 Classification.

We will classify the step methods into two groups:

(a) *The single-step methods.* The approximate integration in $(t_i, t_{i+1})$ uses only the results obtained for $t_i$. One thus complies with the two fundamental properties of paragraph 12.

(b) *The multistep methods.* The approximate integration in $(t_i, t_{i+1})$ brings in the results obtained for

$$t_i, t_{i-1}, t_{i-2}, \ldots, t_{i-p},$$

the number $p$ being dependent on the utilized formulas. The second property of paragraph 12 is not complied with. These methods are the subject of Chapters 3, 4, 5, 6, 7, 8.

#### 15.1 Picard's iteration.

Picard's method consists of forming by iteration a sequence of functions

$$y_1(t), y_2(t), \ldots, y_r(t), \ldots$$

tending in the limit toward the solution in the whole interval under consideration (or at least in a partial interval of a larger length than the length of intervals utilized in the methods inspired by the Cauchy-Lipschitz idea).

As a matter of fact, Picard's method requires a succession of quadratures which, in the exact form, are possible only in exceptional cases; outside of these cases it is better to use approximate quadrature formulas. The amount of calculation to be performed is, therefore, much greater than that required for the same precision by the step methods.

#### 15.2 Global methods.

If we try to derive the philosophy of Picard's method, we see that it consists of working directly in the whole interval $(a, b)$ or at least in a considerable part of the latter. We call the *global methods* the methods possessing this characteristic. They can, moreover, stand on different principles. We will briefly explain these methods in Chapter 10. Their interest will probably be mainly theoretical.

### 16.1  The use of Taylor's series.

The method of Taylor's series consists of developing the solution in an entire series, if possible in the whole interval under consideration. In order to come to an existence theorem, it is necessary to make hypotheses about analyticity. Incidentally, the solution thus found will converge, in general, only in the interior of a well-defined circle. Rather frequently, it will define only the solution in a partial interval. To pass to a computational method, it is necessary to replace the series (infinite but not usable) by a limited expansion determined by a certain order.

The method thus comprised is a global method. In effect, this procedure is very rarely usable because the calculation of the coefficients of the expansion (that is to say, of the successive derivatives at the starting point) becomes inextricable. However, here is an example.

Let the equation be

$$y' = y, \quad \text{with} \quad y(0) = 1.$$

we have

$$y^{(n)}(0) = y^{(n-1)}(0) = \ldots = y(0) = 1,$$

whence the series:

$$y(t) = 1 + \frac{t}{1!} + \frac{t^2}{2!} + \cdots + \frac{t^n}{n!} + \cdots.$$

We note that, in this case, the problem refers to the summation of a series, a subject which we will not study here.

In the same way, we would treat equations such as

$$y' = ty, \quad y'' = ty, \quad \text{etc.}$$

### 16.2  Another use of Taylor's series.

Another way of utilizing Taylor's series consists of dividing the interval of integration into partial intervals in each of which one takes only a small number of terms. Then one falls back on the principle of the single-step methods. Incidentally, the Taylor's series plays an important part in the theory of approximate integration methods, in the computation of errors, and the comparison of formulas.

### 17.  Composite methods.

These are methods which require several distinct principles. For example, one would integrate by a step method and then improve by an iteration over the whole interval of integration or over a partial interval. One obtains thus methods which eventually will be very powerful, but the use of which is very cumbersome.

## III  GENERAL CONSIDERATION OF NUMERICAL METHODS

### 18.1  Errors[1]

By *error*, we will designate the difference:

approximate value — exact value

This difference can arise:

—from the replacement of the exact integration by an approximate integration (truncation error).

—from an error in the data of the problem (coefficients, initial values) (data error or systematic error); we will hardly speak of this kind of errors.

—from round-off error in the computations (errors of computation).

The truncation error interests us both by its generation and by its effect on the result. On the other hand, the other errors interest us only by their effects on the result, their generation having nothing to do with the approximate integration of the differential equations.

### 18.2  The different problems of errors.

We will distinguish several problems relative to the evaluation of the error:

—one supposes as known the approximate values and the exact values; here it is no longer a problem of error. This case is hence without interest.

—one does not know either the approximate values or the exact values. This problem is the problem of the a priori error. The practice of computation would be much simplified if it were possible to solve such a problem. Unfortunately, one cannot say so at all in general.

—one knows the approximate values but not the exact values. The problem of determination of the error, in this case, will be called the *principal problem*.

—one knows the exact values but not the approximate values. The problem of determination of the error, in this case, will be called the *secondary problem*.

The principal problem is the one which is encountered by the numerical analyst. The secondary problem presents a theoretical interest, for example, to compare the different methods of numerical analysis.

### 18.3  The linearized theory of errors.

Very often, when the errors are small and little sensitive to a small variation in the data, and when one is content to evaluate the principal part

---

[1]We distinguish clearly between the *errors* inherent to any approximate calculation and reproducible and the *mistakes* resulting from incorrect use of operation rules or of the apparatus. The mistakes have to be disclosed by tests; we will not deal with this problem here.

of the error, one can present a simplified theory, called the linearized theory
of errors.

### 19.1  The amount of computation; horners

The laborious part in the approximate integration of a more complicated
system will be the computation of the quantities

$$Y_i(\ldots y_j^{(k)} \ldots).$$

Adopting a name due to Ostrowski, we call a *horner* the evaluation of a set
of these quantities. The number of horners necessary to effect a certain
approximate integration will serve as a measure of the amount of computation of a method.

### 19.2  Possibilities of verification and evaluation of errors.

Verification possibilities and bases for the evaluation of an error are
naturally interesting characteristics for a method. We shall point them out
when the occasion arises.

### 19.3  The use of the computation material.

The literature relative to the use of calculating machines for integrating
differential initial value problems is relatively rich. For the programmed
machines, one can consult, for example: Alt, Anderson, Anderson, and
Johnson; Anderson, Ball, and Voss; Bohan, Brock, and Murray [1]; Edelman, Feinstein, and Schwarzschild; Froberg, Gorn, Grandwell, Graves,
Hellermann, Herget [1, 2], Kjelberg, Lotkin [3], Murray, National Physical
Laboratory, Ralston and Wilf, Sabliet, Sneider, Womersley.

On other subjects consult: Bruck, Carter, and Sadler; Collatz [1], Hausmann and Schwarzschild, Lindberger, Marchant [1, 2, 3, 4], Nowakowski,
Wilkes [1].

When one is working with an electronic computer, another important
consideration is the number of memory units necessary for either the numbers or the program. This consideration plays an essential part with machines
whose internal memory—or, at least, a rapidly accessible internal memory—
has only a limited capacity.

### Problem

Prove the following: Suppose that for the differential equation $y' = f(x, y)$
two functions $U_0(x)$ and $u_0(x)$ have been found such that
  (a)  $U_0(x)$ and $u_0(x)$ are defined in the interval $x_0 \leqslant x \leqslant x_0 + a$.
  (b)  $U_0(x_0) = u_0(x_0) = y_0$.
  (c)  $U_0'(x) - f(x, U_0(x)) > 0$, $u_0'(x) - f(x, u_0(x)) < 0$

for $x_0 \leqslant x \leqslant x_0 + a$.

If, in the domain defined by

$$x_0 \leqslant x \leqslant x_0 + a, \qquad u_0(x) \leqslant y \leqslant U_0(x),$$

$f(x, y)$ is continuous and a monotonic increasing function of $y$ for every fixed $x$, then the sequence formed from $U_0(x)$ by means of the recurrence formula

$$U_n = y_0 + \int_{x_0}^{x} f(x, U_{n-1}) dx$$

is monotonically decreasing and converges to the solution of $y' = f(x, y)$ satisfying the initial condition $y(x_0) = y_0$.

Analogously, the sequence formed from $u_0(x)$ by means of the recurrence formula

$$u_n = y_0 + \int_{x_0}^{x} f(x, u_{n-1}) dx$$

is monotonically increasing and converges to the same solution.

# PART I

# THE SINGLE-STEP METHODS

# 2

## GENERALITIES ON THE SINGLE-STEP METHODS EULER'S METHOD—TAYLOR'S SERIES

### I GENERALITIES

In all that follows we will use the equilibrated resolved form in the condensed form

$$x^{(p)} = X(x, x' \ldots, x^{(p-1)}, t).$$

The independent variable may or may not be present.

#### 1. The step of integration.

The approximate solution will be determined for the successive values of

$$a = t_0, t_1, \ldots, t_n.$$

We will set

$$h_{i+1} = t_{i+1} - t_i.$$

$h_{i+1}$ is the length of the $(i + 1)$st step; very often, $h_{i+1}$ will be constant. We will then omit the index. In this case, we will have

$$t_i = t_0 + hi.$$

#### 2.1 Notations relative to the error.

By $x^{(p-k)}(t_i)$ we will designate the column of the exact values of the derivative of order $p - k$, and by $x_i^{(p-k)}$ the column of the corresponding approximate values.

The errors at the abscissa $\{t_i\}$ are given by the columns

$$\mathcal{E}_i^{(p-k)} = x_i^{(p-k)} - x^{(p-k)}(t_i), \qquad k = 0, \ldots, p - 1.$$

## 2.2 Error at one step

Let $x_i(t)$ be the solution of the differential system passing through the point

$$t_i, x_i, x_i', \ldots, x_i^{(p-1)}.$$

If the next step were carried out without error, we would determine

$$x_i^{(p-k)}(t_{i+1}).$$

Actually we commit:

—truncation error, resulting from the use of an approximate integration method.

—a round-off error because of the loss of digits in the various arithmetic operations. In reality, we determine

$$x_{i+1}^{(p-k)}.$$

We call the *error at one step* the totality of the columns

$$\tau_{i+1}^{(p-k)} = x_{i+1}^{(p-k)} - x_i^{(p-k)}(t_{i+1}).$$

We can distinguish:

—the truncation error at one step.
—the round-off error at one step.

## 2.3 Principles common to most single-step methods.

One considers the step $h_{i+1} = t_{i+1} - t_i$ as infinitesimally small, and one strives to find for $x_{i+1}^{(p-k)}$, which is assumed to be calculated without any round-off error, such expressions that the error columns of the method at one step $\tau_{i+1}^{(p-k)}$ are infinitesimally small in $h_{i+1}$ of an order as high as possible.

## 2.4 Order of a single-step method.

If

$$\tau_{i+1}^{(p-1)}, \tau_{i+1}^{(p-2)}, \ldots, \tau_{i+1}$$

are infinitesimally small in

$$h_{i+1}^{\omega_1+1}, h_{i+1}^{\omega_2+1}, \ldots, h_{i+1}^{\omega_p+1},$$

respectively, one says that the method is of the order

$$\omega = (\omega_1, \omega_2, \ldots, \omega_p).$$

## 3. Rule of the preservation of orders.

If one studies the error not after one step but after 2, 3, ..., n steps (n being fixed) (for simplicity, we will assume that the steps are equal), one finds that the error is a rather complicated combination of errors over the several steps. It seems interesting to pose the condition that the error after $n$ steps ($n$ fixed) be an infinitesimal in $h$ of the same order as the error over one step. This rule will be called *the rule of preservation of orders.*

*Remark.* It would be erroneous to believe that the error at a fixed abscissa is an infinitesimal of the same order as those of the above-mentioned studies. It is quite evident that to attain a fixed abscissa, a number of steps are necessary, which increase indefinitely as $1/h$ when $h$ tends to zero.

## II  EULER'S METHOD[1]

*Euler's method,* also called the method of the tangent, is a single-step method.[2] We are going to apply it successively to the case of a first order equation and to the case of an equation of order $p$, or more generally to a system in resolved form.

### 4.1  Equation of the first order.

Let the problem be

$$y' = Y(y, t), \qquad y(t_0) = y_0.$$

We set

$$y_{i+1} = y_i + hY_i,$$

supposing, to shorten the notation, that $h = t_{i+1} - t_i$ is constant.

The preceding formula consists of starting from the point $(t_i, y_i)$ and then of moving along the tangent to the integral curve passing through this point, to the point with abscissa $t_{i+1}$ (see Fig 2-1).

We can, by choice, say that the method gives the isolated successive points, or a function formed by portions of linear functions:

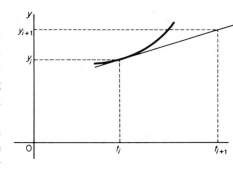

**Fig. 2-1**

$$\eta_i(t) = y_i + (t - t_i)Y_i, \qquad t_i \leqslant t \leqslant t_{i+1}.$$

### 4.2  Example.

$$y' = y - 1.5\,e^{-0.5t}, \qquad y(0) = 1.$$

[1]See Euler.
[2]Historically, this is the first method of approximate integration (1786).

| $t$ | $h = 0.2$ | $h = 0.1$ | $h = 0.05*$ | $y$ exact |
|---|---|---|---|---|
| 0 | 1 | 1 | 1 | 1 |
| 0.1 | | 0.95 | 0.950,60 | 0.951,23 |
| 0.2 | 0.9 | 0.902,32 | 0.903,55 | 0.904,84 |
| 0.3 | | 0.856,82 | 0.858,72 | 0.860,71 |
| 0.4 | 0.808,55 | 0.813,40 | 0.816,00 | 0.818,73 |
| 1.0 | 0.575,69 | 0.590,11 | 0.598,04 | 0.606,53 |
| 2.0 | 0.272,43 | 0.315,32 | 0.340,20 | 0.367,88 |
| 3.0 | −0.025,72 | 0.080,77 | 0.146,55 | 0.223,13 |

*One has noted a result for two.

We observe that the results are not very good, especially toward the end of the calculation, and that they improve as the step decreases.

### 5.1  Truncation error at one step. Theoretical evaluation.

The truncation error in one step is, by virtue of Taylor's formula,

$$y_{i+1} - y_i(t_{i+1}) = \frac{-h^2}{2} y''(\xi),$$

with $t_i \leqslant \xi \leqslant t_{i+1}$. The method is hence of the first order.

### 5.2  Truncation error at one step. Practical evaluation.

One can write

$$y'' = Y'_y Y + Y'_t.$$

If one admits that $Y'_y$ and $Y'_t$ each count one horner, the evaluation of the error at one step counts two horners, i.e., twice as much as the calculation itself, which is prohibitive. One can, fortunately, give for

$$y''(\xi)$$

an expression which uses only values already computed. As a matter of fact,

$$Y_{i+1} = Y(y_{i+1}, t_{i+1}) = Y(y_i + hY_i, t_i + h) = Y_i + hy''_i + \cdots$$

Consequently,

$$\tfrac{1}{2}(Y_{i+1} - Y_i) \approx \tfrac{1}{2} hy'',$$

from which the approximate expression for the truncation error at one step is obtained:

$$\frac{h}{2}(Y_i - Y_{i+1}).$$

**5.3 Example.**

Let us take up again the example of 4.2. We find for $h = 0.2$:

| $t_i$ | Calculated error | Actual error |
|---|---|---|
| 0.2 | −0.004,27 | −0.004,84 |
| 0.4 | −0.003,77 | −0.004,27 |
| 0.6 | −0.003,29 | −0.003,74 |
| 0.8 | −0.002,84 | −0.003,24 |
| 1.0 | −0.002,40 | −0.002,75 |
| 2.0 | −0.000,18 | −0.000,30 |
| 3.0 | +0.003,07 | +0.003,22 |

In order to estimate the quality of this approximation, we have deter-mined

$$\eta = \frac{\sum |\text{actual error} - \text{calculated error}|}{\sum |\text{actual error}|} \approx 11\%.$$

*Remark* 1. The evaluation of the error over an interval and no longer over one step will be shown in Chapters 9 and 10.

*Remark* 2. The round-off error in this case is negligible compared to the truncation error.

**6.1 Systems in canonical form.**

We will give the method, which is general, for the system:

$$u' = U(u, y, t), \qquad u(t_0) = u_0,$$
$$y' = Y(u, y, t), \qquad y(t_0) = y_0.$$

We will call *Euler's method* the following integration procedure:

$$u_{i+1} = u_i + hU_i,$$
$$y_{i+1} = y_i + hY_i.$$

The method consists of starting from the point $(t_i, u_i, y_i)$ and then moving along the tangent to the integral curve passing through this point, to the point with abscissa $t_{i+1}$.

**6.2 Example.**

$$y' = z, \qquad z' = u, \qquad u' = v, \qquad v' = y,$$
$$y(0) = z(0) = u(0) = v(0) = 1, \qquad h = 0.1.$$

We find

| $t$ | $y = z = u = v$ | Exact solution |
|---|---|---|
| 0 | 1 | 1 |
| 0.1 | 1.1 | 1.1052 |
| 0.2 | 1.21 | 1.2214 |
| 0.3 | 1.331 | 1.3499 |
| 0.4 | 1.4641 | 1.4918 |
| 0.5 | 1.6105 | 1.6487 |
| 1.0 | 2.5937 | 2.7183 |

The considerations of paragraphs 5.1 and 5.2 carry over without modification to systems in canonical form. Let us remark only that, if we call a horner the evaluation of a pair of functions, such as $Y$ and $Z$, the calculation of the second derivative counts three horners in the case of two unknown functions.

As a matter of fact,

$$y'' = Y'_y Y + Y'_z Z + Y'_t,$$
$$z'' = Z'_y Y + Z'_z Z + Z'_t.$$

### 7.1 Euler's method for any system in resolved form.

We will demonstrate Euler's method on the system:

$$u' = U(u, y, y', t), \qquad u(t_0) = u_0, \qquad y(t_0) = y_0, \qquad y'(t_0) = y'_0,$$
$$y'' = Y(u, y, y', t).$$

We will call Euler's method the following integration procedure:

$$u_{i+1} = u_i + hU_i,$$

$$y_{i+1} = y_i + hy'_i + \frac{h^2}{2} Y_i,$$

$$y'_{i+1} = y'_i + h Y_i.$$

### 7.2 Example.

$$y'' = y, \qquad y(0) = y'(0) = 1, \qquad h = 0.1$$

| $t$ | $y'_i$ | $y_i$ | $y = y' = e^t$ |
|---|---|---|---|
| 0 | 1 | 1 | 1 |
| 0.1 | 1.1 | 1.105 | 1.1052 |
| 0.2 | 1.2105 | 1.2205 | 1.2214 |
| 0.3 | 1.3226 | 1.3477 | 1.3498 |
| 0.4 | 1.4673 | 1.4877 | 1.4918 |
| 0.5 | 1.6161 | 1.6418 | 1.6487 |
| 1.0 | 2.6251 | 2.6823 | 2.7183 |

## 8. Truncation error at one step.

Let us return to the notations of 7.1. The truncation error at one step is obviously given for $u$ by

$$\frac{-h^2}{2} u''(\eta), \qquad t_i < \eta < t_{i+1};$$

for $y$ by

$$\frac{-h^3}{6} y'''(\eta);$$

for $y'$ by

$$\frac{-h^2}{2} y'''(\eta);$$

hence this is a method of order $(1, 2)$.

Likewise, as in the case of an equation of the first order, one can replace approximately the above-mentioned expressions by

$$\frac{h}{2} (U_i - U_{i+1}),$$

$$\frac{h^2}{6} (Y_i - Y_{i+1}),$$

$$\frac{h}{2} (Y_i - Y_{i+1}),$$

which gives a practical evaluation of the truncation error at one step.

### 9. Remarks on the preceding formulas.

(a) These formulas cause an asymmetry, the development of $y$ being pushed further than that of $u$ and $y'$. We will show in 11.2 that they satisfy the rule of the preservation of orders.

(b) A transition to the equilibrated resolved form still permits the use of Euler's method. Indeed, if we write in the system of 7.1

$$v' = u,$$

$$\begin{cases} v'' = X(v', y, y', t), \\ y'' = Y(v', y, y', t) \end{cases}$$

Euler's method consists of writing

$$v_{i+1} = v_i + hu_i + \frac{h^2}{2} U_i,$$

$$\begin{cases} u_{i+1} = u_i + hU_i, \\ y_{i+1} = y_i + hy'_i + \frac{h^2}{2} Y_i, \\ y'_{i+1} = y'_i + hY_i. \end{cases}$$

The first formula can be neglected, since $v$ actually does not interest us.

### 10. Is it necessary to pass to the canonical form?[1]

Let us take up the system of 7.1. One can associate it with the canonical form

[1]Ceschino-Kuntzmann [2].

$$\begin{cases} u'^* = U^*(u^*, y^*, v^*, t), \\ y'^* = v^*, \\ v'^* = Y^*(u^*, y^*, v^*, t). \end{cases}$$

Euler's formula for this system is written as

$$u_{i+1}^* = u_i^* + hU_i^*,$$

$$y_{i+1}^* = y_i^* + hv_i^*,$$

$$v_{i+1}^* = v_i^* + hY_i^*.$$

We note immediately that these two formulas, in the case of the canonical form, differ solely by the absence of the term

$$\frac{h^2}{2} Y_i^* \quad \text{in} \quad y_{i+1}^*$$

The principal part of the error over one step of $y$ in this method is hence

$$\frac{h}{2} (-v_{i+1}^* + v_i^*) = -\frac{h^2}{2} Y_i^*.$$

In other words, the expression $y_{i+1}$ is unquestionably more accurate than $y_{i+1}^*$.

This is just what one notes when comparing the examples of 6.2 and 7.2 (6.2 gives the numerical values corresponding to the canonical form of 7.2).

One might be tempted to believe that this is always the case. A simple example will disillusion us. Let us consider the problem:

$$y'' = y, \quad y(0) = -y'(0) = 2.7183, \quad h = 0.1.$$

|     | Second order equation | | Canonical form | |
| --- | --- | --- | --- | --- |
| $t$ | $-y_i$ | $y_i$ | $y_i^* = -y_i'^*$ | $y$ exact |
| 0   | 2.7183 | 2.7183 | 2.7183 | 2.7183 |
| 0.1 | 2.4465 | 2.4601 | 2.4465 | 2.4596 |
| 0.2 | 2.2005 | 2.2278 | 2.2019 | 2.2255 |
| 0.3 | 1.9777 | 2.0189 | 1.9817 | 2.0137 |
| 0.4 | 1.7758 | 1.8312 | 1.7835 | 1.8221 |
| 0.5 | 1.5927 | 1.6627 | 1.6052 | 1.6487 |
| 1.0 | 0.8970 | 1.0532 | 0.9479 | 1.0000 |
| 1.5 | 0.4450 | 0.7247 | 0.5597 | 0.6065 |
| 2.0 | 0.1166 | 0.5873 | 0.3305 | 0.3679 |

One ascertains that $y_i$ is at first better than $y_i^*$, but as $y_i'$ is much worse than $y_i'^*$, $y_i$ eventually also becomes much worse than $y_i^*$.

This shows the unreliability of certain reasonings based on orders of infinitesimals. Without a doubt, after an infinitely small step (or even after a fixed number of steps), the formula of 7.1 gives better results than that of 8.1. On the other hand, one cannot assert anything at the abscissa $t_0 + l$, because the number of steps necessary to attain this abscissa increases indefinitely, when $h$ tends towards zero.

We will take up this question in the chapter devoted to the propagation of errors.

### 11.1 Variants of Euler's method.

The comparison of the formulas found in the case for a general system and in the case of a system in canonical form suggests the following most general variant. Let us consider the system

$$y^{(p)} = Y(y, y', \ldots, y^{(p-1)}, z, \ldots, z^{(q-1)}, t),$$
$$z^{(q)} = Z(y, y', \ldots, y^{(p-1)}, z, \ldots, z^{(q-1)}, t).$$

We write the successive approximation formulas

$$y_{i+1} = y_i + hy_i + \cdots + \frac{h^a}{a!} y_i^{(a)},$$

$$y'_{i+1} = y'_i + hy''_i + \cdots + \frac{h_1^a}{a_1!} y_i^{(a_1+1)},$$

$$\vdots$$

$$y_{i+1}^{(p-1)} = y_i^{(p-1)} + hY_i,$$

$$z_{i+1} = z_i + hz'_i + \cdots + \frac{h^\beta}{\beta!} z_i^{(\beta)},$$

$$z'_{i+1} = z'_i + hz''_i + \cdots + \frac{h^{\beta_1}}{\beta_1!} z_i^{(\beta_1+1)},$$

$$\vdots$$

$$z_{i+1}^{(q-1)} = z_i^{(q-1)} + hZ_i$$

with

$$\alpha, \alpha_1 + 1, \ldots \leqslant p, \qquad \beta, \beta_1 + 1, \ldots \leqslant q.$$

When the upper bound $p$ (or $q$) is attained, the corresponding derivative is obviously to be replaced by

$$Y(y_i, y'_i, \ldots, y_i^{(p-1)}, z_i, \ldots, z^{(q-1)}, t_i) \qquad \text{(or } Z\text{)}$$

Euler's method for the system itself consists of taking

$$\alpha = \alpha_1 + 1 = \alpha_2 + 2 = \cdots = p,$$
$$\beta = \beta_1 + 1 = \beta_2 + 2 = \cdots = q.$$

Euler's method for the system in canonical form consists of taking

$$\alpha = \alpha_1 = \cdots = 1,$$
$$\beta = \beta_1 = \cdots = 1.$$

### 11.2  Preservation of orders.

Let us examine which conditions the rule of preservation of orders involves.

Let us consider the first integration step for the above-mentioned system. The orders, in which the different quantities are exact, are the following:

| $y_1$ | $y_1'$ | $y_1^{(p-1)}$ | $z_1$ | $z_1'$ | $z_1^{(q-1)}$ | $Y_1$ | $Z_1$ |
|-------|--------|---------------|-------|--------|---------------|-------|-------|
| $\alpha$ | $\alpha_1$ | 1 | $\beta$ | $\beta_1$ | 1 | 1 | |

After the second step, we find the following orders:

$$y_2 \qquad \text{Min } (\alpha, \alpha_1 + 1, \ldots),$$
$$y_2' \qquad \text{Min } (\alpha_1, \alpha_2 + 1 \ldots),$$
$$y_2^{(p-1)} \qquad \text{Min } (\alpha_{p-1}, 2),$$
$$z_2 \qquad \text{Min } (\beta, \beta_1 + 1, \ldots),$$
$$z_2' \qquad \text{Min } (\beta_1, \beta_2 + 1, \ldots),$$
$$z_2^{(q-1)} \qquad \text{Min } (\beta_{q-1}, 2).$$

The rule of preservation of orders requires that these orders be at least those of analogous quantities, relative to the first step. This brings about

$$\alpha \leqslant \alpha_1 + 1 \leqslant \alpha_2 + 2 \ldots \leqslant p,$$
$$\beta \leqslant \beta_1 + 1 \leqslant \beta_2 + 2 \ldots \leqslant q.$$

We will accept only the formulas which satisfy these conditions. It is easy to verify that Euler's formulas for a system and those for its canonical form satisfy these conditions.

Here is another example of the formula satisfying these conditions. It is relative to the fourth order equation:

$$y'''' = Y(y, y', y'', y''', t),$$

$$y_{i+1} = y_i + hy_i', \qquad y_{i+1}' = y_i' + hy_i'',$$

$$y_{i+1}'' = y_i'' + hy_i''' + \frac{h^2}{2} Y_i, \qquad y_{i+1}''' = y_i''' + hY_i.$$

### III  TAYLOR'S SERIES

We have already spoken about the very unusual use of the Taylor's series method as a global method. Here we will show its use as a step method.

### 12.1  Case of an equation of the first order.

Let the equation be

$$y' = Y(y, t).$$

We pass from point $i$ to point $i + 1$ by means of the formula

$$y_{i+1} = y_i + hy_i' + \frac{h^2}{2} y_i'' + \cdots + \frac{h^r}{r!} y_i^{(r)},$$

which necessitates the evaluation of $r$ successive derivatives at point $i$. We will study this evaluation in section IV.

It is obviously a question of:

—a single-step method.

—a generalization of Euler's method.

### 12.2 Example.

$$y' = -2ty^2, \qquad y(0) = 1, \qquad h = 0.2$$

$$y_{i+1} = y_i + hy_i' + \frac{h^2}{2} y_i''$$

| $t$ | $y_i$ | $y$ exact |
|-----|-------|-----------|
| 0   | 1        | 1         |
| 0.2 | 0.96     | 0.961,54  |
| 0.4 | 0.855,07 | 0.862,07  |
| 0.6 | 0.724,85 | 0.735,29  |
| 0.8 | 0.599,67 | 0.609,76  |
| 1   | 0.492,29 | 0.500,00  |
| 2   | 0.199,91 | 0.200,00  |

### 13. Case of any system in resolved form.

Let the system be

$$u' = U(u, y, y', t),$$
$$y'' = Y(u, y, y', t).$$

We will use the formulas

$$u_{i+1} = u_i + hU_i + \cdots + \frac{h^r}{r!} u_i^{(r)},$$

$$y_{i+1} = y_i + hy_i' + \cdots + \frac{h^{r+1}}{(r+1)!} y_i^{(r+1)},$$

$$y_{i+1}' = y_i' + hY_i + \cdots + \frac{h^r}{r!} y_i^{(r+1)}.$$

## IV  EVALUATION OF SUCCESSIVE DERIVATIVES

### 14. Derivation of intermediary expressions.

We will treat immediately the case of a system of any order. We shall then give the formulas relative to a certain number of particular cases. We obtain a larger degree of symmetry in the formulas by reverting to the case where the independent variable does not occur explicitly. It is not a restriction of generality if we suppose the system in the equilibrated resolved form written in condensed notation:

$$x^{(p)} = X(x^{(p-1)}, x^{(p-2)}, \ldots, x).^1$$

We set

$$x^{(p-1)}(t) = u(t) + u^*(t), \qquad x^{(p-2)}(t) = v(t) + v^*(t), \text{ etc.,}$$

with

$$u(t) = x^{(p-1)}(0) + tx^{(p)}(0),$$

$$v(t) = x^{(p-2)}(0) + tx^{(p-1)}(0) + \frac{t^2}{2!} x^{(p)}(0),$$

$$u^*(t) = \frac{t^2}{2!} x^{(p+1)}(0) + \frac{t^3}{3!} x^{(p+2)}(0) + \cdots,$$

$$v^*(t) = \frac{t^3}{3!} x^{(p+1)}(0) + \frac{t^4}{4!} x^{(p+2)}(0) + \cdots.$$

The developments of $u^*(t)$, $v^*(t)$ are in reality limited developments which we will stop when the necessary order has been attained. One will note that the gap between $u$ and $u^*$, $v$ and $v^*$ is exactly at the term $x^{(p)}(0)$. Let us consider

$$X(u + \bar{u}, v + \bar{v}, \ldots) \tag{1}$$

where $\bar{u}$, $\bar{v}$ denote the arbitrary but infinitely small quantities in $t$ of the same order as $u^*$, $v^*$, .... We are going to write a development of (1) in powers of

$$\bar{u}, \bar{v}, \ldots.$$

We have

$$X(u, v, \ldots) + X_u \bar{u} + X_v \bar{v} + \cdots + \frac{1}{2!} X_{uu} \bar{u}\bar{u} + X_{uv} \bar{u}\bar{v} + \cdots.$$

$X(u, v, \ldots)$ is a column function of $t$ which we shall develop following Taylor's formula:

$$X(u, v, w, \ldots) = X_0 + tC_1 + \frac{t^2}{2!} C_2 + \frac{t^3}{3!} C_3 + \cdots.$$

$X_u$, $X_v$, ... are quantities with two indices which one can write in matrix form (jacobian matrices). The $\bar{u}$, $\bar{v}$, as well as the products $X_u \bar{u}$, are columns. We write

$$X_u = J_1 + tK_1 + \frac{t^2}{2!} L_1 + \frac{t^3}{3!} M_1 + \cdots,$$

$$X_v = J_2 + tK_2 + \frac{t^2}{2!} L_2 + \cdots.$$

---

[1]In this whole section, we will arrange the derivatives of $x$ in an order opposite to the customary usage.

The $X_{u,\,u}$ are quantities with three indices. $X_{u,\,u}\bar{u}\bar{u}$ represent the condensed product of this quantity with three indices by the two quantities with one index of $\bar{u}$, $\bar{u}$; this is, therefore, a quantity with one index. We write

$$X_{u,\,u} = R_{u,\,u} + t S_{u,\,u} + \cdots ,$$
$$X_{u,\,v} = R_{u,\,v} + t S_{u,\,v} + \cdots .$$

To obtain expressions for the successive derivatives of $x(t)$ we are going to write the development in powers of $t$ of

$$X(u + u^*, v + v^*, \ldots)$$

Practically, we are going to stop with terms in $t^5$. One has

$$X_0 + tC_1 + \frac{t^2}{2!}C_2 + \frac{t^3}{3!}C_3 + \frac{t^4}{4!}C_4 + \frac{t^5}{5!}C_5$$

$$+ \left(J_1 + tK_1 + \frac{t^2}{2!}L_1 + \frac{t^3}{3!}M_1\right)u^* + \left(J_2 + tK_2 + \frac{t^2}{2!}L_2\right)v^*$$

$$+ (J_3 + tK_3)w^* + J_4 s^* + (R_{u,\,u} + t S_{u,\,u})\frac{u^* u^*}{2!}$$

$$+ R_{u,\,v} u^* v^*.$$

Now let us replace $u^*$, $v^*$, ... by their values; we obtain

$$X_0 + tC_1 + \frac{t^2}{2!}[C_2 + J_1 x^{(p+1)}(0)] + \frac{t^3}{3!}[C_3 + 3K_1 x^{(p+1)}(0) + J_1 x^{(p+2)}(0)$$

$$+ J_2 x^{(p+1)}(0)] + \frac{t^4}{4!}[C_4 + 6L_1 x^{(p+1)}(0) + 4K_1 x^{(p+2)}(0) + J_1 x^{(p+3)}(0)$$

$$+ 4K_2 x^{(p+1)}(0) + J_2 x^{(p+2)}(0) + J_3 x^{(p+1)}(0) + 3R_{u,\,u} x^{(p+1)}(0)x^{(p+1)}(0)]$$

$$+ \frac{t^5}{5!}[C_5 + 10M_1 x^{(p+1)}(0) + 10L_1 x^{(p+2)}(0) + 5K_1 x^{(p+3)}(0) + J_1 x^{(p+4)}(0)$$

$$+ 10L_2 x^{(p+1)}(0) + 5K_2 x^{(p+2)}(0) + J_2 x^{(p+3)}(0) + 5K_3 x^{(p+1)}(0)$$

$$+ J_3 x^{(p+2)}(0) + J_4 x^{(p+1)}(0) + 10R_{u,\,u} x^{(p+1)}(0)x^{(p+2)}(0)$$

$$+ 15S_{u,\,u} x^{(p+1)}(0)x^{(p+1)}(0) + 10R_{u,\,v} x^{(p+1)}(0)x^{(p+1)}(0)].$$

### 15. Final formulas

The coefficients of $t$, $t^2/2!$, $t^3/3!$, $t^4/4!$, $t^5/5!$ are

$$x^{(p+1)}, \; x^{(p+2)}, \; x^{(p+3)}, \; x^{(p+4)}, \; x^{(p+5)}.$$

But each of these expressions contains preceding derivatives which remain to be replaced by their values. We then obtain the final expressions:

$$x^{(p+1)} = C_1 ,$$
$$x^{(p+2)} = C_2 + J_1 C_1 ,$$
$$x^{(p+3)} = C_3 + 3K_1 C_1 + J_2 C_1 + J_1 C_2 + J_1^2 C_1 ,$$

$$x^{(p+4)} = C_4 + J_3 C_1 + 4K_2 C_1 + 3R + J_2 C_2 + J_2 J_1 C_1$$
$$+ 4K_1 C_2 + 4K_1 J_1 C_1 + J_1 C_3 + J_1 J_2 C_1 + 3J_1 K_1 C_1$$
$$+ J_1^3 C_1 + J_1^2 C_2 + 6L_1 C_1 .$$

For simplicity, set

$$R = R_{u,u} C_1 C_1 .$$

$$x^{(p+5)} = C_5 + J_1 C_4 + J_1^2 C_3 + 5K_1 C_3 + J_2 C_3 + J_1^3 C_2$$
$$+ 4J_1 K_1 C_2 + J_1 J_2 C_2 + J_3 C_2 + 5K_1 J_1 C_2 + J_2 J_1 C_2$$
$$+ 5K_2 C_2 + 10L_1 C_2 + 10M_1 C_1 + 10L_2 C_1 + 10L_1 J_1 C_1$$
$$+ 5K_3 C_1 + 5K_2 J_1 C_1 + 15K_1^2 C_1 + 5K_1 J_2 C_1 + 5K_1 J_1^2 C_1$$
$$+ J_4 C_1 + J_3 J_1 C_1 + 3J_2 K_1 C_1 + J_2^2 C_1 + J_2 J_1^2 C_1$$
$$+ J_1 J_3 C_1 + 4J_1 K_2 C_1 + J_1 J_2 J_1 C_1 + 4J_1 K_1 J_1 C_1$$
$$+ J_1^2 J_2 C_1 + 3J_1^2 K_1 C_1 + J_1^4 C_1 + 6J_1 L_1 C_1 + 3J_1 R$$
$$+ 10R' + 10R'' + 10R''' + 15S,$$

$$R' = R_{u,u} C_1 C_2 ,$$
$$R'' = R_{u,u} C_1 (J_1 C_1),$$
$$R''' = R_{u,v} C_1 C_1,$$
$$S = S_{u,u} C_1 C_1 .$$

**16.1 Simplification in the case of one unknown function without the independent variable.**

A demonstration, whose details we will not give, shows that

$$ABC_i = BAC_i.$$

$A$ and $B$ denote matrices of the types $J$ or $K$. This brings about the following simplifications:

$$\frac{d^{p+4} x}{dt^{p+4}} = C_4 + J_3 C_1 + 4K_2 C_1 + 3R + J_2 C_2 + 2J_2 J_1 C_1$$
$$+ 4K_1 C_2 + 7K_1 J_1 C_1 + J_1 C_3 + J_1^3 C_1 + J_1^2 C_2 + 6L_1 C_1 ,$$

$$\frac{d^{p+5} x}{dt^{p+5}} = C_5 + J_1 C_4 + J_1^2 C_3 + 5K_1 C_3 + J_2 C_3 + J_1^3 C_2$$
$$+ 9J_1 K_1 C_2 + 2J_1 J_2 C_2 + J_3 C_2 + 5K_2 C_2 + 10L_1 C_2$$
$$+ 10M_1 C_1 + 10L_2 C_1 + 16L_1 J_1 C_1 + 5K_3 C_1 + 9K_2 J_1 C_1$$
$$+ 15K_1^2 C_1 + 8K_1 J_2 C_1 + 12K_1 J_1^2 C_1 + J_4 C_1 + 2J_3 J_1 C_1$$
$$+ J_2^2 C_1 + 3J_2 J_1^2 C_1 + J_1^4 C_1 + 3J_1 R + 10R' + 10R''$$
$$+ 10R''' + 15S.$$

### 16.2 Case $p = 1$.

The case $p = 1$ presents simplifications as a result of the disappearance of the terms

$$J_2, J_3, \ldots, K_2, K_3, \ldots, K''''.$$

Finally, if we denote by $X$ the columns of the second members

$$C_1 = J_1 X, \qquad C_2 = K_1 X, \ldots,$$

we then have

$$\frac{d^2 x}{dt^2} = J_1 X,$$

$$\frac{d^3 x}{dt^3} = K_1 X + J_1^2 X,$$

$$\frac{d^4 x}{dt^4} = L_1 X + 3K_1 J_1 X + J_1 K_1 X + J_1^3 X,$$

$$\frac{d^5 x}{dt^5} = M_1 X + 3R + 4K_1^2 X + 4K_1 J_1^2 X + J_1 L_1 X + 3J_1 K_1 J_1 X$$
$$+ J_1^4 X + J_1^2 K_1 X + 6L_1 J_1 X,$$

$$\frac{d^6 x}{dt^6} = N_1 X + J_1 M_1 X + J_1^2 L_1 X + 5K_1 L_1 X + J_1^3 K_1 X + 4J_1 K_1^2 X$$
$$+ 5K_1 J_1 K_1 X + 10L_1 K_1 X + 10M_1 J_1 X + 10L_1 J_1^2 X$$
$$+ 15K_1^2 J_1 X + 5K_1 J_1^3 X + 4J_1 K_1 J_1^2 X + 3J_1^2 K_1 J_1 X$$
$$+ J_1^5 X + 6J_1 L_1 J_1 X + 3J_1 R + 15S + 10R' + 10R''.$$

### 16.3 Case where two preceding simplifications occur simultaneously.

If we have one unknown function and $p = 1$, we obtain formulas yet more reduced:

$$\frac{d^5 x}{dt^5} = M_1 X + J_1 L_1 X + 4K_1^2 X + J_1^2 K_1 X + 7K_1 J_1^2 X + J_1^4 X$$
$$+ 6L_1 J_1 X + 3R.$$

$$\frac{d^6 x}{dt^6} = N_1 X + J_1 M_1 X + J_1^2 L_1 X + 5K_1 L_1 X + J_1^3 K_1 X$$
$$+ 9J_1 K_1^2 X + 10L_1 K_1 X + 10M_1 J_1 X + 16L_1 J_1^2 X$$
$$+ 15K_1^2 J_1 X + 12K_1 J_1^3 X + J_1^5 X + 3J_1 R + 15S$$
$$+ 10R' + 10R''.$$

### 16.4 Independence of the groups of terms.

A quite laborious verification, which we will not reproduce here, permits us to be sure that each of the preceding groups contains a term which does not appear in any of the others, which assures their independence.

## Problems

Obtain the values of $y$ corresponding to $x = \pm 0.5$ for each of the following problems by using (a) Taylor series, and (b) Euler's method, rounding the results to four decimal places and estimating the errors:

1. $y' = x^2 + y^2$,      $y(0) = 0$.
2. $y'' = -y$,           $y(0) = 0$,      $y'(0) = 1$.
3. $y' = -x + y$,      $y(0) = 1.5$.

Do the same for the system

$$y' = x + y + z, \qquad z' = y - z, \qquad y(0) = 1, \qquad z(0) = -2.$$

# 3 RUNGE-KUTTA METHOD[1]

By the name *Runge-Kutta method* we will denote a collection of single-step methods based on a common principle. In this chapter, we propose to give a synthetic exposition of this collection of methods, starting with their general definition. As a preliminary step we will study the improved tangent methods, the Euler-Cauchy, and the classical Runge-Kutta methods for the case of a first order equation.

## I  THE IMPROVED TANGENT METHOD FOR AN EQUATION OF THE FIRST ORDER

### 1.1  The formula.

Let the equation of the first order be

$$y' = Y(y, t).$$

Euler's method is of order 1. One can ask if it would not be more advantageous to make the tangent occur not at the point $t_i$ but at a point with abscissa $t_i + h/2$. Indeed, on an arc, the point where the tangent is parallel to the chord joining the ends is generally found towards the middle. Naturally, it is impossible to determine exactly the point of the integral curve with abscissa $t_i + h/2$, but one can determine it approximately by setting (Fig. 3-1)

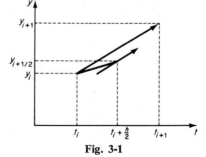

**Fig. 3-1**

[1]Kutta, Runge [1, 2].

37

$$y_{i+1/2} = y_i + \frac{h}{2} Y_i,$$

which leads to the formulas:

$$\begin{cases} y_{i+1/2} = y_i + \dfrac{h}{2} Y_i, \\ y_{i+1} = y_i + hY_{i+1/2}, \end{cases} \tag{1}$$

with

$$Y_{i+1/2} = Y\left(y_{i+1/2}, t_i + \frac{h}{2}\right).$$

The ensemble of formulas (1) constitutes the improved tangent method.

### 1.2 Examples.

1.  $\qquad\qquad y' = -y, \qquad y(0) = 1, \qquad h = 0.1.$

| $t$ | $y_i$ | Error | $t$ | $y_i$ | Error |
|-----|-------|-------|-----|-------|-------|
| 0   | 1.000,00 |            | 2.5 | 0.082,45 | $-36$ |
| 0.1 | 0.905,00 | $-14 \cdot 10^{-5}$ | 3.0 | 0.050,05 | $-26 \cdot 10^{-5}$ |
| 0.2 | 0.819,02 | $-29$      |     |          |       |
| 0.3 | 0.741,21 | $-39$      | 3.5 | 0.030,39 | $-19$ |
| 0.4 | 0.670,80 | $-48$      | 4.0 | 0.018,44 | $-12$ |
| 0.5 | 0.607,07 | $-59$      |     |          |       |
|     |          |            | 4.5 | 0.011,19 | $-8$  |
| 1.0 | 0.368,54 | $-66$      | 5.0 | 0.006,796 | $-5.8$ |
| 1.5 | 0.223,73 | $-60$      |     |          |       |
| 2.0 | 0.135,82 | $-48$      |     |          |       |

2.  $\qquad\qquad y' = y - 1.5e^{-0.5t}, \qquad y(0) = 1.$

| $t$ | $h = 0.4$ | $h = 0.2$ | $y$ exact |
|-----|-----------|-----------|-----------|
| 0   | 1         | 1         | 1         |
| 0.2 |           | 0.904,63  | 0.904,84  |
| 0.4 | 0.817,10  | 0.818,29  | 0.818,73  |
| 0.6 |           | 0.740,11  | 0.740,82  |
| 0.8 | 0.666,57  | 0.669,31  | 0.670,32  |
| 1.0 |           | 0.605,16  | 0.606,53  |
| 1.2 | 0.542,16  | 0.547,01  | 0.548,81  |
| 2.0 | 0.351,25  | 0.363,34  | 0.367,88  |
| 2.8 | 0.200,41  | 0.236,17  | 0.246,60  |
| 4.0 | $-0.016,04$ | 0.100,51 | 0.135,34  |
| 4.8 | $-0.241,36$ | 0.013,43 | 0.090,72  |

3.                          $y' = -ty,$     $y(0) = 1,$     $h = 0.1.$

| $t$ | $y_i$ | $y$ exact |
|---|---|---|
| 0 | 1 | 1 |
| 0.1 | 0.995 | 0.995,012 |
| 0.2 | 0.980,150 | 0.980,199 |
| 0.3 | 0.955,891 | 0.955,997 |
| 0.4 | 0.922,937 | 0.923,116 |
| 0.5 | 0.882,235 | 0.882,497 |

## 2.1 Truncation error at one step.

We will content ourselves here in giving the formulas. The justification will be carried over to paragraph 16, where we will treat a more general case.

By $y_i(t)$ we still denote the integral curve which passes through the point $t_i, y_i,$ and set

$$Y_i(t) = Y(y_i(t), t).$$

The truncation error over one step

$$y_{i+1} - y_i(t_{i+1})$$

has theoretically for the principal part

$$-h^3 \left( \frac{y'''}{24} + \frac{y'' Y'_y}{8} \right).$$

The method is, therefore, of order 2. However, one can give the following practical approximate expression (supposing negligible round-off error):

$$\frac{h}{12} \left( -5 Y_{i+1} + 12 Y_{i+1/2} - 8 Y_i + Y_{i-1} \right).$$

## 2.2 Examples.

Let us return to the equation $y' = -y,$ with $y(0) = 1$; $h = 0.1.$ We find the following results:

| $t$ | Calculated error | Actual error |
|---|---|---|
| 0.2 | 0.000,16 | 0.000,14 |
| 0.3 | 0.000,14 | 0.000,13 |
| 0.4 | 0.000,12 | 0.000,13 |
| 0.5 | 0.000,11 | 0.000,11 |
| 1.0 | 0.000,07 | 0.000,06 |
| 1.5 | 0.000,04 | 0,000,04 |
| 2.0 | 0.000,02 | 0.000,03 |
| 2.5 | 0.000,02 | 0.000,01 |
| 3.0 | 0.000,01 | 0.000,01 |

$$\eta = 8\%^1$$

[1]For the definition of $\eta$, see Chapter 2, paragraph 5.3.

For

$$y' = y - 1.5e^{-0.5t}, \qquad y(0) = 1, \qquad h = 0.2,$$

we find

|  | Calculated | Actual |
|---|---|---|
| $t$ | error | error |
| 0.4 | −0.000,17 | −0.000,18 |
| 0.6 | −0.000,15 | −0.000,17 |
| 0.8 | −0.000,14 | −0.000,14 |
| 1.0 | −0.000,13 | −0.000,14 |
| 2.0 | −0.000,07 | −0.000,08 |
| 3.0 | −0.000,03 | −0.000,03 |
| 4.0 | +0.000,01 | +0.000,01 |
| 5.0 | +0.000,09 | +0.000,09 |
| | $\eta = 8\%$ | |

Finally, for

$$y' = -ty, \qquad y(0) = 1, \qquad h = 0.1,$$

we find

|  | Calculated | Actual |
|---|---|---|
| $t$ | error | error |
| 0.2 | 0.000,049 | 0.000,037 |
| 0.3 | 0.000,070 | 0.000,059 |
| 0.4 | 0.000,087 | 0.000,076 |
| 0.5 | 0.000,100 | 0.000,090 |
| | $\eta = 17\%$ | |

*Remark.* In all these examples the round-off error is of minor importance.

## II  THE METHOD OF EULER-CAUCHY FOR AN EQUATION OF THE FIRST ORDER

### 3.1 Formulas.

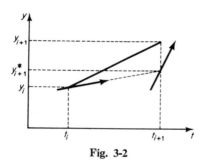

Fig. 3-2

Another manner of improving the tangent method consists of noting that, on a small arc, the slope of the chord is obviously the arithmetic mean of the slopes of the tangents at the end points (Fig. 3-2). Naturally, one cannot determine exactly the slope of the tangent to the integral curve at the point with the abscissa $t_i + h$, but one can determine it approximately by the formulas:

$$y_{i+1}^{*} = y_i + h Y_i, \tag{1}$$
$$Y_{i+1}^{*} = Y(y_{i+1}^{*}, t_{i+1}). \tag{2}$$

We obtain the approximate integration by

$$y_{i+1} = y_i + \frac{h}{2}(Y_i + Y_{i+1}^{*}). \tag{3}$$

### 3.2 Examples.

Let us return to the equation
$$y' = y - 1.5\,e^{-0.5t}, \qquad y(0) = 1.$$

| $t$ | $h = 0.4$ | $h = 0.2$ | $y$ exact |
|---|---|---|---|
| 0 | 1 | 1 | 1 |
| 0.2 | | 0.904,27 | 0.904,84 |
| 0.4 | 0.814,38 | 0.817,53 | 0.818,73 |
| 0.6 | | 0.738,90 | 0.740,82 |
| 0.8 | 0.660,32 | 0.667,56 | 0.670,32 |
| 1.0 | | 0.602,79 | 0.606,53 |
| 2.0 | 0.323,59 | 0.355,49 | 0.367,88 |
| 3.0 | | 0.118,26 | 0.223,13 |
| 4.0 | −0.195,46 | 0.040,25 | 0.135,34 |
| 5.0 | | −0.175,40 | 0.082,08 |

Let another example be
$$y' = -ty, \qquad y(0) = 1, \qquad h = 0.1.$$

| $t$ | $y_i$ | $y$ exact |
|---|---|---|
| 0 | 1 | 1 |
| 0.1 | 0.995 | 0.995,012 |
| 0.2 | 0.980,175 | 0.980,198 |
| 0.3 | 0.955,964 | 0.955,997 |
| 0.4 | 0.923,079 | 0.923,116 |
| 0.5 | 0.882,464 | 0.882,497 |

### 4.1 Truncation error over one step.

Here, too, we will content ourselves with giving the results, returning for justification to paragraph 16. The error over one step has for the principal part

$$h^3 \left( \frac{y'''}{12} - \frac{Y_y' y''}{4} \right).$$

The method is, therefore, of order 2.

However, one can give the following practical approximate expression (supposing negligible round-off error):

$$\frac{h}{12}(-5 Y_{i+1} + 6 Y_{i+1}^{*} - 2 Y_i + Y_{i-1}).$$

## 4.2 Examples.

Let us return to

$$y' = y - 1.5e^{-0.5t}, \qquad y(0) = 1, \qquad h = 0.2.$$

We find

| $t$ | Calculated error | Actual error |
|---|---|---|
| 0.4 | 0.000,46 | 0.000,50 |
| 0.6 | 0.000,41 | 0.000,45 |
| 0.8 | 0.000,38 | 0.000,41 |
| 1.0 | 0.000,34 | 0.000,37 |
| 2.0 | 0.000,19 | 0.000,21 |
| 3.0 | 0.000,09 | 0.000,10 |
| 4.0 | −0.000,02 | −0,000,02 |
| 5.0 | −0.000,23 | −0.000,25 |
| | $\eta = 9.5\%$ | |

The same for

$$y' = -ty, \qquad y(0) = 1, \qquad h = 0.1$$

| $t$ | Calculated error | Actual error |
|---|---|---|
| 0.2 | 0.000,024 | 0.000,011 |
| 0.3 | 0.000,021 | 0.000,010 |
| 0.4 | 0.000,015 | 0.000,005 |
| 0.5 | 0.000,005 | 0.000,003 |
| | $\eta = 124\%$ | |

This last result is rather misleading, but it is easily understood why. Indeed, if we consider the separate representations: of $y'''$ by

$$\frac{Y_{i+1} + Y_{i-1} - 2Y_i}{h^2}$$

and of $Y'_y y''$ by

$$\frac{2}{h^2}(Y_{i+1} - Y^*_{i+1}),$$

we find

| $t$ | $y_i$ | $y'''$ (exact) | $\frac{Y_{i+1} + Y_{i-1} - 2Y_i}{h^2}$ | $Y'_y y''$ (exact) | $\frac{2}{h^2}(Y_i - Y^*_i)$ |
|---|---|---|---|---|---|
| 0 | 1 | | | | |
| 0.1 | 0.995 | 0.297,505 | 0.296,50 | 0.098,505 | 0.1000 |
| 0.2 | 0.980,175 | 0.580,264 | 0.578,08 | 0.188,194 | 0.1950 |
| 0.3 | 0.955,964 | 0.834,556 | 0.831,18 | 0.260,978 | 0.2764 |
| 0.4 | 0.923,079 | 1.048,619 | 1.044,20 | 0.310,155 | 0.3365 |
| 0.5 | 0.882,464 | | | | |

These two representations are good, but the two terms nearly cancel each other, although their difference is known with a rather large relative error.

*Remark.* In all these examples, the round-off error is of minor importance.

## III  THE CLASSICAL RUNGE-KUTTA METHOD FOR A FIRST ORDER EQUATION

### 5.1 Formula.

The classical Runge-Kutta method for a first order equation

$$y' = Y(y, t)$$

consists of performing, at each step, the following computations:

$$y_{i,1} = y_i + \frac{h}{2}\, Y_i, \qquad Y_{i,1} = Y\left(y_{i,1}, t_i + \frac{h}{2}\right),$$

$$y_{i,2} = y_i + \frac{h}{2}\, Y_{i,1}, \qquad Y_{i,2} = Y\left(y_{i,2}, t_i + \frac{h}{2}\right),$$

$$y_{i,3} = y_i + h Y_{i,2}, \qquad Y_{i,3} = Y(y_{i,3}, t_i + h),$$

$$y_{i+1} = y_i + \frac{h}{6}\, (Y_i + 2Y_{i,1} + 2Y_{i,2} + Y_{i,3}).$$

Each step counts four horners. The formulas are applicable without modification to a system in canonical form.

### 5.2 Examples.

1.    $y' = y - 1.5e^{-0.5t}, \qquad h = 0.4, \qquad y(0) = 1.$

| $t$ | $y_i$ | $y$ exact |
|---|---|---|
| 0 | 1 | 1 |
| 0.4 | 0.818,700 | 0.818,731 |
| 0.8 | 0.670,248 | 0.670,320 |
| 1.2 | 0.548,683 | 0.548,812 |
| 1.6 | 0.449,121 | 0.449,329 |
| 3.2 | 0.200,771 | 0.201,897 |
| 4.8 | 0.085,101 | 0.090,718 |

2.    $y' = -2ty^2, \qquad y(0) = 1.$

| $t$ | $h = 0.2$ | $h = 0.1$ | $y$ exact |
|---|---|---|---|
| 0 | 1 | 1 | 1 |
| 0.1 | | 0.990,099 | 0.990,099 |
| 0.2 | 0.961,533 | 0.961,538 | 0.961,539 |

2. (*continued*)

| $t$ | $h=0.2$ | $h=0.1$ | $y$ exact |
|---|---|---|---|
| 0.3 | | 0.917,430 | 0.917,431 |
| 0.4 | 0.862,053 | 0.862,068 | 0.862,069 |
| 1.0 | 0.500,007 | 0.500,000 | 0.500,000 |
| 1.6 | 0.280,914 | 0.280,899 | 0.280,899 |
| 2.0 | 0.200,008 | 0.200,000 | 0.200,000 |

**6. Truncation error at one step. Practical evaluation.**

We will not give the theoretical evaluation here, which is rather complicated. Let us say only that this method is of order 4. Here is one practical evaluation which will be justified later (Chapter 10, paragraph 5).

$$- \frac{h}{20}(Y_{i+1} + 9Y_i + 9Y_{i-1} + Y_{i-2}) + \frac{(11y_{i+1} + 27y_i - 27y_{i-1} - 11y_{i-2})}{60}.$$

(We suppose, as in the preceding methods, the round-off error to be negligible.)

**7. Examples.**

1. $$y' = y - 1.5e^{-0.5t}, \qquad y(0) = 1.$$

| $t$ | Calculated error | Actual error |
|---|---|---|
| 0.2 | $28 \cdot 10^{-8}$ | $28 \cdot 10^{-8}$ |
| 0.4 | 26 | 26 |
| 0.6 | 24 | 23 |
| 0.8 | 21 | 21 |
| 1.0 | 20 | 19 |
| 1.8 | 13 | 13 |

Between 0 and 1, $\eta = 1\%$[1]

2. $$y' = -2ty^2, \qquad y(0) = 1.$$

| $t$ | Calculated error | Actual error |
|---|---|---|
| 0.2 | $360 \cdot 10^{-9}$ | $240 \cdot 10^{-9}$ |
| 0.3 | 406 | 300 |
| 0.4 | 288 | 260 |
| 0.5 | 97 | 120 |
| 0.6 | $-88$ | $-52$ |
| 0.7 | $-255$ | $-200$ |
| 0.8 | $-302$ | $-290$ |
| 0.9 | $-330$ | $-325$ |
| 1.0 | $-322$ | $-323$ |

$\eta = 18\%$[1]

[1]For the definition of $\eta$, see Chapter 2, paragraph 5.3.

*Remark.* In these examples the round-off error is of minor importance.

## IV GENERAL FORMULAS

We consider the equilibrated resolved form in condensed notation

$$x^{(p)} = X(x^{(p-1)}, \ldots, x),$$

the independent variable being absent. As we work only over one step, we may suppose that this step is the first one, with the initial conditions

$$t_0, x_0, \ldots, x_0^{(p-1)}.$$

### 8.1 Notation.

Generalizing what has been done with the improved tangent method, we will consider the values

$$t_\alpha = t_0 + h\theta_\alpha, \qquad \alpha = 0, 1, \ldots, q,$$
$$\theta_0 = 0, \qquad \theta_q = 1,$$

where $q$ will be called the *rank or the degree of the method*.[1] The approximate values of $x, x', \ldots, x^{(p-1)}$ at the points $t_\alpha$ will be given by

$$x_{0,\alpha}^{(p-1)} = x_0^{(p-1)} + h \sum_{\beta=0}^{\alpha-1} A_{\alpha,\beta} X_{0,\beta},$$

$$x_{0,\alpha}^{(p-k)} = x_0^{(p-k)} + \frac{h\theta_\alpha}{1!} x_0^{(p-k+1)} + \cdots + \frac{h^{k-1}\theta_\alpha^{k-1}}{(k-1)!} x_0^{(p-1)} + \frac{h^k}{k!} \sum_{\beta=0}^{\alpha-1} K_{\alpha,\beta} X_{0,\beta},$$

$$x_{0,\alpha} = x_0 + \frac{h\theta_\alpha}{1!} x_0' + \cdots + \frac{h^{p-1}\theta_\alpha^{p-1}}{(p-1)!} x_0^{(p-1)} + \frac{h^p}{p!} \sum_{\beta=0}^{\alpha-1} L_{\alpha,\beta} X_{0,\beta},$$

$$x_1^{(p-k)} = x_{0,q}^{(p-k)}, \qquad k = 1, \ldots, p.$$

We set

$$x_{0,\beta} = X(x_{0,\beta}^{(p-1)}, \ldots, x_{0,\beta}^{(p-k)}, \ldots, x_{0,\beta}).$$

### 8.2 Justification of the notations.

The coefficients $A_{\alpha\beta}$ are used for the $(p-1)$st derivatives, $B_{\alpha\beta}$ for the $(p-2)$nd derivatives, $\ldots$, $K_{\alpha\beta}$ for the $(p-k)$th derivatives, and $L_{\alpha\beta}$ for the unknown functions themselves. These notations merit some explanations. Let us consider the system

$$x^{(p)} = X(x^{(p-1)}).$$

Because of the fact that this system contains only derivatives of order $p$ and $p-1$, its solution will only bring in the coefficients

$$A_{\alpha,\beta}.$$

[1] Ultimately, we will distinguish between these two notions for more general methods.

But in setting

$$x^{(p-1)} = u,$$

the system becomes

$$u' = X(u).$$

Hence, it is justified that the coefficients $A_{\alpha, \beta}$ are used for the $(p - 1)$st derivatives, whatever $p$ is, the coefficients $B_{\alpha\beta}$ for the $(p - 2)$nd derivatives, whatever $p$ is, and so forth.

### 8.3  Practical arrangement.

We will arrange the coefficients of one formula in a triangular matrix form such as

## 9.  Prescribed conditions.

We intend now to determine the quantities which we have, that is to say, the quantities

$$\theta_\alpha, A_{\alpha\beta}, \ldots, L_{\alpha\beta}$$

so as to obtain Taylor developments in powers of $h$, valid up to as high an order as possible, for

$$x_{0, q}, \ldots, x_{0, q}^{(k)}, \ldots, x_{0, q}^{(p-1)},$$

which will be taken as the initial values for a new step.

It is clear that

$$x_{0, q}, \ldots, x_{0, q}^{(k)}, \ldots, x_{0, q}^{(p-1)}$$

are the exact expansions up to the orders $p, \ldots, p - k, \ldots, 1$ if

$$\sum_\beta A_{q\beta} = 1, \qquad \sum_\beta K_{q\beta} = 1, \qquad \sum_\beta L_{q\beta} = 1$$

($\beta$ varies from 0 to $q - 1$).

These conditions must necessarily be verified. We obtain a simplification of the equations by supposing that

$$x_{0, \alpha}, \ldots, x_{0, \alpha}^{(p-k)}, \ldots, x_{0, \alpha}^{(p-1)} \qquad (\beta \text{ varies from 0 to } \alpha - 1)$$

are also exact up to the same order. Then, one obtains the conditions:[1]

[1] In applying the Runge-utta method to the equation

$$y^{(p)} = y^{(p-1)} + 1 - t, \qquad y^{(p-1)}(0) = 0,$$

we can show that the relations

$$\sum_\beta A_{\alpha\beta} = \theta_\alpha$$

are necessary for the validity of the formulas relative to $y^{(p-1)}$ up to order $q$ inclusive.

$$\sum_\beta A_{\alpha\beta} = \theta_\alpha, \qquad \sum_\beta K_{\alpha\beta} = \theta_\alpha^k, \qquad \sum_\beta L_{\alpha\beta} = \theta_\alpha^p$$

($\beta$ varies from 0 to $\alpha - 1$).

Subsequently, we suppose these conditions verified, which is not necessary but which corresponds to the idea of naturally preferring, at the same cost, the most precise formulas. We thus can write

$$x_{0,\alpha}^{(p-1)} = x_0^{(p-1)} + \frac{h\theta_\alpha}{1!} X_0 + h \sum_{\beta=0}^{\alpha-1} A_{\alpha\beta}(X_{0,\beta} - X_0),$$

$$\vdots$$

$$x_{0,\alpha}^{(p-k)} = x_0^{(p-1)} + \frac{h\theta_\alpha}{1!} x_0^{(p-k+1)} + \cdots + \frac{h^k \theta_\alpha^k}{k!} X_0 + \frac{h^k}{k!} \sum_{\beta=0}^{\alpha-1} K_{\alpha\beta}(X_{0,\beta} - X_0),$$

$$\vdots$$

$$x_{0,\alpha} = x_0 + \frac{h\theta_\alpha}{1!} x_0' + \cdots + \frac{h^p \theta_\alpha^p}{p!} X_0 + \frac{h^p}{p!} \sum_{\beta=0}^{\alpha-1} L_{\alpha\beta}(X_{0,\beta} - X_0).$$

### 10.1 Evaluation of $X_{0,\alpha} - X_0$.

Before we start with the establishment of the equations, we are going to give the expression of $X_{0,\alpha} - X_0$ which we will expand in powers of $h$ up to the fourth order. We will consider the intermediate value

$$X^* = X\left(x_0^{(p-1)} + \frac{h\theta_\alpha}{1!} X_0, \ldots, x_0 + \frac{h\theta_\alpha}{1!} x_0' + \cdots + \frac{h^p \theta_\alpha^p}{p!} X_0\right)$$

and develop

$$(X^* - X_0) + (X_\alpha - X^*).$$

The first parenthesis gives a column which is, according to definition (Chapter 2, paragraph 14),

$$h\theta_\alpha C_1 + \frac{h^2 \theta_\alpha^2}{2!} C_2 + \frac{h^3 \theta_\alpha^3}{3!} C_3 + \frac{h^4 \theta_\alpha^5}{4!} C_4.$$

We will develop the second parenthesis as in Chapter 2, paragraph 14. It becomes (if we stop at the fourth order terms)

$$\left(J_1 + \frac{h\theta_\alpha}{1!} K_1 + \frac{h^2 \theta_\alpha^2}{2!} L_1 + \cdots\right) h \sum_\beta A_{\alpha,\beta}(X_{0,\beta} - X_0)$$

$$+ \left(J_2 + \frac{h\theta_\alpha}{1!} K_2 + \cdots\right) \frac{h^2}{2} \sum_\beta B_{\alpha,\beta}(X_{0,\beta} - X_0)$$

$$+ (J_3 + \cdots) \frac{h^3}{3!} \sum_\beta C_{\alpha,\beta}(X_{0,\beta} - X_0)$$

$$+ \frac{h^2}{2!} (R_{u,u} + \cdots) \sum_\beta A_{\alpha,\beta}(X_{0,\beta} - X_0) \sum_\gamma A_{\alpha,\gamma}(X_{0,\gamma} - X_0)$$

from which we will develop, arrange, and replace gradually the $X_{0,\beta} - X_0$ by their values:

$$X_{0,\,\alpha} - X_0 = h\theta_\alpha C_1$$

$$+ h^2 \left[ \frac{\theta_\alpha^2}{2!} C_2 + \sum_\beta A_{\alpha,\,\beta} \theta_\beta J_1 C_1 \right]$$

$$+ h^3 \left[ \frac{\theta_\alpha^3}{3!} C_3 + \sum_\beta A_{\alpha,\,\beta} \theta_\alpha \theta_\beta K_1 C_1 + \frac{1}{2} \sum_\beta B_{\alpha,\,\alpha} \theta_\beta J_2 C_1 \right.$$

$$\left. + \sum_\beta A_{\alpha,\,\beta} \frac{\theta_\beta^2}{2!} J_1 C_2 + \sum_{\beta,\,\gamma} A_{\alpha,\,\beta} A_{\beta,\,\gamma} \theta_\gamma J_1^2 C_1 \right]$$

$$+ h^4 \left[ \frac{\theta_\alpha^4}{4!} C_4 + \sum_\beta A_{\alpha,\,\beta} \frac{\theta_\alpha^2}{2!} \theta_\beta L_1 C_1 + \frac{1}{2} \sum_\beta B_{\alpha,\,\beta} \theta_\alpha \theta_\beta K_2 C_1 \right.$$

$$+ \frac{1}{3!} \sum_\beta C_{\alpha,\,\beta} \theta_\beta J_3 C_1 + \frac{1}{2!} \sum_\beta A_{\alpha,\,\beta} \theta_\beta \sum_\gamma A_{\alpha,\,\gamma} \theta_\gamma R$$

$$+ \sum_\beta A_{\alpha,\,\beta} \frac{\theta_\alpha \theta_\beta^2}{2!} K_1 C_2 + \sum_{\beta,\,\gamma} A_{\alpha,\,\beta} A_{\beta,\,\gamma} \theta_\alpha \theta_\gamma K_1 J_1 C_1$$

$$+ \frac{1}{4} \sum_\beta B_{\alpha,\,\beta} \theta_\beta^2 J_2 C_2 + \frac{1}{2} \sum_{\beta,\,\gamma} B_{\alpha,\,\beta} A_{\beta,\,\gamma} \theta_\gamma J_2 J_1 C_1$$

$$+ \frac{1}{3!} \sum_\beta A_{\alpha,\,\beta} \theta_\beta^3 J_1 C_3 + \sum_{\beta,\,\gamma} A_{\alpha,\,\beta} A_{\beta,\,\gamma} \theta_\beta \theta_\gamma J_1 K_1 C_1$$

$$+ \frac{1}{2} \sum_{\beta,\,\gamma} A_{\alpha,\,\beta} A_{\beta,\,\gamma} \theta_\gamma J_1 J_2 C_1$$

$$\left. + \sum_{\beta,\,\gamma} A_{\alpha,\,\beta} A_{\beta,\,\gamma} \frac{\theta_\gamma^2}{2!} J_1^2 C_2 + \sum_{\beta,\,\gamma,\,\delta} A_{\alpha,\,\beta} A_{\beta,\,\gamma} A_{\gamma,\,\delta} \theta_\delta J_1^3 C_1 \right].$$

## 10.2 Simplification if $p$ is small.

If $p$ is small, some of the above coefficients disappear. They are those $J, K, L$, whose lower index exceeds $p$. For example, if $p = 1$, all the terms $B_{\alpha,\,\beta}$, $C_{\alpha,\,\beta}$ disappear. If $p = 2$, all the terms $C_{\alpha,\,\beta}$ disappear.

## 11.1 Expression of the developments of the exact solution and of the approximate solution.

We are going to write in $x_1^{(p-k)}$ the coefficients of the terms

$$h^{k+1}, \quad h^{k+2}, \quad h^{k+3}, \quad h^{k+4}$$

without fixing $q$ for the moment. For one part, these quantities are

$$\frac{h^{k+1}}{(k+1)!} x_0^{(p+1)} + \frac{h^{k+2}}{(k+2)!} x_0^{(p+2)} + \frac{h^{k+3}}{(k+3)!} x_0^{(p+3)} + \frac{h^{k+4}}{(k+4)!} x_0^{(p+4)}$$

and for the other part, they are the first four terms of the development of

$$\frac{h^k}{k!} \sum_{\alpha=1}^{q-1} K_{q,\,\alpha} (X_{0,\,\alpha} - X_0).$$

The table below shows the different terms and their coefficients. Compare with Lotkin [1].

| | Taylor | Runge-Kutta |
|---|---|---|
| $\frac{h^{k+1}}{k!}C_1$ | $\frac{1}{k+1}$ | $\sum_\alpha K_{q,\alpha}\theta_\alpha$ |
| $\frac{h^{k+2}}{k!}C_2$ | $\frac{1}{(k+1)(k+2)}$ | $\frac{1}{2}\sum_\alpha K_{q,\alpha}\theta_\alpha^2$ |
| $J_1 C_1$ | $\frac{1}{(k+1)(k+2)}$ | $\sum_{\alpha,\beta} K_{q,\alpha}A_{\alpha,\beta}\theta_\beta$ |
| $\frac{h^{k+3}}{k!}C_3$ | $\frac{1}{(k+1)(k+2)(k+3)}$ | $\frac{1}{6}\sum_\alpha K_{q,\alpha}\theta_\alpha^3$ |
| $J_2 C_1$ | $\frac{1}{(k+1)(k+2)(k+3)}$ | $\frac{1}{2}\sum_{\alpha,\beta} K_{q,\alpha}B_{\alpha,\beta}\theta_\beta$ |
| $K_1 C_1$ | $\frac{3}{(k+1)(k+2)(k+3)}$ | $\sum_{\alpha,\beta} K_{q,\alpha}A_{\alpha,\beta}\theta_\alpha\theta_\beta$ |
| $J_1^2 C_1$ | $\frac{1}{(k+1)(k+2)(k+3)}$ | $\sum_{\alpha,\beta,\gamma} K_{q,\alpha}A_{\alpha,\beta}A_{\beta,\gamma}\theta_\gamma$ |
| $J_1 C_2$ | $\frac{1}{(k+1)(k+2)(k+3)}$ | $\frac{1}{2}\sum_{\alpha,\beta} K_{q,\alpha}A_{\alpha,\beta}\theta_\beta^2$ |
| $\frac{h^{k+4}}{k!}C_4$ | $\frac{1}{(k+1)(k+2)(k+3)(k+4)}$ | $\frac{1}{24}\sum_\alpha K_{q,\alpha}\theta_\alpha^4$ |
| $J_3 C_1$ | $\frac{1}{(k+1)(k+2)(k+3)(k+4)}$ | $\frac{1}{6}\sum_{\alpha,\beta} K_{q,\alpha}C_{\alpha,\beta}\theta_\beta$ |
| $K_2 C_1$ | $\frac{4}{(k+1)(k+2)(k+3)(k+4)}$ | $\frac{1}{2}\sum_{\alpha,\beta} K_{q,\alpha}B_{\alpha,\beta}\theta_\alpha\theta_\beta$ |
| $L_1 C_1$ | $\frac{6}{(k+1)(k+2)(k+3)(k+4)}$ | $\frac{1}{2}\sum_{\alpha,\beta} K_{q,\alpha}A_{\alpha,\beta}\theta_\alpha^2\theta_\beta$ |
| $R$ | $\frac{3}{(k+1)(k+2)(k+3)(k+4)}$ | $\frac{1}{2}\sum_\alpha K_{q,\alpha}\left(\sum_\beta \alpha_\beta\theta A_\beta\right)^2$ |
| $\frac{h^{k+4}}{k!}J_2 C_2$ | $\frac{1}{(k+1)(k+2)(k+3)(k+4)}$ | $\frac{1}{4}\sum_{\alpha,\beta} K_{q,\alpha}B_{\alpha,\beta}\theta_\beta^2$ |
| $\left[\rule{0pt}{9pt}\right.J_2 J_1 C_1$ | $\frac{1}{(k+1)(k+2)(k+3)(k+4)}$ | $\frac{1}{2}\sum_{\alpha,\beta,\gamma} K_{q,\alpha}B_{\alpha,\beta}A_{\beta,\gamma}\theta_\gamma$ |
| $\left.\rule{0pt}{9pt}\right]J_1 J_2 C_1$ | $\frac{1}{(k+1)(k+2)(k+3)(k+4)}$ | $\frac{1}{2}\sum_{\alpha,\beta,\gamma} K_{q,\alpha}A_{\alpha,\beta}B_{\beta,\gamma}\theta_\gamma$ |
| $K_1 C_2$ | $\frac{4}{(k+1)(k+2)(k+3)(k+4)}$ | $\frac{1}{2}\sum_{\alpha,\beta} K_{q,\alpha}A_{\alpha,\beta}\theta_\alpha\theta_\beta^2$ |
| $\left[\rule{0pt}{9pt}\right.K_1 J_1 C_1$ | $\frac{4}{(k+1)(k+2)(k+3)(k+4)}$ | $\sum_{\alpha,\beta,\gamma} K_{q,\alpha}A_{\alpha,\beta}A_{\beta,\gamma}\theta_\alpha\theta_\gamma$ |
| $\left.\rule{0pt}{9pt}\right]J_1 K_1 C_1$ | $\frac{3}{(k+1)(k+2)(k+3)(k+4)}$ | $\sum_{\alpha,\beta,\gamma} K_{q,\alpha}A_{\alpha,\beta}A_{\beta,\gamma}\theta_\beta\theta_\gamma$ |
| $J_1 C_3$ | $\frac{1}{(k+1)(k+2)(k+3)(k+4)}$ | $\frac{1}{6}\sum_{\alpha,\beta} K_{q,\alpha}A_{\alpha,\beta}\theta_\beta^3$ |
| $J_1^3 C_1$ | $\frac{1}{(k+1)(k+2)(k+3)(k+4)}$ | $\sum_{\alpha,\beta,\gamma,\delta} K_{q,\alpha}A_{\alpha,\beta}A_{\beta,\gamma}A_{\gamma,\delta}\theta_\delta$ |
| $J_1^2 C_2$ | $\frac{1}{(k+1)(k+2)(k+3)(k+4)}$ | $\frac{1}{2}\sum_{\alpha,\beta,\gamma} K_{q,\alpha}A_{\alpha,\beta}A_{\beta,\gamma}\theta_\gamma^2$ |

If we have only one unknown function, the quantities joined by the square bracket are not distinct. These formulas are valid for all values of $q$. As a matter of fact, we will use them for $q = 1, 2, 3, 4, 5$.

### 11.2 Remark on the possibility of other formulas.

Let us return to paragraph 8.1. We can imagine other formulas. Here, for example, is a second order method:

$$y_{i+1}^* = y_i + hY_i,$$

$$y_{i+1} = y_i + h\sqrt{Y_i\,Y_{i+1}^*}$$

(which consists of replacing the arithmetic mean of the Euler-Cauchy method by a geometric mean). Moreover, this method is applicable to a system in canonical form, but the vector notations are no longer valid.

In comparison to the formulas of the Runge-Kutta type, this formula has the following shortcomings:

—it is inapplicable if $Y_i^*$ and $Y_{i+1}$ have opposite signs which is likely to happen around $Y = 0$.

—the development of the approximate solution causes the appearance of terms which do not enter into the development of the exact derivative.

For the error at one step, one finds

$$h^3 \left[ \frac{C_2 - 2J_1C_1}{12} - \frac{C_1^2}{8\,Y_i} \right],$$

i.e., the error relative to the Euler-Cauchy method is increased by one term which does not enter in the table of paragraph 11.1.

## V  METHODS OF RANK ONE AND TWO

### 12. Case of rank one.

The method of rank one reduces to that of Euler. Returning to the usual notations, where the subscript denotes the number of the step, we write it as

$$x_{i+1} = x_i + hx_i' + \cdots + \frac{h^p}{p!}\, X_i,$$

$$x_{i+1}' = x_i' + hx_i'' + \cdots + \frac{h^{p-1}}{(p-1)!}\, X_i,$$

$$\vdots$$

$$x_{i+1}^{(p-1)} = x_i^{(p-1)} + hX_i.$$

We see that there are no coefficients to determine. Its matrix form is

$$\boxed{1}\quad \boxed{1}\quad \cdots\quad \boxed{1}.$$

The formula is of order $(1, 2, \ldots, p)$.

### 13.1 Case of rank two.

The correctness of the terms $h^{k+1}$ in $y^{(p-k)}$ requires that

$$K_{2,1}\theta_1 = \frac{1}{k+1}.$$

In taking $\theta_1$ to be arbitrary (nonzero), this condition determines all the other coefficients.

The notation of the coefficients in matrix form is

| $\theta_1$ | | |
|---|---|---|
| $1 - \dfrac{1}{2\theta_1}$ | $\dfrac{1}{2\theta_1}$ | |

$\cdots$

| $\theta_1^k$ | | |
|---|---|---|
| $1 - \dfrac{1}{(k+1)\theta_1}$ | $\dfrac{1}{(k+1)\theta_1}$ | |

$\cdots$

We will call this formula RK2. It is of order $(2, 3, 4, \ldots, p+1)$.

### 13.2 Particular cases.

For $p = 1$, $\theta_1 = 1/2$, one obtains the improved tangent method; for $p = 1$, $\theta_1 = 1$, the Euler-Cauchy method.

## 14. Investigation of a representation of $x^{(p-k)}(t)$.[1]

We have an approximate value of

$$x_{i+1} \cdots x_{i+1}^{(p-k)} \cdots x_{i+1}^{(p-1)}$$

valid up to the degrees

$$p+1, \ldots, \qquad k+1, \ldots, \qquad 2.$$

We can ask if it is possible to obtain a representation valid up to the same order for

$$x(t) \cdots x^{(p-k)}(t) \cdots x^{(p-1)}(t) \qquad t \in (t_i, t_{i+1}).$$

Such representation is furnished by

$$\eta_{p-k}(t) = x_i^{(p-k)}(t_i) + \cdots + \frac{(t - t_i)^k}{k!}\left[X_i + \frac{(t - t_i)}{\theta_1(k+1)h}(X_{i,1} - X_i)\right],$$

as we can easily verify.

### 15.1 Truncation error at one step. Theoretical expression.

One obtains the principal part of the truncation error in composing the first nonidentical terms in the two developments in powers of $h$.

For the derivative of order $p - k$, one arrives at

[1]Kuntzmann [1].

$$\frac{h^{k+2}}{k!} \left\{ C_2 \left[ \frac{-1}{(k+1)(k+2)} + \frac{1}{2!} \sum K_{q,\,\alpha} \theta_\alpha^2 \right] \right.$$

$$\left. + J_1 C_1 \left[ \frac{-1}{(k+1)(k+2)} + \sum K_{q,\,\alpha} A_{\alpha,\,\beta} \theta_\beta \right] \right\}$$

which, after replacing the coefficients by their values, reduces itself to

$$\frac{h^{k+2}}{(k+2)!} \left\{ C_2 \left[ -1 + \frac{\theta_1(k+2)}{2} \right] - J_1 C_1 \right\}.$$

### 15.2 Remark on Taylor's series.

For $\theta_1 = 0$, we find

$$-\frac{h^{k+2}}{(k+2)!} (C_2 + J_1 C_1) = -\frac{h^{k+2}}{(k+2)!} x^{(p+2)},$$

i.e., the error term of

$$x_0^{(p-k)} + \frac{h}{1!} x_0^{(p-k+1)} + \cdots + \frac{h^{k+1}}{(k+1)!} x_0^{(p+1)}.$$

This permits us to consider the Taylor series method developed up to $x_0^{(p-k)}$ as the particular case of the Runge-Kutta method of order two, where one takes $\theta_1 = 0$.

### 15.3 Heun's method of order 2.

One will notice that in the formula for the error, one of the terms has a fixed coefficient, and the other has a coefficient which depends on $\theta$ and on $k$. In taking $\theta_1 = 2/3$, one removes the term $C_2$ in the expression of $x^{(p-1)}$. The formulas thus obtained constitute Heun's method of order 2. Their coefficients are written in matrix form:

| 2/3 | |
|---|---|
| 1/4 | 3/4 |

| $(2/3)^k$ | |
|---|---|
| $1 - \dfrac{3}{2(k+1)}$ | $\dfrac{3}{2(k+1)}$ |

### 15.4 Examples.

1.            $y' = y - 1.5e^{-0.5t}, \qquad y(0) = 1, \qquad h = 0.1.$

| $t$ | $y$ Euler-Cauchy | $y$ improved tangent | $y$ Heun | $y$ exact |
|---|---|---|---|---|
| 0.1 | 0.951,158 | 0.951,204 | 0.951,188 | 0.951,229 |
| 0.2 | 0.904,690 | 0.904,784 | 0.904,753 | 0.904,837 |
| 0.3 | 0.860,480 | 0.860,626 | 0.860,577 | 0.860,708 |
| 0.4 | 0.818,418 | 0.818,617 | 0.818,551 | 0.818,731 |
| 0.5 | 0.778,396 | 0.778,654 | 0.778,568 | 0.778,801 |
| 1 | 0.605,549 | 0.606,176 | 0.605,966 | 0.606,531 |

1. (*continued*)

| $t$ | $y$ Euler-Cauchy | $y$ improved tangent | $y$ Heun | $y$ exact |
|---|---|---|---|---|
| 1.5 | 0.470,504 | 0.471,693 | 0.471,294 | 0.472,367 |
| 2 | 0.364,619 | 0.366,700 | 0.366,003 | 0.367,879 |

2. $\qquad y' = -ty, \qquad y(0) = 1, \qquad h = 0.1.$

| $t$ | $y$ Euler-Cauchy | $y$ improved tangent | $y$ Heun | $y$ exact |
|---|---|---|---|---|
| 0.1 | 0.995,000 | 0.995,000 | 0.995,000 | 0.995,012 |
| 0.2 | 0.980,175 | 0.980,149 | 0.980,158 | 0.980,199 |
| 0.3 | 0.955,964 | 0.955,891 | 0.955,915 | 0.955,997 |
| 0.4 | 0.923,079 | 0.922,937 | 0.922,984 | 0.923,116 |
| 0.5 | 0.882,464 | 0.882,235 | 0.882,311 | 0.882,497 |
| 1 | 0.606,718 | 0.605,987 | 0.606,231 | 0.606,531 |
| 1.5 | 0.325,335 | 0.324,391 | 0.324,705 | 0.324,652 |
| 2 | 0.136,318 | 0.135,578 | 0.135,824 | 0.135,335 |

3. $\qquad y' = -2ty^2, \qquad y(0) = 1, \qquad h = 0.1.$

| $t$ | $y$ Euler-Cauchy | $y$ improved tangent | $y$ Heun | $y$ exact |
|---|---|---|---|---|
| 0.1 | 0.990,000 | 0.990,000 | 0.990,000 | 0.990,099 |
| 0.2 | 0.961,366 | 0.961,176 | 0.961,240 | 0.961,538 |
| 0.3 | 0.917,246 | 0.916,742 | 0.916,911 | 0.917,431 |
| 0.4 | 0.861,954 | 0.861,104 | 0.861,390 | 0.862,069 |
| 0.5 | 0.800,034 | 0.798,887 | 0.799,273 | 0.800,000 |
| 1 | 0.500,919 | 0.499,638 | 0.500,073 | 0.500,000 |
| 1.5 | 0.308,659 | 0.307,976 | 0.308,209 | 0.307,692 |
| 2 | 0.200,695 | 0.200,364 | 0.200,478 | 0.200,000 |

4. $\quad y'' + 1.5y' + 0.5y = 0, \qquad y(0) = y'(0) = 1, \qquad h = 0.1.$

| $t$ | $y$ | | | | $y'$ | | | |
|---|---|---|---|---|---|---|---|---|
| | $\theta = 1/2$ | $\theta = 2/3$ | $\theta = 1$ | $y$ exact | $\theta = 1/2$ | $\theta = 2/3$ | $\theta = 1$ | $y'$ exact |
| 0 | 1 | 1 | 1 | 1 | 1 | 1 | 1 | 1 |
| 0.1 | 1.090,42 | 1.090,42 | 1.090,43 | 1.090,43 | 0.812,62 | 0.812,67 | 0.812,75 | 0.812,05 |
| 0.2 | 1.163,24 | 1.163,25 | 1.163,26 | 1.163,15 | 0.647,52 | 0.647,59 | 0.647,74 | 0.646,52 |
| 0.3 | 1.220,56 | 1.220,58 | 1.220,61 | 1.220,38 | 0.502,26 | 0.502,45 | 0.502,64 | 0.501,04 |
| 0.4 | 1.264,28 | 1.264,31 | 1.264,35 | 1.263,96 | 0.375,03 | 0.375,14 | 0.375,36 | 0.373,50 |
| 0.5 | 1.296,08 | 1.296,12 | 1.296,19 | 1.295,61 | 0.263,66 | 0.263,78 | 0.264,01 | 0.261,99 |
| 1 | 1.323,78 | 1.323,87 | 1.324,05 | 1.322,49 | −0.107,82 | −0.107,72 | −0.107,51 | −0.109,42 |
| 1.5 | 1.222,01 | 1.222,14 | 1.222,40 | 1.220,08 | −0.274,34 | −0.274,28 | −0.274,17 | −0.275,34 |
| 2 | 1.067,78 | 1.067,93 | 1.068,22 | 1.065,51 | −0.329,36 | −0.329,35 | −0.329,33 | −0.329,75 |

5.     $y'' = (1 - t^2)y$,     $y(0) = y'(0) = 1$,     $h = 0.1$.

| $t$ | $y$ | | | | $y'$ | | | |
|---|---|---|---|---|---|---|---|---|
| | $\theta_1 = 1/2$ | $\theta_1 = 2/3$ | $\theta_1 = 1$ | $y$ exact | $\theta_1 = 1/2$ | $\theta_1 = 2/3$ | $\theta_1 = 1$ | $y'$ exact |
| 0 | 1 | 1 | 1 | 1 | 1 | 1 | 1 | 1 |
| 0.1 | 1.105,16 | 1.105,16 | 1.105,16 | 1.105,16 | 1.1049 | 1.1048 | 1.1047 | 1.1048 |
| 0.2 | 1.221,26 | 1.221,25 | 1.221,23 | 1.221,25 | 1.2184 | 1.2183 | 1.2180 | 1.2183 |
| 0.3 | 1.349,07 | 1.349,04 | 1.348,98 | 1.349,05 | 1.3388 | 1.3385 | 1.3380 | 1.3385 |
| 0.4 | 1.489,13 | 1.489,08 | 1.488,96 | 1.489,09 | 1,4632 | 1.4628 | 1.4619 | 1.4628 |
| 0.5 | 1.641,69 | 1.641,59 | 1.641,37 | 1.641,61 | 1.5879 | 1.5873 | 1.5860 | 1.5873 |
| 1 | 2.562,22 | 2.561,43 | 2.559,76 | 2.561,50 | 1.9950 | 1.9925 | 1.9872 | 1.9924 |
| 1.5 | 3.417,60 | 3.414,93 | 3.409,43 | 3.415,07 | 1.0694 | 1.0646 | 1.0550 | 1.0647 |
| 2 | 3.172,87 | 3.168,71 | 3.160,32 | 3.168,89 | $-2.5054$ | $-2.5040$ | $-2.5006$ | $-2.5035$ |

## 16. Practical evaluation of the truncation error at one step.

The quantities $C_2$ and $J_1 C_1$, on which the error at one step depends, are difficult to evaluate directly. Fortunately, it is possible to have their approximations from quantities already calculated by supposing the round-off error to be negligible. We operate in the following manner:

$$X_{i,\alpha} - X_i = h\theta_\alpha C_1 + h^2\left[\frac{\theta_\alpha^2}{2} C_2 + J_1 C_1 \sum_\beta A_{\alpha,\beta}\theta_\beta\right],$$

from which we derive

$$\theta_1(X_{i+1} - X_i) - X_{i,1} + X_i = h^2[C_2 + J_1 C_1]\frac{\theta_1}{2} - \frac{\theta_1^2}{2} C_2 h^2$$

$$= h^2\frac{\theta_1}{2}[C_2(1 - \theta_1) + J_1 C_1].$$

Let us consider

$$x^{(p+2)} = C_2 + J_1 C_1.$$

The derivative of order $p + 2$ can be written, except for infinitesimal quantities, by means of the second divided difference of $X$:

$$2\left[\frac{X_{i-1}}{h_i(h_{i+1} + h_i)} - \frac{X_i}{h_i h_{i+1}} + \frac{X_{i+1}}{h_{i+1}(h_{i+1} + h_i)}\right].$$

We have set $h_{i+1} = t_{i+1} - t_i$ (the steps are assumed to be unequal). In utilizing these two expressions, we obtain as an approximate expression of the error at $x_i^{(p-k)}$:

$$-\frac{h_{i+1}^k}{(k+2)!}\left\{\left[2 + \frac{kh_i}{h_i + h_{i+1}}\right] X_{i+1} - \frac{k+2}{\theta_1} X_{i,1}\right.$$

$$+ \left[2\left(\frac{1}{\theta_1} - 1\right) + k\left(\frac{1}{\theta_1} - 1 + \frac{h_{i+1}}{h_i}\right)\right] X_i - \frac{kh_{i+1}^2}{h_i(h_i + h_{i+1})} X_{i-1}\right\}.$$

If the steps are equal, the formulas reduce, for $x^{(p-k)}$, to

$$\frac{h^k}{(k+2)!}\left[-X_{i+1}\left(2+\frac{k}{2}\right)+\frac{k}{2}X_{i-1}+\frac{k+2}{\theta_1}X_{i,1}-\left(\frac{k+2}{\theta_1}-2\right)X_i\right];$$

for $x^{(p-1)}$, to

$$\frac{h}{12}\left[-5X_{i+1}+X_{i-1}+\frac{6}{\theta_1}X_{i,1}+\left(-\frac{6}{\theta_1}+4\right)X_i\right].$$

In the case of the improved tangent method, this reduces to

$$\frac{h}{12}(-5X_{i+1}+12X_{i+1/2}-8X_i+X_{i-1});$$

in that of Euler-Cauchy, to

$$\frac{h}{12}(-5X_{i+1}-2X_i+6X_{i+1}^*+X_{i-1}).$$

One can find examples of the use of these formulas in paragraphs 2.1 and 4.1.


## VI  METHODS OF RANK THREE

### 17. Impossibility of an approximation of $x^{(p-k)}$ in $h^{k+2}$.

If one attempts to write that the value $x_i^{(p-k)}$ is exact up to the terms in $h^{(k+2)}$, one arrives at the conditions:

$$K_{3,1}\theta_1+K_{3,2}\theta_2=\frac{1}{k+1}, \qquad\qquad C_1$$

$$K_{3,1}\theta_1^2+K_{3,2}\theta_2^2=\frac{2}{(k+1)(k+2)}, \qquad C_2$$

$$K_{3,2}A_{2,1}\theta_1=\frac{1}{(k+1)(k+2)}. \qquad J_1C_1$$

One can consider this as a system of three equations in the two quantities $K_{3,1}$ and $K_{3,2}$. Such a system is compatible only if the complete determinant is zero; for example,

$$\begin{vmatrix} \theta_1 & \theta_2 & \dfrac{1}{k+1} \\[2mm] \theta_1^2 & \theta_2^2 & \dfrac{2}{(k+1)(k+2)} \\[2mm] 0 & A_{2,1}\theta_1 & \dfrac{1}{(k+1)(k+2)} \end{vmatrix}=0,$$

which can be written by multiplying the last column by $(k+1)(k+2)$, which is not zero, and by dividing the first column by $\theta_1$:

$$kA_{2,1}\theta_1^2=\theta_1\theta_2-\theta_2^2+2A_{2,1}\theta_1-2A_{2,1}\theta_1^2.$$

By virtue of the third equation, $A_{2,1}\theta_1^2$ cannot be zero. The above-mentioned relation can only be verified at most for one value of $k$. In other words,

$$x_1^{(p-k)}$$

can be exact only up to order $k + 2$ for only one value of $k$. If $p = 1$, one chooses naturally $k = 1$; if $p > 1$, we will examine that which gives the rule of the preservation of orders.

Let us suppose that we have written formulas which give for $x_1^{(p-k)}$ the order $k + 1$ except for $x_1^{(p-r)}$, where the order is $r + 2$. Let us look for the conditions at which these orders will be maintained at the following step. We will distinguish two cases:

(a) $r \neq 1$. $x_1^{(p-1)}$ is exact up to the terms in $h^2$ only. The same holds for $X_1$. All the intermediate $x_{1,\alpha}^{(p-k)}$ of the second step are exact up to the order $k + 1$, and so are the $x_2^{(p-1)}$ relative to the end of the second step. There is no preservation of the orders.

(b) $r = 1$. $x_1^{(p-1)}$ is exact up to the terms in $h^3$ as well as $X_1$. The $x_{1,\alpha}^{(p-k)}$ are exact up to the order $k + 1$ except for $x_{1,\alpha}^{(p-1)}$, which is exact up to the third order, and the same holds for the $x_2^{(p-k)}$ and $x_2^{(p-1)}$ relative to the end of the second step. Hence, there exists a preservation of the orders.

The sensible solution, which we will adopt, consists of taking the third order for the derivative of order $p - 1$, and the order $k + 1$ for the derivative $x^{(p-k)}$ ($k > 1$); in particular, $x^{(p-2)}$ is also of the third order, and $x$ is of order $p + 1$. The methods investigated are hence of order $(3, 3, 4, \ldots, p + 1)$.

If one compares this result with that of paragraph 3.1, one sees that only the first number has increased. We will see in Chapter 9, paragraph 17.2, that this number represents the most important part therein.

### 18. Determination of the coefficients $A_{\alpha, \beta}$.

These coefficients have to satisfy the conditions

$$A_{31}\theta_1 + A_{32}\theta_2 = \frac{1}{2},$$

$$A_{31}\theta_1^2 + A_{32}\theta_2^2 = \frac{1}{3},$$

$$A_{32}A_{21}\theta_1 = \frac{1}{6},$$

completed by the conditions:

$$A_{30} + A_{31} + A_{32} = 1,$$

$$A_{20} + A_{21} = \theta_2,$$

$$A_{10} = \theta_1.$$

Let us give $\theta_1$ and $\theta_2$. The first two conditions determine $A_{31}$, $A_{32}$; the third determines $A_{21}$. The last three determine $A_{30}$, $A_{20}$, $A_{10}$.

**19. Impossibility of a representation of the third order for $x^{(p-1)}(t)$.**

We have seen that it was possible to obtain for $x_i^{(p-1)}$ a representation of the third order. This result does not extend to the interior points of the step.
  In effect, we have to find functions $a(t)$ and $b(t)$ such that

$$\eta_i(t) = x_i^{(p-1)} + \frac{(t-t_i)}{k!}[X_i + a(t)(X_{i,1} - X_i) + b(t)(X_{i,2} - X_i)]$$

has a correct Taylor development up to the term in $h^3$ inclusive which would allow us to solve the system

$$a(t)\theta_1 + b(t)\theta_2 = \frac{(t-t_i)}{2h},$$

$$a(t)\theta_1^2 + b(t)\theta_2^2 = \frac{2(t-t_i)^2}{6h^2},$$

$$b(t)A_{21}\theta_1 = \frac{(t-t_i)^2}{6h^2}.$$

But this system is consistent only for $t = t_i$ and $t = t_{i+1}$.

**20. Truncation error at one step. Theoretical evaluation.**[1]

For the principal part of the error at one step, for $x^{(p-1)}$, one finds easily

$$h^4\left[C_3\left(-\frac{1}{24} - \frac{\theta_1\theta_2}{12} + \frac{\theta_1 + \theta_2}{18}\right) + J_1 C_2\left(-\frac{1}{24} + \frac{\theta_1}{12}\right)\right.$$

$$\left. + K_1 C_1\left(-\frac{1}{8} + \frac{\theta_2}{6}\right) - J_1^2 C_1 \frac{1}{24} + J_2 C_1\left(-\frac{1}{24} + \frac{A_{32}}{2} B_{21}\theta_1\right)\right].$$

The latter term does not exist if $p = 1$.

**21.1 Actual methods for a system in canonical form.**

Nyström proposes $\theta_1 = \theta_2 = 2/3$.

| 2/3 | | |
|-----|-----|-----|
| 0 | 2/3 | |
| 1/4 | 3/8 | 3/8 |

We will call this form RK3 Nyström.
  We can again use $\theta_1 = 1/2$, $\theta_2 = 1$.

| 1/2 | | |
|-----|-----|-----|
| −1 | 2 | |
| 1/6 | 2/3 | 1/6 |

We will call this formula RK3 Classic.

[1]Piaggio.

Conte and Reeves propose $\theta_1 = 0.626,538,3$; $\theta_2 = 0.075,425,9$.

| $\theta_1$ | | |
|---|---|---|
| $\theta_1$ | $-0.551,112,4$ | |
| $\theta_1$ | $0.856,143,5$ | $-0.482,681,8$ |

This choice permits the reduction of the number of necessary memory units (of paragraph 27.1).

### 21.2 Optimal method of the third order.[1]

If, in trying to minimize the sum of the absolute values of the terms in the error at one step, we find

$$\theta_1 = \frac{10 - 2\sqrt{13}}{6} \approx 0.464,816,2,$$

$$\theta_2 = \frac{1 + \sqrt{13}}{6} \approx 0.767,591,9.$$

| $\theta_1$ | | |
|---|---|---|
| $\dfrac{\sqrt{13} - 5}{24}$ $-0.058,102,0$ | $\dfrac{3 + \sqrt{13}}{8}$ $-0.825,693,9$ | |
| $\dfrac{23 - 5\sqrt{13}}{24}$ $0.207,176,8$ | $\dfrac{5 + \sqrt{13}}{24}$ $0.358,564,6$ | $\dfrac{\sqrt{13} - 1}{6}$ $0.434,258,5$ |

We will call this formula RK3 Optimal.

### 21.3 Examples.

1. Let $\qquad y' = -y, \qquad y(0) = 1, \qquad h = 0.1.$

| $t$ | All methods | $y$ exact |
|---|---|---|
| 0 | 1 | 1 |
| 0.1 | 0.904,833 | 0.904,837 |
| 0.2 | 0.818,723 | 0.818,731 |
| 0.3 | 0.740,808 | 0.740,818 |
| 0.4 | 0.670,308 | 0.670,320 |
| 0.5 | 0.606,517 | 0.606,531 |
| 1.0 | 0.367,863 | 0.367,879 |
| 1.5 | 0.223,115 | 0.223,130 |
| 2.0 | 0.135,323 | 0.135,335 |

[1]Kuntzmann [2].

2.        $y' = y - 1.5e^{-0.5t}$,     $y(0) = 1$,     $h = 0.1$.

| $t$ | Nyström | Classic | Conte and Reeves | Optimum | $y$ exact |
|---|---|---|---|---|---|
| 0 | 1 | 1 | 1 | 1 | 1 |
| 0.1 | 0.951,228 | 0.951,228 | 0.951,228 | 0.951,228 | |
| 0.2 | 0.904,834 | 0.904,835 | 0.904,834 | 0.904,835 | 0.904,837 |
| 0.3 | 0.860,703 | 0.860,704 | 0.860,703 | 0.860,705 | |
| 0.4 | 0.818,724 | 0.818,726 | 0.818,724 | 0.818,726 | 0.818,731 |
| 0.5 | 0.778,792 | 0.778,795 | 0.778,792 | 0.778,795 | |
| 1.0 | 0.606,508 | 0.606,517 | 0.606,510 | 0.606,517 | 0.606,531 |
| 1.5 | 0.472,324 | 0.472,340 | 0.472,326 | 0.472,341 | |
| 2.0 | 0.367,805 | 0.367,832 | 0.367,809 | 0.367,835 | 0.367,879 |

3.        $y' = -ty$,     $y(0) = 1$,     $h = 0.1$.

| $t$ | Nyström | Classic | Conte and Reeves | Optimum | $y$ exact |
|---|---|---|---|---|---|
| 0 | 1 | 1 | 1 | 1 | 1 |
| 0.1 | 0.995,011 | 0.995,017 | 0.995,001 | 0.995,013 | 0.995,012 |
| 0.2 | 0.980,196 | 0.980,207 | 0.980,177 | 0.980,199 | 0.980,199 |
| 0.3 | 0.955,994 | 0.956,010 | 0.955,965 | 0.955,999 | 0.955,997 |
| 0.4 | 0.923,112 | 0.923,132 | 0.923,076 | 0.923,118 | 0.923,116 |
| 0.5 | 0.882,492 | 0.882,516 | 0.882,451 | 0.882,500 | 0.882,497 |
| 1.0 | 0.606,523 | 0.606,553 | 0.606,482 | 0.606,537 | 0.606,531 |
| 1.5 | 0.324,635 | 0.324,653 | 0.324,624 | 0.324,650 | 0.323,033 |
| 2.0 | 0.135,302 | 0.135,308 | 0.135,316 | 0.135,314 | 0.135,335 |

4.        $y' = -2ty^2$,     $y(0) = 1$,     $h = 0.1$.

| $t$ | Nyström | Classic | Conte and Reeves | Optimum | $y$ exact |
|---|---|---|---|---|---|
| 0 | 1 | 1 | 1 | 1 | 1 |
| 0.1 | 0.990,088 | 0.990,132 | 0.990,010 | 0.990,102 | 0.990,099 |
| 0.2 | 0.961,521 | 0.961,600 | 0.961,380 | 0.961,547 | 0.961,538 |
| 0.3 | 0.917,412 | 0.917,513 | 0.917,235 | 0.917,448 | 0.917,431 |
| 0.4 | 0.862,051 | 0.862,159 | 0.861,869 | 0.862,094 | 0.862,069 |
| 0.5 | 0.799,983 | 0.800,083 | 0.799,816 | 0.800,031 | 0.800,000 |
| 1.0 | 0.499,965 | 0.500,016 | 0.499,912 | 0.500,003 | 0.500,000 |
| 1.5 | 0.307,652 | 0.307,676 | 0.307,631 | 0.307,672 | 0.307,692 |
| 2.0 | 0.199,971 | 0.199,983 | 0.199,959 | 0.199,981 | 0.200,000 |

## 22. Comparison of the error terms for the different methods.

Here are the numerical values of the coefficients for the methods cited:

|  | $C_3$ | $J_1 C_2$ | $K_1 C_1$ | $J_1^2 C_2$ |
|---|---|---|---|---|
| Nyström $\theta_1 = \theta_2 = 2/3$ | $-1/216$ | $+1/72$ | $-1/72$ | $-1/24$ |
| $\theta_2 = 1/2, \theta_2 = 1$ | $0$ | $0$ | $+1/24$ | $-1/24$ |
| Conte and Reeves | $-0.0066$ | $+0.0105$ | $-0.113$ | $-1/24$ |
| Optimum | $-0.0029$ | $-0.0029$ | $-0.0029$ | $-1/24$ |

According to these formulas, we have to expect that:
— the Nyström formula is often better than the classic formula.
—the formula of Conte and Reeves is deceiving.
—the optimal formula is often the best of all.

The given examples show us how difficult it is to draw conclusions from numerical examples which are few in number. Here are the stated differences (all errors have been multiplied by $10^6$):

|  |  | Nyström | Classic | Conte and Reeves | Optimum |
|---|---|---|---|---|---|
| Ex. 2 | $t = 1$ | 8 | $-22$ | 49 | $-6$ |
|  | $t = 2$ | 33 | 27 | 19 | 21 |
| Ex. 3 | $t = 1$ | 35 | $-16$ | 88 | $-3$ |
|  | $t = 2$ | 29 | 17 | 41 | 19 |
| Ex. 4 | $t = 1$ | 23 | 14 | 21 | 14 |
|  | $t = 2$ | 74 | 47 | 70 | 44 |

## 23.1 Determination of the coefficients $B_{\alpha, \beta}$ and $K_{\alpha, \beta}$ (for $p > 1$).

The exactness of the development of

$$x^{(p-2)}, \ldots, x^{(p-k)}$$

up to the terms in $h^3, \ldots, h^{k+1}$ inclusive necessitate the conditions:

$$B_{1, 0} = \theta_1^2, \qquad\qquad K_{1, 0} = \theta_1^k,$$
$$B_{2, 0} + B_{2, 1} = \theta_2^2, \qquad K_{2, 0} + K_{2, 1} = \theta_2^k,$$
$$B_{3, 0} + B_{3, 1} + B_{3, 2} = 1, \quad K_{3, 0} + K_{3, 1} + K_{3, 2} = 1,$$
$$B_{3, 1}\theta_1 + B_{3, 2}\theta_2 = \frac{1}{3}, \quad K_{3, 1}\theta_1 + K_{3, 2}\theta_2 = \frac{1}{k + 1}.$$

We can impose supplementary conditions by doing away with certain error terms.

The vanishing of the term $J_2 C_1$ in $x^{(p-1)}$ gives

$$\frac{1}{24} - A_{32} B_{21} \frac{\theta_1}{2} = 0, \qquad \text{condition (A)},$$

where $B_{21} = A_{21}/2$.

Another relation will be found when we study the error at one step for $x^{(p-k)}$:

$$\frac{h^{k+2}}{k!}\left\{C_2\left[-\frac{1}{(k+1)(k+2)}+\frac{1}{2}\sum_{\beta}K_{3,\beta}\theta_{\beta}^2\right]\right.$$
$$\left.-J_1C_1\left[\frac{-1}{(k+1)(k+2)}+K_{32}A_{21}\theta_1\right]\right\}.$$

This error contains two terms. We know that it is impossible to do away with both of them at the same time.

An easy calculation proves that, to minimize the sum of their absolute values, it is necessary to make the second term zero. This leads to the condition (B):

$$B_{3,2}=\frac{2-3\theta_1}{12\theta_2(\theta_2-\theta_1)},\qquad K_{3,2}=\frac{2-3\theta_1}{(k+1)(k+2)\theta_2(\theta_2-\theta_1)}.$$

For $\theta_1=\theta_2=2/3$:

$$B_{3,2}=\frac{3}{16},\qquad K_{3,2}=\frac{9}{4(k+1)(k+2)}.$$

All the coefficients $B_{\alpha,\beta}$ are hence determined. For $k>2$ there remains one indeterminate, for example, $K_{2,1}$. The error which remains with $x^{(p-k)}$, $(k>1)$, has as a principal part

$$-C_2\frac{h^{k+2}}{k!}\frac{\theta_1(k-1)}{2(k+1)(k+2)}.$$

### 23.2 Methods available for $p>1$.

Nyström proposes (to complete the table of paragraph 21.1):

| 4/9 | | $B$ |
|---|---|---|
| 4/9 | 0 | |
| 1/2 | 1/4 | 1/4 |

| $(2/3)^k$ | | $K$ |
|---|---|---|
| $(2/3)^k$ | 0 | |
| $\dfrac{2k-1}{2(k+1)}$ | $\dfrac{3}{4(k+1)}$ | $\dfrac{3}{4(k+1)}$ |

We shall call this formula RK3 Nyström I.

Neither $A$ nor $B$ are verified in this way. When trying to verify $A$ and $B$, we arrive at

| 4/9 | | $B$ |
|---|---|---|
| 1/9 | 1/3 | |
| 1/2 | 5/16 | 3/16 |

| $(2/3)^k$ | | $K$ |
|---|---|---|
| $(2/3)^k$ | 0 | |
| $\dfrac{4k^2+6k-4}{4(k+1)(k+2)}$ | $\dfrac{6k+3}{4(k+1)(k+2)}$ | $\dfrac{9}{4(k+1)(k+2)}$ |

We call this formula RK3 Nyström II.

Likewise, for $\theta_1 = 1/2$, $\theta_2 = 1$, we can take:
RK3 Classic I

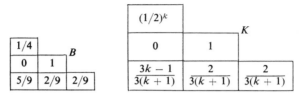

which verifies $A$.
RK3 Classic II

$$
\begin{array}{|c|c|}
\hline
1/4 & \\
\hline
0 & 1 \\
\hline
5/12 & 6/12 & 1/12 \\
\hline
\end{array}
\quad B
$$

$$
\begin{array}{|c|c|c|}
\hline
\multicolumn{3}{|l|}{(1/2)^k} \\
\hline
0 & 1 & \\
\hline
\dfrac{k^2 + k - 1}{(k+1)(k+2)} & \dfrac{2}{k+2} & \dfrac{1}{(k+1)(k+2)} \\
\hline
\end{array}
\quad K
$$

which verifies $A$ and $B$.

Finally, we can complete the optimal formula:

$$
\begin{array}{|c|c|c|}
\hline
\dfrac{38 - 10\sqrt{13}}{9} & & \\
0.216{,}054{,}1 & & \\
\hline
\dfrac{29 - \sqrt{13}}{144} & \dfrac{3 + \sqrt{13}}{16} & \\
0.176{,}350{,}3 & 0.412{,}847{,}0 & \\
\hline
\dfrac{7 - \sqrt{13}}{8} & \dfrac{5 + \sqrt{13}}{24} & \dfrac{\sqrt{13} - 1}{12} \\
0.424{,}306{,}1 & 0.358{,}564{,}6 & 0.217{,}129{,}3 \\
\hline
\end{array}
$$

which verifies $A$ and $B$.

### 23.3 Example.

$$y'' + 1.5y' + 0.5y = 0, \qquad y(0) = y'(0) = 1, \qquad h = 0.1.$$

| $t$ | RK3 NI | RK3 NII | RK3 CI | RK3 CII | RK3 O | $y$ exact |
|---|---|---|---|---|---|---|
| 0 | 1 | 1 | 1 | 1 | 1 | 1 |
| 0.1 | 1.090,40 | 1.090,41 | 1.090,38 | 1.090,41 | 1.090,41 | 1.090,41 |
| 0.2 | 1.163,15 | 1.163,16 | 1.163,11 | 1.163,16 | 1.163,16 | 1.163,16 |
| 0.3 | 1.220,36 | 1.220,37 | 1.220,31 | 1.220,37 | 1.220,37 | 1.220,38 |
| 0.4 | 1.263,94 | 1.263,95 | 1.263,87 | 1.263,95 | 1.263,95 | 1.263,96 |
| 0.5 | 1.295,58 | 1.295,60 | 1.295,50 | 1.295,60 | 1.295,60 | 1.295,61 |
| 1.0 | 1.322,42 | 1.322,44 | 1.322,29 | 1.322,43 | 1.322,44 | 1.322,48 |
| 1.5 | 1.219,98 | 1.220,00 | 1.219,84 | 1.220,00 | 1.220,01 | 1.220,08 |
| 2.0 | 1.065,41 | 1.065,42 | 1.065,27 | 1.065,43 | 1.065,43 | 1.065,51 |

### 24. Error terms for these different methods.

Here are the error terms for $k = 2$:

|            | $C^2$                 | $J_1 C_1$ |
|------------|-----------------------|-----------|
| Nyström I  | 1/72                  | 1/72      |
| Nyström II | 1/72                  | 0         |
| Classic I  | 1/36                  | 5/72      |
| Classic II | 1/96                  | 0         |
| Optimal    | $\dfrac{5 - \sqrt{13}}{144}$ | 0  |

## VII  METHODS OF RANK FOUR

The formulas obtained below are of the order $(4, 4, \ldots, p + 2)$.

### 25.1 Conditions on $A_{\alpha\beta}$.

According to the study of the case $q = 3$, we will first write that the representation of $x_1^{(p-1)}$ is valid up to the terms in $h^4$. This is expressed by the conditions:

$$A_{4,0} + A_{4,1} + A_{4,2} + A_{4,3} = 1,$$

$$A_{3,0} + A_{3,1} + A_{3,2} = \theta_3,$$

$$A_{2,0} + A_{2,1} = \theta_2,$$

$$A_{1,0} = \theta_1,$$

$$\begin{Vmatrix} \theta_1 & \theta_2 & \theta_3 \\ \theta_1^2 & \theta_2^2 & \theta_3^2 \\ \theta_1^3 & \theta_2^3 & \theta_3^3 \end{Vmatrix} \cdot \begin{Vmatrix} A_{4,1} \\ A_{4,2} \\ A_{4,3} \end{Vmatrix} = \begin{Vmatrix} 1/2 \\ 1/3 \\ 1/4 \end{Vmatrix} \qquad \begin{matrix} C_1 \\ C_2 \\ C_3 \end{matrix} \qquad \begin{matrix} (1) \\ (2) \\ (3) \end{matrix}$$

$$\begin{Vmatrix} \theta_2 & \theta_1 & \theta_1 \\ \theta_2^2 & \theta_1^2 & \theta_1^2 \\ \theta_3\theta_2 & \theta_3\theta_1 & \theta_2\theta_1 \end{Vmatrix} \cdot \begin{Vmatrix} A_{4,3} & A_{3,2} \\ A_{4,3} & A_{3,1} \\ A_{4,2} & A_{2,1} \end{Vmatrix} = \begin{Vmatrix} 1/6 \\ 1/12 \\ 1/8 \end{Vmatrix} \qquad \begin{matrix} J_1 C_1 \\ J_1 C_2 \\ K_1 C_1 \end{matrix} \qquad \begin{matrix} (4) \\ (5) \\ (6) \end{matrix}$$

$$A_{4,3} A_{3,2} A_{2,1} \theta_1 = 1/24 \qquad\qquad J_1^2 C_1 \qquad (7)$$

On the whole, the first relations determine $A_{4,0}$, $A_{4,1}$, $A_{4,2}$, $A_{4,3}$, which are the coefficients of the approximate quadrature at the abscissas $0$, $\theta_1$, $\theta_2$, $\theta_3$. The relations (4), (5), and (6) determine $A_{3,2}$, $A_{3,1}$, $A_{2,1}$. Consequently, relation (7) gives a condition of compatibility between $\theta_1$, $\theta_2$, $\theta_3$. A computation, a little laborious but easy, shows that this condition is

$$\theta_3 = 1.$$

### 25.2 Study of a determinant.

Let us consider the determinant:

$$\begin{vmatrix} \theta_1 & \theta_2 & \theta_3 \\ \theta_1^2 & \theta_2^2 & \theta_3^2 \\ 0 & A_{2,1}\theta_1 & A_{3,2}\theta_2 + A_{3,1}\theta_1 \end{vmatrix}$$

We are going to show that it is nonzero.

Let us consider the determinant obtained, forming the combination of columns with the following multipliers:

$$1.0, 0; \ A_{4,1}, A_{4,2}, A_{4,3}; \ A_{4,1}\theta_1, A_{4,2}\theta_2, A_{4,3}\theta_3.$$

We arrive at

$$\begin{vmatrix} \theta_1 & 1/2 & 1/3 \\ \theta_1^2 & 1/3 & 1/4 \\ 0 & 1/6 & 1/8 \end{vmatrix} = \theta_1^2(1/18 - 1/16) \neq 0.$$

### 25.3 Approximate representation of $x^{(p-1)}(t)$.

The fact that $\theta_3 = 1$ suffices to prove that it is not possible to obtain a representation of $x^{(p-1)}(t)$ exact up to the terms in $h^4$ inclusive.

One the other hand, it is possible to find a representation of $x^{(p-1)}(t)$ of order 3. Indeed, one is led to solve the system

$$a(t)\theta_1 + b(t)\theta_2 + c(t)\theta_3 = \frac{(t - t_i)^2}{2},$$

$$a(t)\theta_1^2 + b(t)\theta_2^2 + c(t)\theta_3^2 = \frac{(t - t_i)^3}{3},$$

$$b(t)A_{21}\theta_1 + c(t)[A_{32}\theta_2 + A_{31}\theta_1] = \frac{(t - t_i)^3}{6}.$$

But we just proved that the determinant of this system is nonzero.

### 26.1 Error of the method at one step for $x^{(p-1)}$. Theoretical evaluation.[1]

The latter is obtained by comparison of the terms neglected in Taylor's development and in that of the approximate integration formulas. These terms are of several types:

—some contain only $A_{\alpha, \beta}$, and these consequently cannot be cancelled at all.

—others contain $B_{\alpha, \beta}$, $C_{\alpha, \beta}$, and these will be studied further.

### 26.2 Error terms not containing $B_{\alpha, \beta}$, $C_{\alpha, \beta}$.

We find

$$\frac{1}{24}\left(\frac{1}{20} - \frac{\theta_1 + \theta_2}{12} + \frac{\theta_1\theta_2}{6}\right) \qquad C_4$$

[1]Albrecht, Bieberbach, and Bukovics [3], Gautschi [2], Lotkin [1], Vejvoda [1].

$$\frac{1}{24}\left(\frac{-\theta_2}{2} + \frac{3}{10}\right) \qquad\qquad L_1 C_1$$

$$\frac{1}{24}\left(-\frac{12}{20} - \frac{\theta_1}{2} + \theta_1\theta_2\right) + \frac{\psi}{2} \qquad R$$

$$\frac{1}{24}\left(\frac{-\theta_1}{2} + \frac{1}{5}\right) \qquad\qquad K_1 C_2$$

$$+\frac{1}{120} \qquad\qquad K_1 J_1 C_1$$

$$\frac{4}{24}\left(-\frac{1}{20} + \frac{\theta_1 + \theta_2}{12} - \frac{\theta_1\theta_2}{6}\right) \qquad J_1 C_3$$

$$-\frac{3}{120} + \frac{\theta_2}{24} \qquad\qquad J_1 K_1 C_1$$

$$-\frac{1}{120} \qquad\qquad J_1^3 C_1$$

$$\frac{1}{24}\left(-\frac{1}{5} + \frac{\theta_1}{2}\right) \qquad\qquad J_1^2 C_2$$

We have denoted by $\psi$ the quantity

$$\frac{\theta_1^2(26\theta_2 - 18) + \theta_1(27 - 42\theta_2 + 6\theta_2^2) + (4\theta_2 - 3)(3 - \theta_2)}{48(2\theta_1 - 1)[3 - 4(\theta_1 + \theta_2) + 6\theta_1\theta_2]}.$$

The coefficient of $R$ takes an indeterminate form for $\theta_1 = \theta_2 = 1/2$. In re-calculating this quantity, we find

$$-\frac{3}{120} + \frac{1}{48}(1 + A_{21}).$$

### 27.1 Actual formulas for $\theta_1 = \theta_2 = 1/2$.

For any $\theta_1$ and $\theta_2$, equations (1) through (7) determine entirely the coefficients $A_{\alpha,\beta}$. This is not the case for

$$\theta_1 = \theta_2 = \frac{1}{2}.$$

The equations give only

$$A_{43} = \frac{1}{6},$$

$$A_{32} + A_{31} = 1, \qquad A_{41} + A_{42} = \frac{2}{3},$$

$$A_{42} A_{21} = \frac{1}{6}, \qquad A_{32} A_{21} = \frac{1}{2}.$$

The Runge-Kutta formula RK4 Classical uses the coefficients:

| 1/2 | | | |
|-----|-----|-----|-----|
| 0 | 1/2 | | |
| 0 | 0 | 1 | |
| 1/6 | 1/3 | 1/3 | 1/6 |

Applying the preceding formula, one notes that in the calculation of $X_{i,2}$, the number of the quantities to be conserved simultaneously is maximum (four per function): $x_i$, $X_i$, $X_{i,1}$, and $X_{1,2}$, or

$$x_i + h(A_{20}\, X_i + A_{21}\, X_{i,1}), \qquad x_1 + h(A_{30}\, X_i + A_{31}\, X_{i,1}),$$
$$x_i + h(A_{40}\, X_i + A_{41}\, X_{i,1}), \qquad X_{i,2}.$$

However, these quantities are independent, unless the condition

$$\begin{vmatrix} 1 & A_{20} & A_{21} \\ 1 & A_{30} & A_{31} \\ 1 & A_{40} & A_{41} \end{vmatrix} = 0$$

is valid, which reduces the number of quantities to be conserved simultaneously to three. To realize this condition, Gill proposes that

$$\theta_1 = \theta_2 = \frac{1}{2}.$$

| 1/2 | | | |
|-----|-----|-----|-----|
| $(\sqrt{2} - 1)/2$ | $(2 - \sqrt{2})/2$ | | |
| 0 | $-\sqrt{2}/2$ | $1 + \sqrt{2}/2$ | |
| 1/6 | $(2 - \sqrt{2})/6$ | $(2 + \sqrt{2})/6$ | 1/6 |

We will call this formula RK4 Gill. See also Blum. The following has also been proposed with a view to using a binary computer (Strachey, cited by D. W. Martin).

| 1/2 | | | |
|------|------|------|------|
| $-1/2$ | 1 | | |
| 0 | 1/2 | 1/2 | |
| 1/6 | 2/6 | 2/6 | 1/6 |

**27.2  Other available formulas.**

We encounter in the literature choices other than $\theta_1 = \theta_2 = 1/2$. For example,

$$\theta_1 = \frac{1}{3}, \qquad \theta_2 = \frac{2}{3} \qquad \text{(Boulton)}$$

$$\theta_1 = 1, \qquad \theta_2 = \frac{1}{2} \qquad \text{(Ince, appendix B)}$$

$$\theta_1 = \frac{1}{2}, \qquad \theta_2 = 0 \qquad \text{(Mineur).}$$

### 27.3  Optimal method of rank four.[1]

Let us seek to determine $\theta_1$ and $\theta_2$ in order to minimize components of the error at one step. We are led to take $\theta_1 = 2/5$, $\theta_2 = 3/5$.

| 2/5 | | | |
|---|---|---|---|
| −3/20 | 3/4 | | |
| 19/44 | −15/44 | 40/44 | |
| 55/360 | 125/360 | 125/360 | 55/360 |

We will call this formula the RK4 Optimal.

### 28. Table summarizing the truncation error at one step (terms not containing $B_{\alpha,\beta}$, $C_{\alpha,\beta}$).

| | $C_4$ | $L_1 C_1$ | $R$ | $K_1 C_2$ | $K_1 J_1 C_1$ | $J_1 C_3$ | $J_1 K_1 C_1$ | $J_1^3 C_1$ | $J_1^2 C_2$ |
|---|---|---|---|---|---|---|---|---|---|
| Classic | $\cdots$ | $\cdots$ | $+\dfrac{1}{160}$ | $-\dfrac{1}{480}$ | $+\dfrac{1}{120}$ | $-\dfrac{4}{2880}$ | $-\dfrac{1}{240}$ | $-\dfrac{1}{120}$ | $+\dfrac{1}{480}$ |
| Gill | $+\dfrac{1}{2880}$ | $+\dfrac{1}{480}$ | $-\dfrac{\sqrt{2}}{96}+\dfrac{1}{60}$ | | | | | | |
| Optimal | $+\dfrac{1}{3600}$ | $0$ | $\dfrac{3}{880}$ | $0$ | $+\dfrac{1}{120}$ | $-\dfrac{4}{3600}$ | $0$ | $-\dfrac{1}{120}$ | $0$ |

### 29. Examples.[2]

1. $\qquad y' = y - 1.5e^{-0.5t}, \qquad y(0) = 1, \qquad h = 0.1.$

| $t$ | Classic | Gill | Optimum | $y$ exact |
|---|---|---|---|---|
| 0 | 1 | | | |
| 0.1 | 0.951,229,40 | 9401 | 941 | 942 |
| 0.2 | 0.904,837,36 | 736 | 738 | 742 |
| 0.3 | 0.860,707,89 | 789 | 792 | 798 |
| 0.4 | 0.818,730,63 | 063 | 067 | 075 |
| 0.5 | 0.778,800,62 | 062 | 067 | 078 |
| 1.0 | 0.606,530,26 | 025 | 038 | 066 |
| 1.5 | 0.472,365,78 | 578 | 601 | 655 |
| 2.0 | 0.367,878,09 | 809 | 869 | 944 |

[1]Kuntzmann [2].

[2]In this example, and in others which follow, we will only write the last figures of each number.

2.        $y' = -ty,$     $y(0) = 1,$     $h = 0.1.$

| $t$ | Classic | Gill | Optimum | $y$ exact |
|---|---|---|---|---|
| 0 | 1 | | | |
| 0.1 | 0.995,012,48 | 249 | 248 | 248 |
| 0.2 | 0.980,198,68 | 868 | 866 | 867 |
| 0.3 | 0.955,997,48 | 749 | 745 | 748 |
| 0.4 | 0.923,116,35 | 635 | 629 | 634 |
| 0.5 | 0.882,496,90 | 691 | 681 | 690 |
| 1.0 | 0.606,530,73 | 074 | 046 | 066 |
| 1.5 | 0.324,653,00 | 300 | 266 | 247 |
| 2.0 | 0.135,336,63 | 663 | 637 | 538 |

3.        $y' = -2ty^2,$     $y(0) = 1,$     $h = 0.1.$

| $t$ | Classic | Gill | Optimum | $y$ exact |
|---|---|---|---|---|
| 0 | 1 | | | |
| 0.1 | 0.990,098,9 | 990 | 989 | 990 |
| 0.2 | 0.961,538,1 | 383 | 379 | 385 |
| 0.3 | 0.917,430,6 | 308 | 301 | 312 |
| 0.4 | 0.862,068,2 | 684 | 674 | 690 |
| 0.5 | 0.799,999,2 | 994 | 982 | 000 |
| 1.0 | 0.500,000,6 | 008 | 996 | 000 |
| 1.5 | 0.307,693,3 | 935 | 927 | 923 |
| 2.0 | 0.200,000,7 | 008 | 004 | 000 |

## 30. Impossibility of a formula exact up to the term in $h^{k+3}$ for $x^{(p-k)}$, $k \neq 1$.

In writing the conditions, which the coefficients $K_{\alpha, \beta}$, have to satisfy, we find

$$\sum K_{4\alpha}\theta_\alpha = \frac{1}{k+1}, \qquad\qquad C_1 \qquad\qquad (8)$$

$$\sum K_{4\alpha}\theta_\alpha^2 = \frac{2}{(k+1)(k+2)}, \qquad\qquad C_2 \qquad\qquad (9)$$

$$\sum K_{4\alpha}\theta_\alpha^3 = \frac{6}{(k+1)(k+2)(k+3)}, \qquad\qquad C_3 \qquad\qquad (10)$$

$$\sum K_{4\alpha}A_{\alpha\beta}\theta_\beta = \frac{1}{(k+1)(k+2)}, \qquad\qquad J_1 C_1 \qquad\qquad (11)$$

$$\sum K_{4\alpha}A_{\alpha\beta}\theta_\beta^2 = \frac{2}{(k+1)(k+2)(k+3)}, \qquad\qquad J_1 C_2 \qquad\qquad (12)$$

$$\sum K_{4\alpha}A_{\alpha\beta}\theta_\alpha\theta_\beta = \frac{3}{(k+1)(k+2)(k+3)}, \qquad\qquad K_1 C_1 \qquad\qquad (13)$$

$$K_{43}A_{32}A_{21}\theta_1 = \frac{1}{(k+1)(k+2)(k+3)}, \qquad\qquad J_1^2 C_1 \qquad\qquad (14)$$

Thus, we have seven equations for the three unknowns $K_{41}$, $K_{42}$, $K_{43}$.

Let us take equations (10), (12), and (14). Their determinant is

$$A_{32} A_{21} \theta_1 \cdot A_{21} \theta_1^2 \theta_1^3$$

It is, therefore, nonzero. On the other hand, their second members are proportional to those of equations (3), (5), and (7) of paragraph 25.1. Therefore, we have

$$K_{4\alpha} = A_{4,\alpha} \frac{24}{(k+1)(k+2)(k+3)}.$$

But if we substitute it into (8), we find

$$\frac{12}{(k+1)(k+2)(k+3)} = \frac{1}{(k+1)},$$

which is incorrect for $k > 1$. Hence, it is only possible to obtain $x^{(p-k)}$ up to the order $h^{k+2}$.

### 31.1 Determination of the coefficients $B_{\alpha, \beta}$, $K_{\alpha, \beta}$.

One can, therefore, impose only for $k > 1$

$$\sum K_{4\alpha} \theta_\alpha = \frac{1}{k+1}, \qquad\qquad C_1 \qquad\qquad (8)$$

$$\sum K_{4\alpha} \theta_\alpha^2 = \frac{2}{(k+1)(k+2)}, \qquad C_2 \qquad\qquad (9)$$

$$\sum K_{4\alpha} A_{\alpha\beta} \theta_\beta = \frac{1}{(k+1)(k+2)}. \qquad J_1 C_1 \qquad (11)$$

Equations (8), (9), and (11) have a nonzero determinant (25.2). The $K_{4\alpha}$ are hence completely determined.

One can, moreover, give the following expressions:

$$K_{4\alpha} = A_{4\alpha} \left[ \frac{6(3k-2) + 24\theta_\alpha(1-k)}{(1+k)(2+k)} \right].$$

To obtain other relations, let us attempt to make the terms in $x^{(p-1)}$ of order $h^5$ involving $B_{\alpha,\beta}$ and $C_{\alpha,\beta}$ vanish. One arrives at

$$\frac{1}{120} - \frac{1}{6} \sum A_{4,\alpha} C_{\alpha,\beta} \theta_\beta = 0, \qquad J_3 C_1$$

$$\frac{4}{120} - \frac{1}{2} \sum A_{4,\alpha} B_{\alpha,\beta} \theta_\alpha \theta_\beta = 0, \qquad K_2 C_1 \qquad (1)$$

$$\frac{1}{120} - \frac{1}{4} \sum A_{4,\alpha} B_{\alpha,\beta} \theta_\beta^2 = 0, \qquad J_2 C_2 \qquad (2)$$

$$\frac{1}{120} - \frac{1}{2} \sum A_{4,\alpha} B_{\alpha,\beta} A_{\beta,\gamma} \theta_\gamma = 0, \qquad J_2 J_1 C_1 \qquad (3)$$

$$\frac{1}{120} - \frac{1}{2} \sum A_{4,\alpha} A_{\alpha,\beta} B_{\beta,\gamma} \theta_\gamma = 0, \qquad J_1 J_2 C_1 \qquad (4)$$

Let us recall that, in addition,

$$\frac{1}{24} - \frac{1}{2} \Sigma \ A_{4,\alpha} B_{\alpha,\beta} \theta_\beta = 0, \qquad J_2 C_1 \tag{5}$$

a condition relative to the vanishing of a term of $h^4$. One can satisfy (1), (3), (4), and (5) by taking

$$A_{43} B_{32} = \frac{4(1 - 2\theta_1)}{120\theta_2(\theta_2 - \theta_1)}, \qquad A_{42} B_{21} = \frac{2}{120\theta_1(1 - \theta_2)},$$

$$A_{43} B_{31} = \frac{12\theta_2 + 2\theta_1\theta_2 - 10\theta_2^2 - 4}{120\theta_1(1 - \theta_2)(\theta_2 - \theta_1)}.$$

If $\theta_1 = \theta_2 = 1/2$, the second members are equal to

$$\frac{8}{120}, \qquad \frac{8}{120}, \qquad \frac{4}{120}.$$

The preceding considerations determine the $B_{\alpha,\beta}$. There remain the indeterminancies for

$$K_{\alpha,\beta}, p \geqslant 3, a < 4.$$

### 31.2 Actual methods.

Let us first take as coefficients $A_{\alpha,\beta}$, those of RK4 Classical. Nyström, Zurmühl [1, 2] propose:

| 1/4 | | | |
|-----|-----|-----|-----|
| 1/4 | 0 | $B$ | |
| 0 | 0 | 1 | |
| 1/3 | 1/3 | 1/3 | 0 |

| $(1/2)^k$ | | | |
|-----------|-----------|-----------|-----------|
| $(1/2)^k$ | 0 | $K$ | |
| 0 | 0 | 1 | |
| $\dfrac{k^2}{(k+1)(k+2)}$ | $\dfrac{2k}{(k+1)(k+2)}$ | $\dfrac{2k}{(k+1)(k+2)}$ | $\dfrac{2-k}{(k+1)(k+2)}$ |

We will call this formula the RK4 Classical Zurmühl. It does not satisfy the conditions posed in paragraph 31.1. To satisfy them, it is necessary to set:

| 1/4 | | | |
|------|-----|-----|-----|
| 1/20 | 1/5 | $B$ | |
| 2/5 | 1/5 | 2/5 | |
| 1/3 | 1/3 | 1/3 | 0 |

We will call this formula RK4 Classical, Variant I.

Here are likewise the coefficients by taking for the optimal formula:

| 4/25 | | | |
|---|---|---|---|
| 3/50 | 3/10 | $B$ | |
| 1/2 | 3/22 | 4/11 | |
| 11/36 | 15/36 | 10/36 | 0 |

| $(2/5)^k$ | | | |
|---|---|---|---|
| $(3/5)^k$ | 0 | $K$ | |
| 0 | 0 | 1 | |
| $\dfrac{12k^2 - 3k + 2}{12(k + 1)(k + 2)}$ | $\dfrac{35k - 10}{12(k + 1)(k + 2)}$ | $\dfrac{15k + 10}{12(k + 1)(k + 2)}$ | $\dfrac{22 - 11k}{12(k + 1)(k + 2)}$ |

### 31.3 Example.

$$y'' + 1.5y' + 0.5y = 0, \qquad y(0) = y'(0) = 1, \qquad h = 0.1.$$

| $t$ | RK4 CZ | RK4 CV | RK4 O | $y$ exact |
|---|---|---|---|---|
| 0 | 1 | 1 | 1 | 1 |
| 0.1 | 1.090,405,1 | 1.090,404,9 | 1.090,401,0 | 1.090,405,4 |
| 0.2 | 1.163,156,7 | 1.163,156,5 | 1.163,156,6 | 1.163,157,4 |
| 0.3 | 1.220,376,4 | 1.220,376,1 | 1.220,376,2 | 1.220,377,2 |
| 0.4 | 1.263,961,9 | 1.263,961,5 | 1.263,961,6 | 1.263,962,9 |
| 0.5 | 1.295,610,2 | 1.295,609,7 | 1.295,609,8 | 1.295,611,1 |
| 1.0 | 1.322,483,7 | 1.322,482,9 | 1.322,483,0 | 1.322,484,3 |
| 1.5 | 1.220,075,8 | 1.220,074,9 | 1.220,074,8 | 1.220,075,7 |
| 2.0 | 1.065,512,6 | 1.065,511,6 | 1.065,511,5 | 1.065,511,9 |

### 32.1 Truncation error at one step for $x^{(p-1)}$.

This error is that given for $p = 1$, completed for the following terms:

| | $J_3 C_1$ | $K_2 C_1$ | $J_2 C_2$ | $J_2 J_1 C_1$ | $J_1 J_2 C_1$ |
|---|---|---|---|---|---|
| Zurmühl | Can be made zero | +1/120 | +1/480 | +1/80 | −1/120 |
| Variant I | by a convenient | 0 | +1/480 | 0 | 0 |
| Optimal | choice of the $C_{\alpha\beta}$[1] | 0 | +1/600 | 0 | 0 |

One sees that the coefficients of the terms are rather important. The Variant I or the optimal formula has to bring considerable improvements.

### 32.2 Truncation error at one step for $x^{(p-k)}$, $k \neq 1$.

This error has for its principal part, except for the term $h^{k+3}/k!$,

$$\frac{-(k - 1)}{(k + 1)(k + 2)}\left[\frac{2 + k}{4(3 + k)} - \frac{\theta_1 + \theta_2}{3} + \frac{2\theta_1\theta_2}{3}\right] \qquad C_3$$

[1]It suffices to set $\sum_{\alpha,\,\beta} A_{4,\,\alpha} C_{\alpha,\,\beta}\,\theta_\beta = 1/20$.

$$\frac{-(k-1)(k-2)}{(k+1)(k+2)(k+3)20} \qquad J_2 C_1$$

$$\frac{k-1}{4(k+1)(k+2)(k+3)}[-3(k+2)+4\theta_2(k+3)] \qquad K_1 C_1$$

$$\frac{-(k-1)(k+2)}{4(k+1)(k+2)(k+3)} \qquad J_1^2 C_1$$

$$\frac{k-1}{4(k+1)(k+2)(k+3)}[k+2-2\theta_1(k+3)] \qquad J_1 C_2$$

We are going to give these remaining error terms for the above-mentioned formulas and $k = 2$. There is a common factor $h^5/2$.

| Zurmühl & Variant I | $C_3$ | $J_2 C_1$ | $K_1 C_1$ | $J_1^2 C_1$ | $J_1 C_2$ |
|---|---|---|---|---|---|
| | $-1/360$ | 0 | $-2/240$ | $-4/240$ | $1/240$ |
| Optimal | $-1/450$ | 0 | 0 | $-4/240$ | 0 |

One sees that the coefficients are rather large and that the optimal formula is more advantageous.

## VIII  INVESTIGATION OF THE CASE $q \geqslant 5$

### 33.1 Basic formulas.

Here are the equations to establish for obtaining a representation of $x_1^{(p-1)}$ up to the term $h^5$, when we have the simplest case of one first order equation:

$$\begin{Vmatrix} \theta_1 & \theta_2 & \theta_3 & \theta_4 \\ \theta_1^2 & \cdots & \cdots & \cdots \\ \theta_1^3 & \cdots & \cdots & \cdots \\ \theta_1^4 & \cdots & \cdots & \theta_4^4 \end{Vmatrix} \begin{Vmatrix} A_{51} \\ A_{52} \\ A_{53} \\ A_{54} \end{Vmatrix} = \begin{Vmatrix} 1/2 \\ 1/3 \\ 1/4 \\ 1/5 \end{Vmatrix} \begin{matrix} C_1 \\ C_2 \\ C_3 \\ C_4 \end{matrix} \begin{matrix} (1) \\ (2) \\ (3) \\ (4) \end{matrix}$$

$$\begin{Vmatrix} \theta_3 & \theta_2 & \theta_1 & \theta_2 & \theta_1 & \theta_1 \\ \theta_3^2 & \theta_2^2 & \theta_1^2 & \theta_2^2 & \theta_1^2 & \theta_1^2 \\ \theta_3^3 & \theta_2^3 & \theta_1^3 & \theta_2^3 & \theta_1^3 & \theta_1^3 \\ \theta_4\theta_3 & \theta_4\theta_2 & \theta_4\theta_1 & \theta_3\theta_2 & \theta_3\theta_1 & \theta_2\theta_1 \\ \theta_4\theta_3^2 & \theta_4\theta_2^2 & \theta_4\theta_1^2 & \theta_3\theta_2^2 & \theta_3\theta_1^2 & \theta_3\theta_1^2 \\ \theta_4^2\theta_3 & \theta_4^2\theta_2 & \theta_4^2\theta_1 & \theta_3^2\theta_2 & \theta_3^2\theta_1 & \theta_2^2\theta_1 \end{Vmatrix} \begin{Vmatrix} A_{54}A_{43} \\ A_{54}A_{42} \\ A_{54}A_{41} \\ A_{53}A_{32} \\ A_{53}A_{31} \\ A_{52}A_{21} \end{Vmatrix} = \begin{Vmatrix} 20/120 \\ 10/120 \\ 6/120 \\ 15/120 \\ 8/120 \\ 12/120 \end{Vmatrix} \begin{matrix} J_1 C_1 \\ J_1 C_2 \\ J_1 C_1 \\ K_1 C_1 \\ K_1 C_2 \\ L_1 C_1 \end{matrix} \begin{matrix} (5) \\ (6) \\ (7) \\ (8) \\ (9) \\ (10) \end{matrix}$$

$$\begin{Vmatrix} \theta_2 & \theta_1 & \theta_1 & \theta_1 \\ \theta_2^2 & \theta_1^2 & \theta_1^2 & \theta_1^2 \\ \theta_2(\theta_3 + \theta_4) & \theta_1(\theta_4 + \theta_3) & \theta_1(\theta_4 + \theta_2) & \theta_1(\theta_3 + \theta_2) \end{Vmatrix} \times$$

$$\times \begin{Vmatrix} A_{54}A_{43}A_{32} \\ A_{54}A_{43}A_{31} \\ A_{53}A_{32}A_{21} + A_{54}A_{42}A_{21} \end{Vmatrix} = \begin{Vmatrix} 5/120 \\ 2/120 \\ 7/120 \end{Vmatrix} \qquad \begin{aligned} & J_1^2 C_1 && (11) \\ & J_1^2 C_2 && (12) \\ & K_1 J_1 C_1 + J_1 K_1 C_1 && (13) \end{aligned}$$

$$A_{54}A_{43}A_{32}A_{21}\theta_1 = \frac{1}{120} \qquad J^3 C_1 \qquad (14)$$

There remains, to be complete, a nonlinear condition which will not be of use to us.

### 33.2 Impossibility of attaining the fifth order for $q = 5$.

Equations (1), (2), (3), and (4) determine $A_{54}$, $A_{53}$, $A_{52}$, $A_{51}$, which, with $A_{50}$, are the coefficients of the approximate quadrature at the abscissas 0, $\theta_1, \theta_2, \theta_3, \theta_4$. Consequently, equations (5) through (10) determine the other coefficients. Finally, there remain a certain number of conditions. In solving (1), (2), (3), and (4), one arrives at

$$120\theta_2(\theta_4 - \theta_2)(\theta_3 - \theta_2)(\theta_1 - \theta_2)A_{52} =$$
$$= 60\theta_1\theta_3\theta_4 - 40(\theta_1\theta_3 + \theta_1\theta_4 + \theta_3\theta_4) + 30(\theta_1 + \theta_3 + \theta_4) - 24. \quad (15)$$

On the other hand, one concludes from (11) and (12):

$$120\theta_2(\theta_2 - \theta_1)A_{54}A_{43}A_{32} = 2 - 5\theta_1.$$

Then, combining with (14), we have

$$120\theta_2(\theta_2 - \theta_1)A_{54}A_{43}A_{32}A_{21}\theta_1 = (2 - 5\theta_1)A_{21}\theta_1 = \theta_2(\theta_2 - \theta_1). \quad (16)$$

Finally, from (5), (8), and (10), one arrives at

$$120\theta_1(\theta_2 - \theta_3)(\theta_2 - \theta_4)A_{52}A_{21}\theta_1 = 12 - 15(\theta_3 + \theta_4) + 20\theta_3\theta_4. \quad (17)$$

From (16) and (17) one deduces

$$120\theta_2(\theta_2 - \theta_3)(\theta_2 - \theta_4)(\theta_2 - \theta_1)A_{52} = [12 - 15(\theta_3 + \theta_4) + 20\theta_3\theta_4](2 - 5\theta_1).$$

In comparing this value with (15), one arrives at

$$\theta_1[-40\theta_3\theta_4 + 35(\theta_3 + \theta_4) - 30] = 0,$$

and as $\theta_1 \neq 0$

$$40\theta_3\theta_4 - 35(\theta_3 + \theta_4) + 30 = 0. \quad (18)$$

From (11) and (13), one deduces

$$120[A_{54}A_{42}A_{21}\theta_1(\theta_2 - \theta_3) + A_{53}A_{32}A_{21}\theta_1(\theta_2 - \theta_4)] = 7 - 5(\theta_3 + \theta_4),$$

and from there

$$120\theta_2(\theta_2 - \theta_1)[A_{54}A_{42}(\theta_2 - \theta_3) + A_{53}A_{32}(\theta_2 - \theta_4)]$$
$$= (2 - 5\theta_1)[7 - 5(\theta_3 + \theta_4)]. \quad (19)$$

The system from (5) through (10) gives
$$120\theta_2(\theta_2 - \theta_1)(\theta_3 - \theta_4)A_{53}A_{32} = 8 - 10\theta_4 - 15\theta_1 + 20\theta_1\theta_4,$$
and the system (5), (6), and (7) gives
$$120\theta_2(\theta_2 - \theta_1)(\theta_2 - \theta_3)[A_{53}A_{32} + A_{54}A_{42}] = 6 - 10(\theta_1 + \theta_3) + 20\theta_1\theta_3,$$
or, in adding,
$$120\theta_2(\theta_2 - \theta_1)[A_{53}A_{32}(\theta_2 - \theta_4) + A_{54}A_{42}(\theta_2 - \theta_3)]$$
$$= 14 - 25\theta_1 - 10(\theta_3 + \theta_4) + 20\theta_1(\theta_3 + \theta_4). \tag{20}$$
In comparing (19) and (20), one finds
$$2\theta_1 = \theta_1(\theta_3 + \theta_4),$$
or, since $\theta_1 \neq 0$:
$$2 = \theta_3 + \theta_4. \tag{21}$$
From (18) and (21), it follows immediately that
$$\theta_3 = \theta_4 = 1.$$
(5) and (8), therefore, give
$$120\,A_{52}\,A_{21}\theta_1(1 - \theta_2) = 5.$$
(8) and (10) give
$$120\,A_{52}\,A_{21}\theta_2\theta_1(1 - \theta_2) = 3.$$
Finally, (6) and (9) give
$$120\,A_{52}\,A_{21}\theta_1^2(1 - \theta_2) = 2.$$
From this, one concludes that
$$\theta_1 = \frac{2}{5}, \qquad \theta_2 = \frac{3}{5}.$$
Returning to equations (1) through (4), one sees that $\theta_1$ and $\theta_2$ are such that
$$\begin{vmatrix} 1 & 1 & 1 & 1/2 \\ \theta_1 & \theta_2 & 1 & 1/3 \\ \theta_1^2 & \theta_2^2 & 1 & 1/4 \\ \theta_1^3 & \theta_2^3 & 1 & 1/5 \end{vmatrix} \neq 0.$$
Therefore, there does not exist a formula for $q = 5$, even if the equation is linear.

### 33.3 Formulas of rank five and of order (4, 5).

For
$$\theta_1 = \theta_2 = \frac{1}{2}, \qquad \theta_3 = 1, \qquad \theta_4 = \frac{3}{4},$$

Nyström proposes

| 1/2 | | | | | |
|---|---|---|---|---|---|
| 0 | 1/2 | | | *A* | |
| 0 | 0 | 1 | | | |
| 15/64 | 24/64 | 6/64 | 3/64 | | |
| 1/6 | 1/3 | 1/3 | 1/6 | 0 | |

| 1/4 | | | | | |
|---|---|---|---|---|---|
| 1/4 | 0 | | | *B* | |
| 0 | 0 | 1 | | | |
| 15/32 | 0 | 0 | 3/32 | | |
| 13/45 | 21/45 | 21/45 | 6/45 | −16/45 | |

For the same values of $\theta_i$, Ceschino [3] proposes

| 1/2 | | | | | |
|---|---|---|---|---|---|
| −1/4 | 3/4 | | | *A* | |
| 0 | 1/3 | 2/3 | | | |
| 15/64 | 26/64 | 4/64 | 3/64 | | |
| 3/18 | 8/18 | 4/18 | 3/18 | 0 | |

| 1/4 | | | | | |
|---|---|---|---|---|---|
| 0 | 1/4 | | | *B* | |
| 1/3 | 1/3 | 1/3 | | | |
| 24/64 | 3/64 | 3/64 | 6/64 | | |
| 13/45 | 28/45 | 14/45 | 6/45 | −16/45 | |

### 33.4  Formulas of rank six and of order 5.

It is impossible to attain the fifth order for $x$ with $q = 5$; for this it is necessary to use a formula of rank six. Here is one proposed by Nyström. It is valid for a system in canonical form:

$$\theta_1 = \frac{1}{3}, \quad \theta_2 = \frac{2}{5}, \quad \theta_3 = 1, \quad \theta_4 = \frac{2}{3}, \quad \theta_5 = \frac{4}{5}.$$

| 1/3 | | | | | |
|---|---|---|---|---|---|
| 4/25 | 6/25 | | | *A* | |
| 1/4 | −12/4 | 15/4 | | | |
| 6/81 | 90/81 | −50/81 | 8/81 | | |
| 6/75 | 36/75 | 10/75 | 8/75 | 0 | |
| 23/192 | 0 | 125/192 | 0 | −81/192 | 125/192 |

Such a formula and those of a higher rank appear never to have been used. The choice of the values of $\theta$ has not been discussed.

### 33.5 Formulas of rank eight and of order 6.

Huta [1, 2] has given formulas, the $\theta$ and the $A_{\alpha, \beta}$ of which are indicated on pages 94 and 95. The author has not given any example, and no one seems ever to have used these formulas. Although the author has established them for only one equation, they are valid for a system in the canonical form.

$$\theta_1 = \frac{1}{9}, \qquad \theta_2 = \frac{1}{6}, \qquad \theta_3 = \frac{2}{6}, \qquad \theta_4 = \frac{3}{6},$$

$$\theta_5 = \frac{4}{6}, \qquad \theta_6 = \frac{5}{6}, \qquad \theta_7 = 1.$$

$A$

| | | | | | | | |
|---|---|---|---|---|---|---|---|
| $\frac{1}{9}$ | | | | | | | |
| $\frac{1}{24}$ | $\frac{3}{24}$ | | | | | | |
| $\frac{1}{6}$ | $\frac{-3}{6}$ | $\frac{4}{6}$ | | | | | |
| $\frac{278}{544}$ | $\frac{-945}{544}$ | $\frac{840}{544}$ | $\frac{99}{544}$ | | | | |
| $\frac{-106}{6}$ | $\frac{273}{6}$ | $\frac{-104}{6}$ | $\frac{-107}{6}$ | $\frac{48}{6}$ | | | |
| $\frac{110,974}{45,648}$ | $\frac{-236,799}{45,648}$ | $\frac{68,376}{45,648}$ | $\frac{103,803}{45,648}$ | $\frac{-10,240}{45,648}$ | $\frac{1,926}{45,648}$ | | |
| $\frac{-101,195}{25,994}$ | $\frac{222,534}{25,994}$ | $\frac{-71,988}{25,994}$ | $\frac{-26,109}{25,994}$ | $\frac{-20,000}{25,994}$ | $\frac{-72}{25,994}$ | $\frac{22,824}{25,994}$ | |
| $\frac{41}{840}$ | $0$ | $\frac{216}{840}$ | $\frac{27}{840}$ | $\frac{272}{840}$ | $\frac{27}{840}$ | $\frac{216}{840}$ | $\frac{41}{840}$ |

$A$

| | | | | | | | |
|---|---|---|---|---|---|---|---|
| $\frac{1}{9}$ | | | | | | | |
| $\frac{1}{24}$ | $\frac{3}{24}$ | | | | | | |
| $\frac{1}{6}$ | $\frac{-3}{6}$ | $\frac{4}{6}$ | | | | | |
| $\frac{-5}{8}$ | $\frac{27}{8}$ | $\frac{-24}{8}$ | $\frac{6}{8}$ | | | | |
| $\frac{221}{9}$ | $\frac{-981}{9}$ | $\frac{867}{9}$ | $\frac{-102}{9}$ | $\frac{1}{9}$ | | | |
| $\frac{-183}{48}$ | $\frac{678}{48}$ | $\frac{-472}{48}$ | $\frac{-66}{48}$ | $\frac{80}{48}$ | $\frac{3}{48}$ | | |
| $\frac{716}{82}$ | $\frac{-2,079}{82}$ | $\frac{1,002}{82}$ | $\frac{834}{82}$ | $\frac{-454}{82}$ | $\frac{-9}{82}$ | $\frac{72}{82}$ | |
| $\frac{41}{840}$ | $0$ | $\frac{216}{840}$ | $\frac{27}{840}$ | $\frac{272}{840}$ | $\frac{27}{840}$ | $\frac{216}{840}$ | $\frac{41}{840}$ |

## Problems

By use of the Runge-Kutta method calculate to four decimal places the solutions to the following differential equations in the given intervals, using a step size of 0.2 and estimating the error.

1.          $y' = y - x,$          $y(0) = 1.5,$      $(0 \leqslant x \leqslant 1).$

2.          $y' = \dfrac{y}{x} - y^2,$       $y(1) = 1,$        $(1 \leqslant x \leqslant 2).$

3.          $y' = -2x(y + x^2),$      $y(0) = 0,$        $(0 \leqslant x \leqslant 1).$

4.          $y'' = -\dfrac{0.0003}{y^2} + 0.01(y')^2, \; y(0) = 1,$

$$y'(0) = 0 \qquad (0 \leqslant x \leqslant 0.8).$$

Repeat the above for the system

$$y' = z + 1, \qquad z' = y - x, \qquad y(0) = 1, \qquad z(0) = 1 \quad (0 \leqslant x \leqslant 1).$$

# 4 RELATIONSHIPS OF THE RUNGE-KUTTA PRINCIPLE WITH THE VARIOUS SINGLE-STEP METHODS

### 1. Generalities.

In the preceding chapter, we have presented the Runge-Kutta methods of various orders. If one reflects on the common principle which is the basis of these methods, one notices that this principle is after all quite natural, if one lays the following foundations. Let the system be

$$x^{(p)} = X(x, x', \ldots, x^{(p-1)}, t).$$

(a) The only two choices one is permitted to make are:
—to calculate $X$ for different values of the variables.
—to form linear combinations of these $X'$s and of the $x, x', \ldots$ at the outset of the step.

(b) The standard which serves to measure the degree of exactness obtained is the order of the infinitesimal in relation to the step.

If one adopts these foundations, the Runge-Kutta method is not only the most natural, but even the only one possible, and every other method can be judged by comparison with it. The present chapter, in part, is a development of this idea, and in part contains various tentative bases for the detailed modifications of the basic principle of the Runge-Kutta method. Besides, these modifications can be put to various other uses.

## I  THE BLAESS METHOD[1]

### 2. Outline of the method.

Let us take up a system in the equilibrated resolved form:

$$x^{(p)} = X(x, \ldots, x^{(p-1)}, t).$$

[1]Blaess, Borkmann, Bukowics [1, 2], Zurmühl [1].

We suppose that one has applied Euler's method to this system.

One obtains thus the system of values

$$x_0, x_0', \ldots, x_0^{(p-1)}$$
$$x_1, x_1', \ldots, x_1^{(p-1)}$$
$$\vdots$$
$$x_r, x_r', \ldots, x_r^{(p-1)}$$

(initial values)

with

$$x_{j+1} = x_j + hx_j' + \cdots + \frac{h^p}{p!} X_j,$$

$$x_{j+1}' = x_j' + hx_j'' + \cdots + \frac{h^{p-1}}{(p-1)!} X_j,$$

$$\vdots$$

$$x_{j+1}^{(p-1)} = x_j^{(p-1)} + \frac{h}{1!} X_j.$$

These various values correspond to those of Taylor's expansions correct up to the orders $p, p-1, \ldots, 1$.

One asks if it were not possible to obtain better accuracy at a certain point with abscissa $t_0 + a^*$ by combining these results. One can easily see that such a combination can only be in the form

$$x^* = x_0 + a^* x_0' + \cdots + \frac{a^{*p-1}}{(p-1)!} x_0^{(p-1)} + \frac{a^{*p}}{p!} [L_{r+1,0} X_0 + \cdots + L_{r+1,r} X_r],$$

$$\vdots$$

$$x^{*(p-1)} = x_0^{(p-1)} + a^* [A_{r+1,0} X_0 + \cdots + A_{r+1,r} X_r].$$

Indeed, the first terms are those of the Taylor expansion, and in the corrective terms it is useless to have other things appear than the $X_i$, since all other quantities refer to these.

In the original Blaess method, the steps were assumed to be equal, and the point $t_0 + a^*$ coincided with the very end of the last step. We neglect these two restrictions.

### 3.1 Relation with the Runge-Kutta method.

One can easily verify that the formulas of paragraph 2 may be written as

$$x_i = x_0 + \frac{(h_1 + \cdots + h_i)}{1!} x_0' + \cdots + \frac{(h_1 + \cdots + h_i)^{p-1}}{p-1!} x_0^{(p-1)}$$

$$+ \frac{(h_1 + h_2 + \cdots + h_i)^p}{p!} X_0 + \frac{(h_2 + \cdots + h_i)^p}{p!} (X_1 - X_0)$$

$$+ \frac{(h_3 + \cdots + h_i)^p}{p!} (X_2 - X_1) + \cdots + \frac{h_i^p}{p!} (X_{i-1} - X_{i-2}),$$

and, likewise,

$$x_i^{(p-k)} = x_0^{(p-k)} + \cdots + \frac{(h_1 + h_2 + \cdots + h_i)^{k-1}}{(k-1)!} x_0^{(p-1)}$$

$$+ \frac{(h_1 + \cdots + h_i)^k}{k!} X_0 + \frac{(h_2 + \cdots + h_i)^k}{k!}(X_1 - X_0)$$

$$+ \cdots + \frac{h_i^k}{k!}(X_{i-1} - X_{i-2})$$

$$x_i^{(p-1)} = x_0^{(p-1)} + (h_1 + \cdots + h_i) X_0 + (h_2 + \cdots + h_i)(X_1 - X_0) + \cdots$$

$$\cdots + h_i(X_{i-1} - X_{i-2}).$$

This can be considered as the following Runge-Kutta formula:

$$\theta_1 = \frac{h_1}{a*}, \qquad \theta_2 = \frac{h_1 + h_2}{a*}, \qquad \theta_i = \frac{h_1 + h_2 + \cdots + h_i}{a*}.$$

| | | | | |
|---|---|---|---|---|
| $h_1/a*$ | | | | $A$ |
| $h_1/a*$ | $h_2/a*$ | | | |
| $h_1/a*$ | $h_2/a*$ | $h_3/a*$ | | |
| $h_1/a*$ | $h_2/a*$ | $h_3/a*$ | $h_4/a*$ | |

| | | | |
|---|---|---|---|
| $h_1^k/a*^k$ | | $K$ | |
| $\dfrac{(h_1 + h_2)^k - h_2^k}{a*^k}$ | | $\dfrac{h_2^k}{a*^k}$ | |
| $\dfrac{(h_1 + h_2 + h_3)^k - (h_2 + h_3)^k}{a*^k}$ | $\dfrac{(h_2 + h_3)^k - h_3^k}{a*^k}$ | $\dfrac{h_3^k}{a*^k}$ | |

Let us examine what the relations of the Runge-Kutta theory are, which are exact for these systems of values.

### 3.2 Investigation of $A_{\alpha,\beta}$.

One verifies that for $i \leqslant r$

$$\sum_\beta A_{\alpha,\beta} = \frac{h_1 + h_2 + \cdots + h_\alpha}{a*} = \theta_\alpha.$$

The exactness of the term $h$ in $x^{*(p-1)}$ is expressed by the condition

$$\sum_\alpha A_{r+1,\alpha} = 1.$$

The exactness of the term $h^2$ is translated into

$$\sum_\alpha A_{r+1,\alpha} \frac{(h_1 + \cdots + h_\alpha)}{a*} = 1/2; \qquad (1)$$

that of the term $h^3$ by

$$\sum_\alpha A_{r+1,\alpha} \frac{(h_1 + \cdots + h_\alpha)^2}{a*^2} = 1/3, \qquad (2)$$

$$\sum_{\alpha,\beta} A_{r+1,\alpha} A_{\alpha,\beta} \theta_\beta = 1/6. \tag{3}$$

Relation (3) is written as

$$\sum_\alpha A_{r+1,\alpha} \sum_\beta \frac{h_{\beta+1}}{a^*} \frac{(h_1 + \cdots + h_\beta)}{a^*} = 1/6,$$

or also

$$\sum_\alpha A_{r+1,\alpha} \frac{[(h_1 + h_2 + \cdots + h_\alpha)^2 - h_1^2 - h_2^2 - \cdots - h_\alpha^2]}{2a^{*2}} = 1/6.$$

Comparing with (2), one concludes that

$$\sum_\alpha A_{r+1,\alpha} \frac{(h_1^2 + h_2^2 + \cdots + h_\alpha^2)}{a^{*2}} = 0. \tag{4}$$

### 3.3  Incompatibility of the system if the steps are equal.

If the steps are equal, (1) and (4) are incompatible, whatever $r$ and $a^*$ are. Hence one cannot, by correction, make the term $h^3$ of $x^{(p-1)}$ disappear. The formulas proposed by Blaess hence correspond to a particularly unfortunate configuration.

### 3.4  Example of a formula with unequal steps.

Let us take

$$\frac{h_1}{a^*} = 2/5, \qquad \frac{h_2}{a^*} = 1/5, \qquad \frac{h_3}{a^*} = 2/5.$$

In trying to verify (1), (2), and (3), one obtains

$$A_{4,0} = 46/36, \qquad A_{4,1} = -190/36, \qquad A_{4,2} = 215/36, \qquad A_{4,3} = -35/36,$$

i.e.,

$$x_3^* = x_0 + \frac{a^*}{36} [46\, X_0 - 190\, X_1 + 215\, X_2 - 35\, X_3],$$

the successive steps having the lengths $2a^*/5$, $a^*/5$, $2a^*/5$.

### 3.5  Investigation of the $K_{\alpha,\beta}$.

Once more one has

$$\sum_\beta K_{\alpha,\beta} = \theta_\alpha^k, \qquad \alpha = 1, 2, \ldots, r.$$

In order to make the term $h^k$ disappear in $x^{(p-k)}$, it is necessary that

$$\sum_\alpha K_{r+1,\alpha} = 1.$$

To make the term $h^{k+1}$ disappear, it is necessary that

$$\sum_\alpha K_{r+1,\alpha} \frac{(h_1 + \cdots + h_\alpha)}{a^*} = \frac{1}{k+1}, \tag{1}$$

and for the term $h^{k+2}$, it is necessary that

$$\sum_\alpha K_{r+1,\alpha} \frac{(h_1 + \cdots + h_\alpha)^2}{a^{*2}} = \frac{2}{(k+1)(k+2)} \tag{2}$$

and

$$\sum_\alpha K_{r+1,\alpha} \left[ \frac{(h_1 + h_2 + \cdots + h_\alpha)^2 - h_1^2 - h_2^2 - \cdots - h_\alpha^2}{2a^{*2}} \right] = \frac{1}{(k+1)(k+2)}. \tag{3}$$

Comparing with (2), one arrives at

$$\sum_\alpha K_{r+1,\alpha} \frac{(h_1^2 + \cdots + h_\alpha^2)}{a^{*2}} = 0. \tag{5}$$

The relations are the same as those above, except for the second members. They are still incompatible if the steps are equal.

### 3.6 The Blaess classical formula.

The Blaess classical formula is relative to the case $p = 2$, $r = 5$, and $a^* = 5h$.

$$x_5'^* = x_0' + \frac{5h}{120} (8X_0 + 29X_1 + 24X_2 + 24X_3 + 24X_4 + 11X_5),$$

$$x_5^* = x_0 + 5hx_0' + \frac{25h^2}{1200} (71X_0 + 268X_1 + 120X_2 + 72X_3 + 69X_4),$$

which one can also write as

$$x_5'^* = x_5' + \frac{h}{24} (-16X_0 + 5X_1 + 11X_5),$$

$$x_5^* = x_5 + \frac{h^2}{48} (-145X_0 + 100X_1 + 45X_4).$$

One can give formulas which permit the improvement of the intermediary points. One can also augment the order attained in making the matrix $J_1$ appear (Borkmann).

### 4. Final remarks.

This method presupposes the validity of the representation by a polynomial giving the same improvement over all steps. This hypothesis may not be reasonable.

—One can apply the same idea to other methods, for instance, the improved tangent method. We will not give formulas, as these methods do not seem to be of great interest.

—We will give the principle for the improvement of the results of a first integration (Picard's method) in Chapter 10, paragraph 24.

## II  IMPLICIT RUNGE-KUTTA FORMULAS

The implicit term can be understood with two different meanings; the first consists of solving at each intermediate step an implicit condition which gives the intermediate value $x_{i,\,\alpha}$. The second one consists of writing an implicit system containing all the $x_{i,\,\alpha}$ at the same time.

The first idea, which we study hereafter, leads to results of no significant value, as the gain compared to the explicit formulas does not compensate for the inconvenience of having to solve an implicit relation.

On the other hand, the second idea, studied in Section III and in Chapter 9 does lead to interesting results.

### 5. Simple implicit Runge-Kutta method.

For the system

$$x^{(p)} = X(x, \ldots, x^{(p-1)})$$

let us consider formulas of the following type:

$$
\begin{cases}
x_{i,1} = x_i + h\theta_1 x_i' + \cdots + \dfrac{h^p}{p!}\,\theta_1^p X_i + \dfrac{h^p}{p!}\,L_{1,1}(X_{i,1} - X_i), \\[2mm]
\qquad\qquad \vdots \\[2mm]
x_{i,1}^{(p-k)} = x_i^{(p-k)} + \cdots + \dfrac{h^k}{k!}\,\theta_1^k X_i + \dfrac{h^k}{k!}\,K_{1,1}(X_{i,1} - X_i), \\[2mm]
\qquad\qquad \vdots \\[2mm]
x_{i,1}^{(p-1)} = x_i^{(p-1)} + h\theta_1 X_i + \dfrac{h}{1!}\,A_{1,1}(X_{i,1} - X_i),
\end{cases}
$$

$$
\begin{cases}
x_{i,2} = x_i + hx_i' + \cdots + \dfrac{h^p}{p!}\,[L_{2,2}(X_{i,2} - X_i) + L_{2,1}(X_{i,1} - X_i)], \\[2mm]
\qquad\qquad \vdots \\[2mm]
x_{i,2}^{(p-1)} = x_i^{(p-1)} + h\theta_2 X_i + \dfrac{h}{1!}\,[A_{2,2}(X_{i,2} - X_i) + A_{2,1}(X_{i,1} - X_i)], \\[2mm]
\qquad\qquad \vdots \\[2mm]
x_{i,q} = x_{i+1} \quad x_{i,q}^{(p-k)} = x_{i+1}^{(p-k)} \quad x_{i,q}^{(p-1)} = x_{i+1}^{(p-1)}.
\end{cases}
$$

One can try to determine the $\theta_i$ and the coefficients $L_{i,j}, \ldots, A_{i,j}$ in such a manner as to obtain expansions valid up to as high an order as possible. The calculations necessary do not essentially differ from those for the Runge-Kutta formula. It suffices to modify the systems of acceptable values of the indices by taking $0 \leqslant \beta \leqslant \alpha$.

### 6. Investigation for $q = 1$.

One has necessarily $\theta_1 = 1$. The vanishing of the term $h^{k+1}$ requires the condition

$$\frac{1}{k+1} = \Sigma\, K_{q,\alpha}\theta_\alpha,$$

i.e.,

$$K_{1,1} = \frac{1}{k+1}.$$

The formulas are the following:

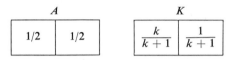

This formula is of order $(2, 3, \ldots, p + 1)$. It will be called the trapezoidal formula, because for $p = 1$, it is written as

$$x_{i+1} = x_i + \frac{h}{2}(X_i + X_{i+1}).$$

### 7. Truncation error at one step.

One can evaluate the truncation error at one step usually by starting from the first neglected terms. We will limit ourselves to systems in canonical form, and we will use an elementary reasoning:

$$x(t_{i+1}) \approx x_i + hX_i + \frac{h^2}{2} x_i'' + \frac{h^3}{6} x_i''',$$

$$x_{i+1} \approx x_i + \frac{h}{2}\left(X_i + X_i + hX_i'' + \frac{h^2}{2} x_i'''\right),$$

whence

$$x_{i+1} - x(t_{i+1}) \approx \frac{h^3}{12} x_i'''.$$

The error at one step is thus of the same order as for the explicit formulas with $q = 2$.

### 8.1 Application to the case of a linear system.

Let the linear system be

$$y' = a(t)y + b(t)z + c(t),$$
$$z' = d(t)y + e(t)z + f(t).$$

The method leads to the expressions

$$y_{i+1} = y_i + \frac{h}{2}[a_i y_i + b_i z_i + c_i + a_{i+1} y_{i+1} + b_{i+1} z_{i+1} + c_{i+1}],$$

$$z_{i+1} = z_i + \frac{h}{2}[d_i y_i + c_i z_i + f_i + d_{i+1} y_{i+1} + c_{i+1} z_{i+1} + f_{i+1}].$$

One will have to solve a system of two equations of the first degree with two unknowns $y_{i+1}, z_{i+1}$.

### 8.2 Application by iteration.

In the general case, it will be necessary to use one iteration. One starts with an arbitrary value $x_{i+1}^{[0]}$ and one determines it successively.

$$x_{i+1}^{[r]} = x_i + \frac{h}{2}(X_i + X_{i+1}^{[r-1]}).$$

The convergence of this iteration is a subject of a general nature. We recall only the conditions. The iteration converges, provided that all the eigenvalues of the matrix $hJ_1$ in absolute value are smaller than 1, and it converges rapidly if all the eigenvalues of the above-mentioned matrix are in absolute value considerably smaller than 1 (for example, if their moduli do not exceed 0.1).

### 9. Relation with the Euler-Cauchy method.

The Euler-Cauchy method can be written as

$$x_{i+1}^{[0]} = x_i + hX_i,$$

$$x_{i+1}^{[1]} = x_i + \frac{h}{2}(X_i + X_{i+1}^{[0]}).$$

It consists thus of taking as a starting value the one given by the tangent method and of using only the first round of the iteration.

We are going to compare the trapezoidal and Euler-Cauchy methods from the points of view of precision and amount of calculation.

(*a*) *Precision.* The error at one step of the trapezoidal method is one of the two error terms of the Euler-Cauchy method. In other words, there can be a gain in certain cases by utilizing the trapezoidal method (for example, by continuing the iteration defined by the Euler-Cauchy method), but this gain will never be very important.

(*b*) *Amount of calculation for the linear case.* We suppose an $n$th order linear system in the canonical form ($n$ large). Both of the two methods to be compared utilize the calculation of the coefficients at $t_i$ and $t_{i+1}$ and hence that of the $X_i$.

The Euler-Cauchy method requires the calculation of $x_{i+1}^{[0]}$ and of $X_{i+1}^{[0]}$, then of $x_{i+1}$. The total takes about $2n + n^2$ multiplications. The trapezoidal method requires the solving of a linear system, which takes about $n^3/3$ multiplications. One sees that the trapezoidal method can be competitive only for $n$ very small ($n \leqslant 3$).

(*c*) *Amount of calculation when one works with iterations.* The Euler-Cauchy method is the best unless one succeeds in finding an initial value of the iteration which is better than that one given by the tangent.

### 10. Investigation for $q = 2$.

The vanishing of the terms in $h^{k+1}$ and $h^{k+2}$ requires that

$$\frac{1}{k+1} = K_{2,2}\theta_2 + K_{2,1}\theta_1, \qquad\qquad C_1$$

$$\frac{2}{(k+1)(k+2)} = K_{2,2}\theta_2^2 + K_{2,1}\theta_1^2, \qquad\qquad C_2$$

$$\frac{1}{(k+1)(k+2)} = K_{2,2}(A_{2,2}\theta_2 + A_{2,1}\theta_1) + K_{2,1}A_{1,1}\theta_1, \qquad J_1 C_1$$

with $\theta_2 = 1$. The first two relations determine $K_{2,2}$ and $K_{2,1}$, provided that $\theta_1 \neq 1$. By remarking that $A_{2,2}\,\theta_2 + A_{2,1}\,\theta_1 = 1/2$ we find that the compatibility of the three equations of $K_{2,2}$ and $K_{2,1}$ gives

$$A_{1,1} = \theta_1/2.$$

The $K_{1,1}$ except for $A_{1,1}$ are indeterminate. These formulas are of order $(3, 4, \ldots, p + 2)$.

### 11. Efficient formulas.

For $p = 1$, we propose

$$\theta_1 = 1/2,$$

| 1/4 | 1/4 | |
|-----|-----|-----|
| 1/6 | 2/3 | 1/6 |

We will call this formula RKI 2 Classic. It is of order 3.

### 12. Investigation for $q = 3$.

The vanishing of the terms of the first three orders leads to an easily written system of equations. We will not examine in detail the solution of this system, which is of little interest. We will only give an actual formula for $p = 1$:

$$\theta_1 = 1/3, \qquad \theta_2 = 2/3, \qquad \theta_3 = 1.$$

| 1/6 | 1/6 | $A$ | |
|------|-----|------|-----|
| 1/12 | 1/2 | 1/12 | |
| 1/8 | 3/8 | 3/8 | 1/8 |

The formula is of order 4. We will call it RKI 3. It is easy to understand why the investigation of formulas in this direction is of little use. For a given order, one gains about one horner if no iteration is necessary. But if an iteration is necessary, the formula is nothing but the Runge-Kutta formula, where one is called to take up again the same abscissas several times. Such a restriction is only a waste of the parameters.

### III    TOTALLY IMPLICIT RUNGE-KUTTA FORMULAS[1]

### 13.1 Principle.

Strictly speaking, in the Runge-Kutta method, the summation over $\beta$ extends to $X_{i,\beta}$ already calculated in the interior of the step.

[1]Hammer and Hollingsworth [3], Henrici [2, 3], Ionescu [1, 2], Stoller and Morrison.

In the methods of Section II, we have extended the summation to values already calculated and to the one in process of calculation. Here we propose to extend the summation to all the values of $X_{i,\beta}$ relative to one and the same step which they would have, or to all those values which are not yet calculated.

These methods seem like the extension to differential systems of approximate quadrature formulas. The theory of this problem will be presented in Chapter 9. Essentially, we will give here some formulas which can be actually used.

### 13.2  Variation of indices.

One will notice that the calculation of $X_i$ (the value of $X$ relative to the start of the step) will no longer be prescribed. With regard to the variation of the indices $\alpha$ and $\beta$, one can, therefore, consider two distinct cases.

(a) One does not compute $X_i$ and hence also not $X_{i,q}$. It is, therefore, convenient to take the following notations:

$$0 \leqslant \alpha \leqslant q, \qquad 0 \leqslant \beta \leqslant q - 1$$

($X_{i,0}$ is thus distinct from $X_i$). We will call these formulas *open-type formulas*.

(b) One computes $X_i$ and hence also $X_{i,q}$; $X_{i,0}$ will usually be identical with $X_i$. We will have the variations:

$$1 \leqslant \alpha \leqslant q, \qquad 0 \leqslant \beta \leqslant q.$$

We will call these formulas *closed-type formulas*. In the two cases, the formulas to be used are those of Chapter 3, Section II, with the variation of the indices which have just been indicated.

### 14.1  Runge-Kutta-Gauss formulas for $q = 1$.

The index $\alpha$ takes the values 0 and 1; $\beta$ takes the value 0:

$$K_{0,0} = \theta_0^k, \qquad K_{1,0} = 1.$$

The exactness up to degree $k + 1$ requires that

$$K_{0,0}\theta_0 = \frac{1}{k+1}.$$

This is possible only for $p = 1$. One has, therefore, for the system in canonical form

$$x' = X(x, t),$$

the formula

$$\theta_0 = 1/2, \qquad \begin{array}{c|c} 1/2 & A \\ \hline 1 & \end{array}$$

We will call this formula RKT 1. It is of order 2. Let us write it explicitly as

$$x_{i,0} = x_i + \frac{h}{2} X_{i,0},$$

$$x_{i+1} = x_i + h X_{i,0}.$$

### 14.2 Interest in these formulas.

These formulas are only usable in very particular cases, for example, for linear systems. Let us apply the preceding formula, which costs only one horner per step, to the equation

$$y' = ay.$$

We have

$$y_{i,0} = y_i + \frac{ah}{2} y_{i,0},$$

$$y_{i+1} = y_i + ah\, y_{i,0},$$

or, in setting $ah = k$:

$$y_{i,0} = \frac{y_i}{1 - k/2},$$

$$y_{i+1} = y_i\left(1 + \frac{k}{1 - k/2}\right) = y_i\left(\frac{1 + k/2}{1 - k/2}\right) = y_i(1 + k + k^2/2 + k^3/4 + \cdots).$$

### 14.3 Example.

Let the system be

$$\begin{cases} y' = z, \\ z' + 1.5z + 0.5\,y = 0, \end{cases}$$

$$y(0) = z(0) = 1, \qquad h = 0.1.$$

| $t$ | $z$ | $y$ | $y$ exact |
|---|---|---|---|
| 0.1 | 0.8118 | 1.0906 | 1.0904 |
| 0.2 | 0.6461 | 1.1635 | 1.1632 |
| 0.3 | 0.5005 | 1.2208 | 1.2204 |
| 0.4 | 0.3729 | 1.2645 | 1.2640 |
| 0.5 | 0.2613 | 1.2962 | 1.2956 |
| 1.0 | −0.1102 | 1.3232 | 1.3225 |
| 1.5 | −0.2760 | 1.2206 | 1.2201 |
| 2.0 | −0.3303 | 1.0659 | 1.0655 |

### 15.1 Runge-Kutta-Gauss formula for $q = 2$.

We will still limit ourselves to a system in canonical form, and we will attempt to write it with an exactness up to the terms in $h^4$ inclusive. We arrive at the conditions:

$$A_{0,0} + A_{0,1} = \theta_0, \qquad A_{1,0} + A_{1,1} = \theta_1, \qquad A_{2,0} + A_{2,1} = 1,$$

$$A_{2,0}\theta_0 + A_{2,1}\theta_1 = 1/2, \qquad A_{20}(A_{0,1}\theta_1 + A_{0,0}\theta_0) + A_{21}(A_{1,1}\theta_1 + A_{1,0}\theta_0) = 1/6,$$

$$A_{2,0}\theta_0^2 + A_{21}\theta_1^2 = 1/3, \quad A_{20}\theta_0(A_{0,1}\theta_1 + A_{00}\theta_0) + A_{21}\theta_1(A_{11}\theta_1 + A_{10}\theta_0) = 1/8,$$
$$A_{2,0}\theta_0^3 + A_{21}\theta_1^3 = 1/4, \quad A_{20}(A_{0,1}\theta_1^2 + A_{00}\theta_0^2) + A_{21}(A_{11}\theta_1^2 + A_{10}\theta_0^2) = 1/12,$$
$$(A_{20}A_{00} + A_{21}A_{10})(A_{01}\theta_1 + A_{00}\theta_0) + (A_{20}A_{01} + A_{21}A_{11})(A_{10}\theta_0 + A_{11}\theta_1) = 1/24.$$

All these conditions are compatible if one takes

$$\theta_0 + \theta_1 = 1, \qquad \theta_0\theta_1 = 1/6.$$

Setting $\delta = \theta_0 - \theta_1$, we find

$$A$$

| | |
|---|---|
| 1/4 | $1/4 + \delta/2$ |
| $1/4 - \delta/2$ | 1/4 |
| 1/2 | 1/2 |

We will call this formula RKT 2. It is of order 4.

### 15.2 Example.

$$\begin{cases} y' = z, \quad z' + 1.5z + 0.5y = 0, \\ y(0) = z(0) = 1, \quad h = 0.1. \end{cases}$$

| $t$ | $y'$ | $y$ | $y$ exact |
|---|---|---|---|
| 0.1 | 0.812,053,74 | 1.090,405,41 | 1.090,405,44 |
| 0.2 | 0.646,518,01 | 1.163,157,35 | 1.163,157,42 |
| 0.3 | 0.501,039,48 | 1.220,377,16 | 1.220,377,24 |
| 0.4 | 0.373,499,53 | 1.263,962,77 | 1.263,763,82 |
| 0.5 | 0.261,991,41 | 1.295,611,04 | 1.295,611,16 |
| 1.0 | −0.109,421,96 | 1.322,484,13 | 1.322,484,31 |
| 1.5 | −0.275,341,80 | 1.220,075,43 | 1.220,075,72 |
| 2.0 | −0.329,752,44 | 1.065,511,39 | 1.065,511,92 |

### 15.3 Runge-Kutta-Gauss formula for $q = 3$.

One can find a set of values for $\theta_0$, $\theta_1$, $\theta_2$ and for the $A_{ij}$ in a manner so as to attain the order 6. The coefficients are the following:

| | | |
|---|---|---|
| 5/36 | $8/36 + \delta/3$ | $5/36 + \delta/6$ |
| $5/36 - 5\delta/24$ | 8/36 | $5/36 + 5\delta/24$ |
| $5/36 - \delta/6$ | $8/36 - \delta/3$ | 5/36 |
| 5/18 | 8/18 | 5/18 |

We will call this formula RKT 3. It is of order 6.

$$\theta_0 + \theta_2 = 1, \qquad \theta_0\theta_2 = 1/10, \qquad \theta_1 = 1/2, \qquad \delta = \theta_0 - \theta_2.$$

The $\theta_i$ are those of the three-points quadrature formula of Gauss. We will return to this problem in the theoretical part.

### 15.4 Examples.

1. Let us apply the preceding method to $y' = y$, $y(0) = 1$. We find

$$y(h) = \frac{1 + h/2 + h^2/10 + h^3/120}{1 - h/2 + h^2/10 - h^3/120},$$

which is exact up to order 6. Besides, one can compute the principal error terms, which are

$$\frac{h^7 + h^8}{7 \times 14400},$$

and thus very small. For $h = 1$, one finds

$$e \approx 193/71 = 2.718,309.$$

2.  $y' = -2ty^2$, $\qquad y(0) = 1$, $\qquad h = 0.4$.

| $t$ | $y_i$ | $y$ exact |
|---|---|---|
| 0.4 | 0.862,070,86 | 0.862,068,97 |
| 0.8 | 0.609,757,74 | 0.609,756,10 |
| 1.2 | 0.409,836,81 | 0.409,836,07 |
| 1.6 | 0.280,899,21 | 0.280,898,88 |
| 2.0 | 0.200,000,16 | 0.2 |
| 4.0 | 0.058,823,54 | 0.058,823,53 |
| 6.0 | 0.027,027,03 | identical |
| 8.0 | 0.015,384,62 | identical |
| 10.0 | 0.009,900,99 | identical |
| 12.0 | 0.006,896,55 | identical |

### 16.1 Closed-type formula $q = 2$.

Let us set

$$x_{i,1} = x_i + h(A_{10}X_i + A_{11}X_{i1} + A_{12}X_{i+1}),$$
$$x_{i+1} = x_i + h(A_{20}X_i + A_{21}X_{i1} + A_{22}X_{i+1}).$$

The conditions needed to attain order 4 are

$$A_{10} + A_{11} + A_{12} = \theta_1,$$
$$A_{20} + A_{21} + A_{22} = 1,$$
$$A_{21}\theta_1 + A_{22} = 1/2,$$
$$A_{21}\theta_1^2 + A_{22} = 1/3,$$
$$A_{21}\theta_1^3 + A_{22} = 1/4,$$

$$A_{21}\alpha + A_{22}\beta = 1/6, \quad \text{with} \quad \alpha = A_{11}\theta_1 + A_{12},$$
$$A_{21}\theta_1\alpha + A_{22}\beta = 1/8, \qquad \qquad \beta = A_{21}\theta_1 + A_{22},$$
$$(A_{21}A_{11} + A_{22}A_{21})\alpha + (A_{21}A_{12} + A_{22}A_{22})\beta = 1/24,$$
$$A_{21}(A_{11}\theta_1^2 + A_{12}) + A_{22}(A_{21}\theta_1^2 + A_{22}) = 1/12.$$

We find

$$\theta_1 = 1/2.$$

$$A$$

| 5/24 | 8/24 | −1/24 |
|------|------|-------|
| 1/6  | 4/6  | 1/6   |

The value of $\theta_1$ and those of the coefficients $A_{2,0}$, $A_{2,1}$, and $A_{2,2}$ are those of the corresponding closed quadrature formula (Radau-Simpson).

### 16.2 Formulas of the semi-closed type.

One can also give approximate integration formulas corresponding to the semi-closed quadrature formulas, i.e., using $X_i$ at the start of the interval but not at the end. (These formulas are known under the name of Radau formulas.) Here are two examples:

*Case $q = 2$.*

$$x_{i,1} = x_i + h(A_{10} X_i + A_{1,1} X_{i,1}),$$
$$x_{i+1} = x_i + h(A_{20} X_i + A_{2,1} X_{i,1}).$$

One obtains order 3 by taking $\theta_1 = 2/3$.

$$A$$

| 1/3 | 1/3 |
|-----|-----|
| 1/4 | 3/4 |

(We would have found this formula in paragraph 11 by taking $\theta_1 = 2/3$.)

*Case $q = 3$.* Likewise, one obtains order 5 by taking

$$\theta_1 = \frac{6 - \sqrt{6}}{10}, \qquad \theta_2 = \frac{6 + \sqrt{6}}{10}.$$

$$A$$

| $\dfrac{72 + 8\sqrt{6}}{600}$ | $\dfrac{24 + \sqrt{6}}{120}$ | $\dfrac{168 - 73\sqrt{6}}{600}$ |
|---|---|---|
| $\dfrac{72 - 8\sqrt{6}}{600}$ | $\dfrac{168 + 73\sqrt{6}}{600}$ | $\dfrac{24 - \sqrt{6}}{120}$ |
| $\dfrac{4}{36}$ | $\dfrac{16 + \sqrt{6}}{36}$ | $\dfrac{16 - \sqrt{6}}{36}$ |

### 17. The possible use of these formulas by iteration.

Except for the case of linear systems, we can attempt to use these formulas by iteration. Let us consider, for example, the case of the Gauss formula with $q = 3$ of paragraph 15.3. Assuming $x_i$ is known, we can first determine $X_i$, then

$$x_{i,0}^*, \qquad x_{i,1}^*, \qquad x_{i,2}^*,$$

the provisional values of $x_{i,0}$, $x_{i,1}$, and $x_{i,2}$, by using a fourth order Runge-Kutta method whose intermediary abscissas are

$$t_{i,0}, \qquad t_{i,1}, \qquad t_{i,2}.$$

With six horners, we obtain the values of order 4:

$$x_{i,0}^*, \qquad x_{i,1}^*, \qquad x_{i,2}^*.$$

Then we proceed by iteration. One round of iteration costing three horners gives order 5. One last calculation of

$$X_{i,0}, \qquad X_{i,2}, \qquad X_{i,2}$$

costing three horners gives $x_{i+1}$ of order 6. The total cost of the calculation is thus twelve horners per step. By utilizing the values

$$x_i, \qquad X_{i-1,0}, \qquad X_{i-1,1}, \qquad X_{i-1,2}$$

and following the principle of Chapter 8, we can reduce this cost to nine horners per step, and the obtaining

$$x_{i,0}^*, \qquad x_{i,1}^*, \qquad x_{i,2}^*$$

of order 3 does not cost any horners.

## IV   SYSTEMS IN THE FORM $x^{(p)} = X(x, \ldots, x^{(j)}, x^{(j+2)}, \ldots, x^{(p-1)}, t)$. THE PARTICULAR CASE $x'' = X(x, t)$[1]

### 18.1 Simplifications of the computation scheme.

When certain derivatives are absent in the second member, one notes that their calculation is needless at the intermediate points. It suffices to compute them at the points $t_i$, $t_{i+1}$, ....

### 18.2 The vanishing of certain equations.

When the derivative $x^{(p-1)}$ is missing in the second member, certain terms in the table given in Chapter 3, paragraph 11 vanish. This is what happens in particular for the system

$$x'' = X(x),$$

which we are going to study particularly. (We have suppressed the inde-

[1]Albrecht, Laurent [1, 2].

pendent variable, as explained in Chapter 1, paragraph 1.5.) The absence of the first derivative translates itself by the vanishing of the terms

$$J_1 C_1, \quad K_1 C_1, \quad J_1^2 C_1, \quad J_1 C_2, \quad L_1 C_1, \quad R, \quad J_2 J_1 C_1, \quad K_1 C_1,$$
$$K_1 J_1 C_1, \quad J_1 C_3, \quad J_1 J_2 C_1, \quad J_1 K_1 C_1, \quad J_1^3 C_1, \quad J_1^2 C_2.$$

Moreover, there is no second order derivative in $X$; thus $J_3 C_1$ vanishes also.

Finally, the big table giving the Taylor developments for the exact and the approximate solution, carried through to the order $k + 6$, is written:

| | | Taylor | Runge-Kutta |
|---|---|---|---|
| $\dfrac{h^{k+1}}{k!}$ | $C_1$ | $\dfrac{1}{k+1}$ | $\sum_\alpha K_{q,\alpha} \theta_\alpha$ |
| $\dfrac{h^{k+2}}{k!}$ | $C_2$ | $\dfrac{1}{(k+1)(k+2)}$ | $\dfrac{1}{2} \sum_\alpha K_{q,\alpha} \theta_\alpha^2$ |
| $\dfrac{h^{k+3}}{k!}$ | $C_3$ | $\dfrac{1}{(k+1)(k+2)(k+3)}$ | $\dfrac{1}{6} \sum_\alpha K_{q,\alpha} \theta_\alpha^3$ |
| | $J_2 C_1$ | $\dfrac{1}{(k+1)(k+2)(k+3)}$ | $\dfrac{1}{2} \sum_{\alpha,\beta} K_{q,\alpha} B_{\alpha,\beta} \theta_\beta$ |
| $\dfrac{h^{k+4}}{k!}$ | $C_4$ | $\dfrac{1}{(k+1)(k+2)(k+3)(k+4)}$ | $\dfrac{1}{24} \sum_\alpha K_{q,\alpha} \theta_\alpha^4$ |
| | $K_2 C_1$ | $\dfrac{4}{(k+1)(k+2)(k+3)(k+4)}$ | $\dfrac{1}{2} \sum_{\alpha,\beta} K_{q,\alpha} B_{\alpha,\beta} \theta_\alpha \theta_\beta$ |
| | $J_2 C_2$ | $\dfrac{1}{(k+1)(k+2)(k+3)(k+4)}$ | $\dfrac{1}{4} \sum_{\alpha,\beta} K_{q,\alpha} B_{\alpha,\beta} \theta_\beta^2$ |
| $\dfrac{h^{k+5}}{k!}$ | $C_5$ | $\dfrac{1}{(k+1)(k+2)(k+3)(k+4)(k+5)}$ | $\dfrac{1}{5!} \sum_\alpha K_{q,\alpha} \theta_\alpha^5$ |
| | $K_2 C_2$ | $\dfrac{5}{(k+1)(k+2)(k+3)(k+4)(k+5)}$ | $\dfrac{1}{4} \sum_{\alpha,\beta} K_{q,\alpha} B_{\alpha,\beta} \theta_\alpha \theta_\beta^2$ |
| | $J_2 C_3$ | $\dfrac{1}{(k+1)(k+2)(k+3)(k+4)(k+5)}$ | $\dfrac{1}{12} \sum_{\alpha,\beta} K_{q,\alpha} B_{\alpha,\beta} \theta_\beta^3$ |
| | $J_2^2 C_1$ | $\dfrac{1}{(k+1)(k+2)(k+3)(k+4)(k+5)}$ | $\dfrac{1}{4} \sum_{\alpha,\beta,\gamma} K_{q,\alpha} B_{\alpha,\beta} B_{\beta,\gamma} \theta_\gamma$ |
| | $L_2 C_1$ | $\dfrac{10}{(k+1)(k+2)(k+3)(k+4)(k+5)}$ | $\dfrac{1}{4} \sum_{\alpha,\beta} K_{q,\alpha} B_{\alpha,\beta} \theta_\alpha^2 \theta_\beta$ |
| $\dfrac{h^{k+6}}{k!}$ | $C_6$ | $1/D$ | $\dfrac{1}{6!} \sum_\alpha K_{q,\alpha} \theta_\alpha^5$ |
| | $M_2 C_1$ | $20/D$ | $\dfrac{1}{12} \sum_{\alpha,\beta} K_{q,\alpha} B_{\alpha,\beta} \theta_\alpha^3 \theta_\beta$ |
| | $L_2 C_2$ | $15/D$ | $\dfrac{1}{8} \sum_{\alpha,\beta} K_{q,\alpha} B_{\alpha,\beta} \theta_\alpha^2 \theta_\beta^2$ |
| | $K_2 C_3$ | $6/D$ | $\dfrac{1}{12} \sum_{\alpha,\beta} K_{q,\alpha} B_{\alpha,\beta} \theta_\alpha \theta_\beta^3$ |
| | $K_2 J_2 C_1$ | $6/D$ | $\dfrac{1}{4} \sum_{\alpha,\beta,\gamma} K_{q,\alpha} B_{\alpha,\beta} B_{\beta,\gamma} \theta_\alpha \theta_\gamma$ |
| | $J_2 C_4$ | $1/D$ | $\dfrac{1}{2,4!} \sum_{\alpha,\beta} K_{\alpha,\beta} B_{\alpha,\beta} \theta_\beta^4$ |

|  | Taylor | Runge-Kutta |
|---|---|---|
| $J_2 K_2 C_1$ | $4/D$ | $1/4 \sum_{\alpha,\beta,\gamma} K_{q,\alpha} B_{\alpha,\beta} B_{\beta,\gamma} \theta_\beta \theta_\gamma$ |
| $J_2^2 C_2$ | $1/D$ | $1/8 \sum_{\alpha,\beta,\gamma} K_{q,\alpha} B_{\alpha,\beta} B_{\beta,\gamma} \theta_\gamma^2$ |
| $W$ | $10/D$ | $1/8 \sum_{\alpha,\beta,\gamma} K_{q,\alpha} B_{\alpha,\beta} B_{\alpha,\gamma} \theta_\beta \theta_\gamma$ |

One has set

$$D = (k+1)(k+2)(k+3)(k+4)(k+5)(k+6),$$
$$W = \sum_{z,u} X''_{zu} z''' u'''.$$

A tedious but not difficult verification convinces one that the various groups of terms are independent.

### 19. Investigation for $q = 1$ and $q = 2$.

For $q = 1$, one recovers Euler's method without difficulty. For $q = 2$, by taking

$$A_{21} = 1/(2\theta_1), \qquad B_{21} = 1(3\theta_1),$$

one obtains the order $(2, 3)$.

### 20. Possibility of formulas valid up to a higher order for $q = 2$.

Let us remark that, in order to obtain a term $h^3$ exact in $y'$, it suffices to take

$$1/6 = 1/2 A_{2,1} \theta_1^2.$$

Comparing with $A_{21} = 1/(2\theta_1)$, one finds $\theta_1 = 2/3$. This leads to the following coefficients, given by Nyström:

Thus one obtains the order $(3, 3)$. We will call this formula RKS 2 Nyström.

### 21.1 Investigation of the case $q = 3$.

The conditions to be satisfied in order to obtain a formula of order $(4, 4)$ are

$$\begin{cases} B_{32}\theta_2 + B_{31}\theta_1 = 1/3, \\ B_{32}\theta_2^2 + B_{31}\theta_1^2 = 1/6; \end{cases}$$

$$\begin{cases} A_{32}\theta_2 + A_{31}\theta_1 = 1/2, \\ A_{32}\theta_2^2 + A_{31}\theta_1^2 = 1/3; \end{cases}$$

$$\begin{cases} A_{32}\theta_2^3 + A_{31}\theta_1^3 = 1/4, \\ A_{32}B_{21}\theta_1 = 1/12; \end{cases}$$

$$\begin{cases} B_{30} = 1 - B_{31} - B_{32}, \\ B_{20} = \theta_2^2 - B_{21}, \\ A_{30} = 1 - A_{31} - A_{32}. \end{cases}$$

By solving the first two systems one finds

$$B_{31} = \frac{\theta_2/3 - 1/6}{\theta_1(\theta_2 - \theta_1)}, \qquad B_{32} = \frac{\theta_1/3 - 1/6}{\theta_2(\theta_1 - \theta_2)},$$

$$A_{31} = \frac{\theta_2/2 - 1/3}{\theta_1(\theta_2 - \theta_1)}, \qquad A_{32} = \frac{\theta_1/2 - 1/3}{\theta_2(\theta_1 - \theta_2)}.$$

The first equation of the third system then gives

$$-\theta_1\theta_2/2 + (\theta_1 + \theta_2)/3 = 1/4.$$

### 21.2 Efficient formula.[1]

$$\theta_1 = 1/2, \qquad \theta_2 = 1.$$

| | | | $A$ |
|---|---|---|---|
| | | | |
| | | | |
| 1/6 | 4/6 | 1/6 | |

| 1/4 | | $B$ |
|---|---|---|
| 0 | 1 | |
| 1/3 | 2/3 | 0 |

This formula is none other than the classical Runge-Kutta formula for $q = 4$. Indeed, when one applies this formula to an equation not containing $y'$, the two substitutions relative to 1/2 are identical. We will call it RKS 3 Classic.

### 22. Minimization of the remaining errors.

As the error for $x$, one finds

$$\Delta_1 h^5 C_3 + \Delta_2 h^5 J_2 C_1$$

with

$$\Delta_2 = \frac{12\theta_1 - 3}{720(3\theta_1 - 2)}, \qquad \Delta_1 = \frac{-10\theta_1^2 + 12\theta_1 - 3}{720(3\theta_1 - 2)};$$

the minimum of

$$|\Delta_1| + |\Delta_2|$$

is achieved for

$$\theta_1 = 1/4, \qquad \theta_2 = 4/5.$$

[1]Nyström, Zurmühl [1].

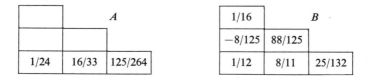

We will call this formula RKS 3 Optimal. Its remaining error for $x$ is $h^5 C_3/1440$. The remaining error for $x'$ is also of order $h^5$.

### 23. Examples.

1.       $y'' = y,$       $y(0) = 1,$       $y'(0) = 1,$       $h = 0.1.$

| $t$ | RKS 3 classic | Error $\times 10^8$ | RKS 3 optimal | Error $\times 10^8$ | Exact solution |
|---|---|---|---|---|---|
| 0.1 | 1.105,170,83 | − 8 | 1.105,170,91 | 0 | 1.105,170,91 |
| 0.2 | 1.221,402,57 | −18 | 1.221,402,73 | − 2 | 1.221,402,75 |
| 0.3 | 1.349,858,51 | −29 | 1.349,858,76 | − 4 | 1.349,858,80 |
| 0.4 | 1.491,824,28 | −41 | 1.491,824,62 | − 7 | 1.491,824,69 |
| 0.5 | 1.648,720,72 | −55 | 1.648,721,17 | −10 | 1.648,721,27 |

2.       $y'' = -y,$       $y(0) = 0,$       $y'(0) = 1,$       $h = 0.1.$

| $t$ | RKS 3 classic | Error $\times 10^9$ | RKS 3 optimal | Error $\times 10^9$ | Exact solution |
|---|---|---|---|---|---|
| 0.1 | 0.099,833,334 | − 82 | 0.099,833,417 | 1 | 0.099,833,416 |
| 0.2 | 0.198,669,167 | −163 | 0.198,669,332 | 2 | 0.198,669,330 |
| 0.3 | 0.295,519,963 | −243 | 0.295,520,210 | 4 | 0.295,520,206 |
| 0.4 | 0.389,418,023 | −319 | 0.389,418,347 | 5 | 0.389,418,342 |
| 0.5 | 0.479,425,149 | −389 | 0.479,425,547 | 9 | 0.479,425,538 |

### 24.1 Formula of rank 4.

Now, we propose to satisfy all the equations up to the order $k + 4$ inclusive. Let us express these equations:

I
$$\begin{cases} B_{43}\theta_3 + B_{42}\theta_2 + B_{41}\theta_1 = 1/3, \\ B_{43}\theta_3^2 + B_{42}\theta_2^2 + B_{41}\theta_1^2 = 1/16, \\ B_{43}\theta_3^3 + B_{42}\theta_2^3 + B_{41}\theta_1^3 = 1/10, \\ B_{43}\theta_3^4 + B_{42}\theta_2^4 + B_{41}\theta_1^4 = 1/15. \end{cases}$$

II
$$\begin{cases} A_{43}\theta_3 + A_{42}\theta_2 + A_{41}\theta_1 = 1/2, \\ A_{43}\theta_3^2 + A_{42}\theta_2^2 + A_{41}\theta_1^2 = 1/3, \\ A_{43}\theta_3^3 + A_{42}\theta_2^3 + A_{41}\theta_1^3 = 1/4, \\ A_{43}\theta_3^4 + A_{42}\theta_2^4 + A_{41}\theta_1^4 = 1/5. \end{cases}$$

III
(a) $B_{42}B_{21}\theta_1 + B_{43}B_{31}\theta_1 + B_{43}B_{32}\theta_2 = 1/30,$
(b) $B_{42}B_{21}\theta_1^2 + B_{43}B_{31}\theta_1^2 + B_{43}B_{32}\theta_2^2 = 1/90,$
(c) $B_{42}B_{21}\theta_2\theta_1 + B_{43}B_{31}\theta_3\theta_1 + B_{43}B_{32}\theta_3\theta_2 = 1/45.$

IV
(a) $A_{42}B_{21}\theta_1 + A_{43}B_{31}\theta_1 + A_{43}B_{32}\theta_2 = 1/12,$
(b) $A_{42}B_{21}\theta_1^2 + A_{43}B_{31}\theta_1^2 + A_{43}B_{32}\theta_2^2 = 1/30,$
(c) $A_{42}B_{21}\theta_2\theta_1 + A_{43}B_{31}\theta_3\theta_1 + A_{43}B_{32}\theta_3\theta_2 = 1/15.$

It is not possible to satisfy all these equations but only to attain the order (5, 5).

Nyström proposes the following two formulas:

$$\theta_1 = 1/5, \qquad \theta_2 = 2/3, \qquad \theta_3 = 1.$$

| A | | | | B | | | |
|---|---|---|---|---|---|---|---|
| | | | | 1/25 | | | |
| | | | | −2/27 | 14/27 | | |
| | | | | 21/35 | −4/35 | 18/35 | |
| 14/336 | 125/336 | 162/336 | 35/336 | 14/168 | 100/168 | 54/168 | 0 |

$$\theta_1 = 2/5, \qquad \theta_2 = 2/3, \qquad \theta_3 = 4/5.$$

| A | | | | B | | | |
|---|---|---|---|---|---|---|---|
| | | | | 4/25 | | | |
| | | | | 4/9 | 0 | | |
| | | | | 8/25 | 8/25 | 0 | |
| 23/192 | 125/192 | −81/192 | 125/192 | 23/96 | 75/96 | −27/96 | 25/96 |

We will call these formulas RKS 4 Nyström.

Laurent proposes to satisfy all the equations except III(b) and IV(c) and to minimize the sum of the absolute values of the coefficients corresponding to these two neglected equations; i.e.,

$$1/8\left|\frac{\theta_1\theta_3}{6} - \frac{2\theta_1}{15} - \frac{\theta_3}{15} + 1/18\right| + 1/4\left|\frac{\theta_2\theta_3}{6} - \frac{2(\theta_2 + \theta_3)}{15} + 1/9\right|.$$

Here is a set of coefficients which achieve, without doubt, a value very close to that of the minimum:

$$\theta_1 = 0.26, \qquad \theta_2 = 0.681,807,380, \qquad \theta_3 = 0.957,041,595.$$

| A | | | |
|---|---|---|---|
| | | | |
| | | | |
| 0.078,394,863 | 0.392,127,923 | 0.394,986,133 | 0.134,521,084 |

| $\theta_1^2$ | | B | |
|---|---|---|---|
| 0.001,866,906 | 0.462,994,397 | | |
| 0.382,009,290 | 0.232,354,585 | 0.301,564,739 | |
| 0.156,729,713 | 0.580,349,338 | 0.251,363,322 | 0.011,557,635 |

We will call this formula RKS 4 Laurent. It is of order (5, 5). The errors for $x$ have for the principal part

$$0.000,18 \quad h^6 \quad J_2 C_2,$$

$$0.000,34 \quad h^6 \quad K_2 C_1.$$

### 24.2 Examples.

1.          $y'' = y, \quad y(0) = 1, \quad y'(0) = 1.$

| $t$ | Solution by RKS 3 classic | Error $\times 10^8$ | Solution by RKS 4 Laurent | Error $\times 10^8$ | Exact solution |
|---|---|---|---|---|---|
| 0.1 | 1.105,170,83 | −8 | 1.105,170,91 | 0 | 1.105,170,91 |
| 0.2 | 1.221,402,57 | −18 | 1.221,402,74 | −1 | 1.221,402,75 |
| 0.3 | 1.349,858,51 | −29 | 1.349,858,78 | −2 | 1.349,858,80 |
| 0.4 | 1.491,824,28 | −41 | 1.491,824,66 | −3 | 1.491,824,69 |
| 0.5 | 1.648,720,72 | −55 | 1.648,721,22 | −5 | 1.648,721,27 |
| 1 | 2.718,280,32 | −150 | 2.718,281,72 | −10 | 2.718,281,82 |
| 2 | 7.389,049,49 | −660 | 7.389,055,72 | −35 | 7.389,056,09 |
| 4 | 54.598,066,2 | −8380 | 54.598,144,3 | −570 | 54.598,150,0 |

2.          $y'' = -y, \quad y(0) = 0, \quad y'(0) = 1.$

| $t$ | Solution by RKS 3 classic | Error $\times 10^9$ | Solution by RKS 4 Laurent | Error $\times 10^9$ | Exact solution |
|---|---|---|---|---|---|
| 0.1 | 0.099,833,334 | −82 | 0.099,833,417 | +1.2 | 0.099,833,416 |
| 0.2 | 0.198,669,167 | −163 | 0.198,669,333 | +3 | 0.198,669,330 |
| 0.3 | 0.295,519,963 | −243 | 0.295,520,210 | +4 | 0.295,520,206 |
| 0.4 | 0.389,418,023 | −319 | 0.389,418,347 | +5 | 0.389,418,342 |
| 0.5 | 0.479,425,149 | −389 | 0.479,425,544 | +6 | 0.479,425,538 |

### 25.1 Formulas of rank 5.

Without explaining the details of the calculations, we give two formulas of rank 5, one due to Albrecht.

$$\theta_1 = 1/4, \qquad \theta_2 = 1/2, \qquad \theta_3 = 3/4, \qquad \theta_4 = 1.$$

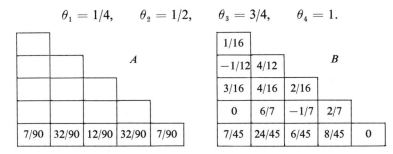

We will call this formula RKS 5 Albrecht. It is of order (6, 6). In the course of a study, for which we return to his thesis, Laurent proposes

$$\theta_1 = 1/4, \qquad \theta_2 = 3/4, \qquad \theta_3 = 1/2, \qquad \theta_4 = 1.$$

A

| | | | | |
|---|---|---|---|---|
| | | | | |
| | | | | |
| | | | | |
| 7/90 | 32/90 | 32/90 | 12/90 | 7/90 |

B

| | | | | |
|---|---|---|---|---|
| 1/16 | | | | |
| 1/16 | 8/16 | | | |
| 1/36 | 6/36 | 2/36 | | |
| 8/21 | 0 | 4/21 | 9/21 | |
| 14/90 | 48/90 | 16/90 | 12/90 | 0 |

We will call this formula RKS 5 Laurent. In comparison with Albrecht's formula, it has the advantage of giving wholly positive coefficients.

### 25.2 Examples.

1. $\qquad y'' = -y, \qquad y(0) = 0, \qquad y'(0) = 1, \qquad h = 0.2.$

| $t$ | Solution by RKS 4 Laurent | Error | Solution by RKS 5 Laurent | Error | Exact solution |
|---|---|---|---|---|---|
| 0.2 | 0.198,669,333 | +3 | 0.198,669,331 | +1 | 0.198,669,330 |
| 0.4 | 0.389,418,352 | +10 | 0.389,418,343 | +1 | 0.389,418,342 |
| 1 | 0.841,471,036 | +51 | 0.841,470,987 | +2 | 0.841,470,985 |
| 2 | 0.909,297,541 | +114 | 0.909,297,436 | +9 | 0.909,297,427 |

2. $\qquad y'' = -y^3, \qquad y(0) = 0.2, \qquad y'(0) = 0, \qquad h = 1.$

| $t$ | Solution by RKS 4 Laurent | Error | Solution by RKS 5 Laurent | Error | Exact solution |
|---|---|---|---|---|---|
| 1 | 0.196,039,546 | 15 | 0.196,039,525 | −6 | 0.196,039,531 |
| 2 | 0.184,610,686 | 27 | 0.184,610,649 | −10 | 0.184,610,659 |

### 26. Another possibility.[1]

Since $x'_{i+1}$ can be calculated after $X_{i+1}$, one can use $X_{i+1}$ in the expression for $x'_{i+1}$. Here are the first two formulas of this type:

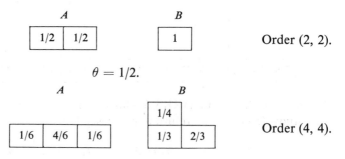

Order (2, 2).

$$\theta = 1/2.$$

Order (4, 4).

This formula is identical to that of paragraph 21.2.

## Problems

Repeat the problems of Chapter 3, using the following methods:
1. RKS 3 Classic.
2. RKS 3 Optimal.
3. RKT 2.
4. RKS 4 Laurent.
Estimate the error of each method. Which would you prefer? Why?

[1]Kuntzmann [7].

# 5  RUNGE-KUTTA TYPE FORMULAS USING HIGHER ORDER DERIVATIVES

### 1. General idea of this chapter.

Now we are going to show a certain number of methods which resort to higher order derivatives than those appearing in the equation. To a certain extent, these methods can remedy the nonexistence of ordinary Runge-Kutta formulas of higher order. The interest in these methods depends essentially on the form of the second member. Generally, they are not applicable when certain quantities occur in the form of a table, or when the number of the functions is too large.

The first procedure which we will present consists of restoring the Runge-Kutta method by means of a transformation. The procedures presented hereafter will actually use higher order derivatives.[1] Let the system be

$$x^{(p)} = X(x, x', \ldots, x^{(p-1)}).$$

One can try to circumvent the difficulty relative to the nonexistence of higher order Runge-Kutta formulas by introducing into the formulas higher order terms. This can be done in several ways, which we will try to review.

(a) The supplementary terms introduced can be total derivatives, for instance,

$$x^{(p+1)}, \qquad x^{(p+2)}.$$

(b) The supplementary terms can only be certain of the terms which we have introduced, for instance, $C_2$, $J_1C_1$, or even $J_1$ multiplied by other columns.

For the other procedure, these supplementary terms can be:

(a) Relative to several intermediate values. One has to make a rather

[1] Bard, Fehlberg [1, 2, 3], Vlasov and Carnyi.

complicated calculation in order to study their influence on the Runge-Kutta formulas.

(b) Relative only to the initial value of the step. Thus there are, by far, fewer modifications to be made in the Runge-Kutta calculations. Moreover, this method has been followed through by several authors.

In any event, it will be interesting to investigate the formulas which, because of the nonexistence of certain coefficients, permit the saving of horners. This study will lead us to the conclusion that one has to impose at the intermediary points approximations of an order appropriate to the number of higher order derivatives which we had decided to use.

# I   PROCEDURE OF THE PREVIOUS DERIVATION[1]

## 2.1 Principle.

Let the differential system be

$$x^{(p)} = X(x, x', \ldots, x^{(p-1)}).$$

We assume that $X$ is differentiable in all variables which occur in the equation as many times as needed. Thus we can write

$$x^{(n+p)} = X_n(x, x', \ldots, x^{(p-1)}).$$

The Runge-Kutta procedure for this $n + p$ order equation simplifies itself, as the second member (right-hand side) does not depend on derivatives of higher order than p $-$ 1. Incidentally, the derivatives $x^{(p)}, \ldots, x^{(n+p-1)}$ need only be calculated at the end of the step, and this by means of the known expressions:

$$x^{(p)} = X, \qquad x^{(p+1)} = X_1, \ldots, x^{(p+n-1)} = X_{n-1}.$$

Therefore, we can focus the effort for the determination of the coefficients which one actually needs. We shall treat in this manner systems of the first order ($p = 1$). by deriving it once. We have only to determine the coefficients $B_{\alpha, \beta}$. Before commencing, let us point out that the previous derivation does not modify the propagation of errors (see Chapter 9, paragraph 18).

## 2.2 Level of the formula.

We see that, for such a formula and in general for all the formulas of this chapter, the rank, i.e., the value of $q$ for which

$$x_{i,q} = x_{i+1},$$

does not coincide with the number of horners, i.e., with the number of $X$ necessary to calculate in order to perform one step. We will reserve the word *level* to characterize this number of horners when it differs from the rank.

[1]Albrecht, Laurent [1], Zurmühl [3].

We will characterize a formula by indicating successively its rank, its level, and its order.

### 3. Formula of rank 2.

With $q = 2$, we can verify the conditions for $B_{\alpha\beta}$ and $\theta_\beta$ up to $h^4$ inclusive. These conditions are

$$B_{21}\theta_1 = 1/3,$$
$$B_{21}\theta_1^2 = 1/6,$$
$$B_{21} + B_{20} = 1,$$

which gives $\theta_1 = 1/2$.

| 1/4 | B |
|-----|-----|
| 1/3 | 2/3 |

We will call this formula RKDP 2, 3, 4 Zurmühl. Actually, it is of rank 2 and of level 3, since one step costs three horners (two calculations for $X_1$ and one for $X$ per step); finally it is of order 4. There is no reason to distinguish between the order of $x$ and the order of $x'$. Necessarily, they are equal, as one obtains $x'$ by starting from $x$ by an explicit formula. The formula seems to be due to Zurmühl. It has later been taken up by Albrecht.

### 4.1 Formula of rank 3.

Now we will verify the conditions for the $B_{\alpha\beta}$ in order to obtain a formula of order 5 with $q = 3$. Furthermore, we will try to satisfy a condition of the next order. Therefore, we have the equations:

$$\text{I} \begin{cases} B_{32}\theta_2 + B_{31}\theta_1 = 1/3, & h^3 \\ B_{32}\theta_2^2 + B_{31}\theta_1^2 = 1/6, & h^4 \\ B_{32}\theta_2^3 + B_{31}\theta_1^3 = 1/10, & h^5 \\ B_{32}\theta_2^4 + B_{31}\theta_1^4 = 1/15, & h^6 \end{cases}$$

$$\text{II} \quad \{ B_{32}B_{21}\theta_1 = 1/30, \quad h^5$$

$$\text{III} \begin{cases} B_{32} + B_{31} + B_{30} = 1, \\ B_{21} + B_{20} = \theta_2^2. \end{cases}$$

In order that system I admit a solution, it is necessary that:

$$\frac{\theta_2\theta_1}{3} - \frac{\theta_1 + \theta_2}{6} + 1/10 = 0,$$

$$\frac{\theta_2\theta_1}{6} - \frac{\theta_1 + \theta_2}{10} + 1/15 = 0,$$

from which one obtains the values of $\theta_1$ and $\theta_2$:[1]

[1] Laurent [1].

$$\theta_1 = \frac{5 - \sqrt{5}}{10} = 0.276,393,202,$$

$$\theta_2 = \frac{5 + \sqrt{5}}{10} = 0.723,606,798.$$

| $\theta_1^2 = \dfrac{3 - \sqrt{5}}{10}$ | $B$ | |
|---|---|---|
| $0$ | $\dfrac{3 + \sqrt{5}}{10}$ | |
| $1/6$ | $\dfrac{5 + \sqrt{5}}{12}$ | $\dfrac{5 - \sqrt{5}}{12}$ |

Bard, who does not write conditions for $h^6$, proposes

$$\theta_1 = 3/10, \qquad \theta_2 = 3/4.$$

| 9/100 | | |
|---|---|---|
| 0 | 9/16 | |
| 15/81 | 50/81 | 16/81 |

We will call these formulas RKDP 3, 4, 5 Laurent and RKDP 3, 4, 5 Bard, respectively.

### 4.2 Examples.

1.    $y' = y - 1.5e^{-0.5t}, \qquad y(0) = 1, \qquad h = 0.4.$

| $t$ | RK4 classic | Error $\times 10^6$ | RKDP2, 3, 4 Zurmühl | Error $\times 10^6$ | RKDP3, 4, 5 Laurent | Error $\times 10^6$ | $y$ exact |
|---|---|---|---|---|---|---|---|
| 0.4 | 0.818,700 | $-$ 31 | 0.818,739 | $+$ 8 | 0.818,731 | 0 | 0.818,731 |
| 0.8 | 0.670,248 | $-$ 72 | 0.670,341 | $+$ 21 | 0.670,320 | 0 | 0.670,320 |
| 1.2 | 0.548,683 | $-$ 129 | 0.548,849 | $+$ 37 | 0.548,812 | 0 | 0.548,812 |
| 1.6 | 0.449,121 | $-$ 208 | 0.449,389 | $+$ 60 | 0.449,329 | 0 | 0.449,329 |
| 2.0 | 0.367,555 | $-$ 324 | 0.367,974 | $+$ 95 | 0.367,879 | 0 | 0.367,879 |
| 4.0 | 0.132,816 | $-2519$ | 0.136,070 | $+735$ | 0.135,333 | $-2$ | 0.135,335 |

2.    $y' = -2ty^2, \qquad y(0) = 1, \qquad h = 0.2.$

| $t$ | RK4 classic | Error $\times 10^6$ | RKDP2, 3, 4 Zurmühl | Error $\times 10^6$ | RKDP3, 4, 5 Laurent | Error $\times 10^6$ | $y$ exact |
|---|---|---|---|---|---|---|---|
| 0.2 | 0.961,533 | $-$ 5 | 0.961,565 | $+27$ | 0.961,539,520 | 1.06 | 0.961,538,461 |
| 0.4 | 0.862,053 | $-16$ | 0.862,150 | $+82$ | 0.862,071,240 | 2.3 | 0.862,068,965 |
| 0.6 | 0.735,279 | $-15$ | 0.735,360 | $+66$ | 0.735,297,534 | 3.4 | 0.735,294,117 |
| 0.8 | 0.609,752 | $-$ 4 | 0.609,780 | $+24$ | 0.609,759,492 | 3.5 | 0.609,756,097 |
| 1.0 | 0.500,007 | $+$ 7 | 0.500,001 | $+$ 1 | 0.500,002,679 | 2.6 | 0.500,000,000 |
| 2.0 | 0.200,008 | $+$ 8 | 0.200,005 | $+$ 5 | 0.200,000,485 | 0.5 | 0.200,000,000 |

3.   $y' = y - 2t/y$,     $y(0) = 1$,     $h = 0.2$.

| $t$ | RK4 classic | Error $\times 10^6$ | RKDP2, 3, 4 Zurmühl | Error $\times 10^6$ | RKDP3, 4, 5 Laurent | Error $\times 10^6$ | $y$ exact |
|---|---|---|---|---|---|---|---|
| 0.2 | 1.183,229,28 | 13 | 1.183,173,99 | − 42 | 1.183,215,97 | +0.01 | 1.183,215,96 |
| 0.4 | 1.341,666,91 | 26 | 1.341,571,91 | − 69 | 1.341,640,90 | +0.11 | 1.341,640,79 |
| 0.6 | 1.483,281,43 | 42 | 1.483,140,47 | − 99 | 1.483,239,90 | +0.20 | 1.483,239,70 |
| 0.8 | 1.612,514,00 | 63 | 1.612,311,87 | − 139 | 1.612,451,86 | +0.31 | 1.612,451,55 |
| 1.0 | 1.732,141,82 | 91 | 1.731,854,60 | − 196 | 1.732,051,26 | +0.45 | 1.732,050,81 |
| 2.0 | 2.236,623,68 | 556 | 2.234,932,45 | −1136 | 2.236,070,64 | +2.66 | 2.236,067,98 |

## 5. Formula of rank 4.

Albrecht proposes the following formula of rank 4:

$$\theta_1 = 1/4, \qquad \theta_2 = 1/2, \qquad \theta_3 = 3/4,$$

| 1/16 | | | |
|---|---|---|---|
| −1/12 | 4/12 | *B* | |
| 3/16 | 4/16 | 2/16 | |
| 14/90 | 48/90 | 12/90 | 16/90 |

which is of order 6, and of level 5.

Laurent tries to verify a condition of the following order:

$$B_{43}\theta_3^5 + B_{42}\theta_2^5 + B_{41}\theta_1^5 = 1/21.$$

In the course of a study, for which we return to his work, he proposes two formulas.

*Formula* 1.

$$\theta_1 = (3 - \sqrt{2})/7 \qquad \theta_2 = 1, \qquad \theta_3 = (3 + \sqrt{2})/7$$
$$\approx 0.226,540,919, \qquad\qquad\qquad \approx 0.630,601,937.$$

| $\theta_1^2$ | | | |
|---|---|---|---|
| 0.051,320,788,3 | | *B* | |
| $\dfrac{\sqrt{2} - 1}{3}$ | $\dfrac{4 - \sqrt{2}}{3}$ | | |
| 0.138,071,187 | 0.861,928,812 | | |
| $\dfrac{92\sqrt{2} - 11}{7203}$ | $\dfrac{626\sqrt{2} + 1752}{7203}$ | $\dfrac{164\sqrt{2} - 124}{7203}$ | |
| 0.016,535,838,9 | 0.366,138,788 | 0.014,984,176,6 | |
| 2/15 | $\dfrac{51 + 10\sqrt{2}}{120}$ | 1/60 | $\dfrac{51 - 10\sqrt{2}}{120}$ |
| 0.133,333,333,3 | 0.542,851,130 | 0.016,666,666,7 | 0.307,148,870 |

*Formula* 2.

$$\theta_1 = (1 - \sqrt{3/7})/2 \qquad \theta_2 = 1/2, \qquad \theta_3 = (1 + \sqrt{3/7})2$$
$$\approx 0.172,673,165, \qquad\qquad\qquad \approx 0.827,326,835.$$

| $\theta_1^2$ | | | |
|---|---|---|---|
| $(3 - 7\sqrt{3/7})/96$ <br> 0.016,485,163,4 | $7(\sqrt{3/7} + 3)/96$ <br> 0.266,485,163 | | |
| $(3 + 5\sqrt{3/7})/21$ <br> 0.298,727,064 | $(7\sqrt{3/7} - 3)/42$ <br> 0.037,680,37 | $2(3 + \sqrt{3/7})/21$ <br> 0.348,062,254 | |
| 0.1 | $49(1 + \sqrt{3/7})/180$ <br> 0.450,433,499 | $32/90$ <br> 0.355,555,556 | $49(1 - \sqrt{3/7})/180$ <br> 0.094,010,945,2 |

For examples of these formulas, the reader is referred to Laurent's thesis.

## II  FORMULAS USING HIGHER ORDER DERIVATIVES AT THE START OF THE STEP

### 6. Principle.

Formulas using higher order derivatives at the start of the step have been presented according to another principle.[1] Let the system be

$$x^{(p)} = X(x, x', \ldots, x^{(p-1)}, t).$$

By generalizing the Runge-Kutta formulas, one writes it as

$$x_{0,\alpha}^{(p-k)} = x_0^{(p-k)} + \frac{h\theta_\alpha}{1!} x_0^{(p-k+1)} + \cdots + \frac{h^{k-1}}{k-1!} \theta_\alpha^{k-1} x_0^{(p-1)}$$

$$+ \frac{h^k}{k!} \theta_\alpha^k X_0 + \frac{h^k}{k!} [h K'_{\alpha,C_1} C_1 + h^2 K'_{\alpha,C_2} C_2 + h^2 K'_{\alpha,J_1C_1} J_1 C_1 \ldots]$$

$$+ \frac{h^k}{k!} \Sigma K_{\alpha,\beta}(X_{0,\beta} - X_0).$$

If we desire to introduce only total derivatives, it suffices to pose the supplementary conditions

$$K'_{C_2} = K'_{J_1C_1}, \text{ etc.}$$

Conforming to a previous remark (Chapter 3, paragraph 11.2), we will not consider expressions other than linear combinations of terms existing in the derivatives.

### 7. Expansion of $X_{0,\alpha} - X_0$.

In order to use these new expressions it is necessary to modify the evaluation of $X_{0\alpha} - X_0$ made in Chapter 3, paragraph 10.1 and the following

[1]Fehlberg [1, 2, 3].

chapters. We will write all these terms up to the terms $h^4$ inclusive by restricting ourselves to the introduction of the supplementary terms $C_1$, $C_2$, $J_1C_1$. An easy calculation, whose details we will omit, shows that it is necessary to write

$$
X_{0,\alpha} - X_0 = h\theta_\alpha C_1 + h^2 \left\{ \theta_\alpha^2 \frac{C_2}{2!} + \left( \sum A_{\alpha,\beta}\theta_\beta + A'_{\alpha,c_1} \right) J_1 C_1 \right\}
$$

$$
+ h^3 \left\{ \theta_\alpha^3 \frac{C_3}{3!} + \left( \sum A_{\alpha,\beta}\frac{\theta_\beta^2}{2!} + A'_{\alpha,c_2} \right) J_1 C_2 + \left( \sum A_{\alpha,\beta}A_{\beta,\gamma}\theta_\gamma \right. \right.
$$

$$
+ A'_{\alpha,J_1c_1} + \sum A_{\alpha\beta}A'_{\beta,c_1} ) J_1^2 C_1 + \left( \sum B_{\alpha\beta}\frac{\theta_\beta}{2} + 1/2 B'_{\alpha,c_1} \right) J_2 C_1
$$

$$
+ \left( \sum A_{\alpha,\beta}\theta_\alpha\theta_\beta + A'_{\alpha,c_1}\theta_\alpha \right) K_1 C_1 \Big\}
$$

$$
+ h^4 \left\{ \theta_\alpha^4 \frac{C_4}{4!} + \left( \sum C_{\alpha\beta}\frac{\theta_\beta}{3!} + \frac{C'_{\alpha,c_1}}{3!} \right) J_3 C_1 + \left( \sum B_{\alpha,\beta}\frac{\theta_\alpha\theta_\beta}{2} \right. \right.
$$

$$
+ 1/2\theta_\alpha B'_{\alpha,c_1} ) K_2 C_1 + \left( \sum A_{\alpha\beta}\frac{\theta_\alpha^2\theta_\beta}{2} + \frac{\theta_\alpha^2}{2}A'_{\alpha,c_1} \right) L_1 C_1
$$

$$
+ \left( \frac{\sum A_{\alpha,\beta}A_{\alpha,\gamma}}{2}\theta_\beta\theta_\gamma + \sum A_{\alpha,\beta}\theta_\beta A'_{\beta,c_1} + 1/2 A'^2_{\alpha,c_1} \right) R
$$

$$
+ \frac{\sum A_{\alpha,\beta}\theta_\beta^3}{3!} J_1 C_3 + \left( \frac{\sum A_{\alpha,\beta}A_{\beta,\gamma}}{2!}\theta_\gamma^2 + \sum A_{\alpha,\beta}A'_{\beta,c_2} \right) J_1^2 C_2
$$

$$
+ (\sum A_{\alpha,\beta}A_{\beta,\gamma}A_{\gamma,\delta}\theta_\delta + \sum A_{\alpha,\beta}A_{\alpha,\gamma}A_{\gamma,c_1} + \sum A_{\alpha,\beta}A'_{\beta,J_1c_1}) J_1^3 C_1
$$

$$
+ \left( \frac{\sum A_{\alpha,\beta}B_{\beta,\gamma}}{2!}\theta_\gamma + \frac{\sum A_{\alpha,\beta}B'_{\beta,c_1}}{2} \right) J_1 J_2 C_1
$$

$$
+ (\sum A_{\alpha,\beta}A_{\beta,\gamma}\theta_\beta\theta_\gamma + \sum A_{\alpha,\beta}A'_{\beta,c_1}\theta_\beta) J_1 K_1 C_1
$$

$$
+ \left( \sum B_{\alpha,\beta}\frac{\theta_\beta^2}{4} + 1/2 B'_{\alpha,c_2} \right) J_2 C_2
$$

$$
+ \left( 1/2 \sum B_{\alpha,\beta}A_{\beta,\gamma}\theta_\gamma + 1/2 B_{\alpha,J_1c_1} + \sum \frac{B_{\alpha,\beta}}{2}A'_{\beta,c_1} \right) J_2 J_1 C_1
$$

$$
+ \left( \frac{\sum A_{\alpha,\beta}}{2}\theta_\alpha\theta_\beta^2 + \theta_\alpha A'_{\alpha,c_2} \right) K_1 C_2 + (\sum A_{\alpha,\beta}A_{\gamma,\beta}\theta_\alpha\theta_\gamma
$$

$$
+ \theta_\alpha A'_{\alpha,J_1c_1} + \sum A_{\alpha,\beta}\theta_\alpha A'_{\beta,c_1}) K_1 J_1 C_1 \Big\} .
$$

## 8. Fundamental table.

From the above, we derive the following table:

| | Taylor | RK with high order terms at the start of the step |
|---|---|---|
| $\frac{h^{k+1}}{k!} C_1$ | $\frac{1}{k+1}$ | $\sum K_{q,\alpha}\theta_\alpha + K'_{q,c_1}$ |

| | Taylor | RK with high order terms at the start of the step |
|---|---|---|
| $\dfrac{h^{k+2}}{k!}\,C_2$ | $\dfrac{1}{(k+1)(k+2)}$ | $1/2 \sum K_{q,\alpha}\theta_\alpha^2 + K'_{q,C_2}$ |
| $J_1 C_1$ | $\dfrac{1}{(k+1)(k+2)}$ | $\sum K_{q,\alpha}A_{\alpha,\beta}\theta_\beta + \sum K_{q,\alpha}A'_{\alpha,C_1} + K'_{q,J_1C_1}$ |
| $\dfrac{h^{k+3}}{k!}\,C_3$ | $\dfrac{1}{(k+1)(k+2)(k+3)}$ | $1/6 \sum K_{q,\alpha}\theta_\alpha^3$ |
| $J_2 C_1$ | $\dfrac{1}{(k+1)(k+2)(k+3)}$ | $1/2 \sum K_{q,\alpha}B_{\alpha,\beta}\theta_\beta + 1/2 \sum K'_{q,\alpha}B'_{\alpha,C_1}$ |
| $K_1 C_1$ | $\dfrac{3}{(k+1)(k+2)(k+3)}$ | $\sum K_{q,\alpha}A_{\alpha,\beta}\theta_\alpha\theta_\beta + \sum K_{q,\alpha}A'_{\alpha,C_1}\theta_\alpha$ |
| $J_1^2 C_1$ | $\dfrac{1}{(k+1)(k+2)(k+3)}$ | $\sum K_{q,\alpha}A_{\alpha,\beta}A_{\beta,\gamma}\theta_\gamma + \sum K_{q,\alpha}A'_{\alpha,J_1C_1}$ <br> $+ \sum K_{q,\alpha}A_{\alpha,\beta}A'_{\beta,C_1}$ |
| $J_1 C_2$ | $\dfrac{1}{(k+1)(k+2)(k+3)}$ | $1/2 \sum K_{q,\alpha}A_{\alpha,\beta}\theta_\beta^2 + \sum K_{q,\alpha}A'_{\alpha,C_2}$ |
| $\dfrac{h^{k+4}}{k!}\,C_4$ | $\dfrac{1}{(k+1)(k+2)(k+3)(k+4)}$ | $1/24 \sum K_{q,\alpha}\theta_\alpha^4$ |
| $J_3 C_1$ | $\dfrac{1}{(k+1)(k+2)(k+3)(k+4)}$ | $1/6 \sum K_{q,\alpha}C_{\alpha,\beta}\theta_\beta + 1/6 \sum K_{q,\alpha}C'_{\alpha,C_1}$ |
| $K_2 C_1$ | $\dfrac{4}{(k+1)(k+2)(k+3)(k+4)}$ | $1/2 \sum K_{q,\alpha}B_{\alpha,\beta}\theta_\alpha\theta_\beta + 1/2 \sum K_{q,\alpha}\theta_\alpha B'_{\alpha,C_1}$ |
| $L_1 C_1$ | $\dfrac{6}{(k+1)(k+2)(k+3)(k+4)}$ | $1/2 \sum K_{q,\alpha}A_{\alpha,\beta}\theta_\alpha^2\theta_\beta + 1/2 \sum K_{q,\alpha}\theta_\alpha^2 A'_{\alpha,C_1}$ |
| $R$ | $\dfrac{3}{(k+1)(k+2)(k+3)(k+4)}$ | $1/2 \sum K_{q,\alpha}A_{\alpha,\beta}A_{\alpha,\gamma}\theta_\beta\theta_\gamma$ <br> $+ \sum K_{q,\alpha}A_{\alpha,\beta}A'_{\beta,C_1}\theta_\beta$ <br> $+ 1/2 \sum K_{q,\alpha}A'^2_{\alpha,C_1}$ |
| $J_2 C_2$ | $\dfrac{1}{(k+1)(k+2)(k+3)(k+4)}$ | $1/4 \sum K_{q,\alpha}B_{\alpha,\beta}\theta_\beta^2 + 1/2 \sum K_{q,\alpha}B'_{\alpha,C_2}$ |
| $J_2 J_1 C_1$ | $\dfrac{1}{(k+1)(k+2)(k+3)(k+4)}$ | $1/2 \sum K_{q,\alpha}B_{\alpha,\beta}A_{\beta,\gamma}\theta_\gamma + 1/2\sum K_{q,\alpha}B_{\alpha,J_1C_1}$ <br> $+ 1/2 \sum K_{q,\alpha}B_{\alpha,\beta}A'_{\beta,C_1}$ |
| $J_1 J_2 C_1$ | $\dfrac{1}{(k+1)(k+2)(k+3)(k+4)}$ | $1/2 \sum K_{q,\alpha}A_{\alpha,\beta}B_{\beta,\gamma}\theta_\gamma$ <br> $+ 1/2 \sum K_{q,\alpha}A_{\alpha,\beta}B'_{\beta,C_1}$ |
| $K_1 C_2$ | $\dfrac{4}{(k+1)(k+2)(k+3)(k+4)}$ | $1/2 \sum K_{q,\alpha}A_{\alpha,\beta}\theta_\alpha\theta_\beta^2 + \sum K_{q,\alpha}\theta_\alpha A'_{\alpha,C_2}$ |
| $K_1 J_1 C_1$ | $\dfrac{4}{(k+1)(k+2)(k+3)(k+4)}$ | $\sum K_{q,\alpha}A_{\alpha,\beta}A_{\beta,\gamma}\theta_\alpha\theta_\gamma$ <br> $+ \sum K_{q,\alpha}\theta_\alpha A'_{\alpha,J_1C_1}$ <br> $+ \sum K_{q,\alpha}A_{\alpha,\beta}\theta_\alpha A'_{\beta,C_1}$ |
| $J_1 K_1 C_1$ | $\dfrac{3}{(k+1)(k+2)(k+3)(k+4)}$ | $\sum K_{q,\alpha}A_{\alpha,\beta}A_{\beta,\gamma}\theta_\beta\theta_\gamma$ <br> $+ \sum K_{q,\alpha}A_{\alpha,\beta}A'_{\beta,C_1}\theta_\beta$ |

| | Taylor | RK with high order terms at the start of the step |
|---|---|---|
| $J_1 C_3$ | $\dfrac{1}{(k+1)(k+2)(k+3)(k+4)}$ | $1/6 \sum K_{q,\alpha} A_{\alpha,\beta} \theta_\beta^3$ |
| $J_1^3 C_1$ | $\dfrac{1}{(k+1)(k+2)(k+3)(k+4)}$ | $\sum K_{q,\alpha} A_{\alpha,\beta} A_{\beta,\gamma} A_{\gamma,\delta} \theta_\delta$ $+ \sum K_{q,\alpha} A_{\alpha,\beta} A_{\beta,\gamma} A'_{\gamma,C_1}$ $+ \sum K_{q,\alpha} A_{\alpha,\beta} A'_{\beta,J_1C_1}$ |
| $J_1^2 C_2$ | $\dfrac{1}{(k+1)(k+2)(k+3)(k+4)}$ | $1/2 \sum K_{q,\alpha} A_{\alpha,\beta} A_{\beta,\gamma} \theta_\gamma^2$ $+ \sum A_{q,\alpha} A_{\alpha,\beta} A'_{\beta,C^2}$ |

## 9. Study of these formulas.

In order to study these formulas we will consider several situations. At first, we will suppose that only one additional derivative is used, and then two such derivatives. We will limit ourselves to a system in canonical form.

### 10.1 One additional derivative with $q = 2$.

In order to obtain the third order with three horners, it suffices to take $\theta_1$ arbitrarily.

| $\theta_1$ | $A$ |   | $\theta_1^2/2$ | $A'$ |
|---|---|---|---|---|
| $1 - 1/(3\,\theta_1^2)$ | $1/(3\,\theta_1^2)$ |   | $1/2 - 1(3\,\theta_1)$ | |

We will call this formula RKT 2, 3, 3.

### 10.2 Actual formulas.

a. We take $\theta_1 = 1/2$, which leads to the formulas

$$x_{i,1} = x_i + \frac{h}{2} X_i + \frac{h^2}{8} x_i'',$$

$$x_{i+1} = x_i + \frac{h}{3} (-X_i + 4 X_{i,1}) - \frac{h^2}{6} x_i''.$$

b. For $\theta_1 = 1$, one finds

| 1 | $A$ |   | 1/2 | $A'$ |
|---|---|---|---|---|
| 2/3 | 1/3 |   | 1/6 | |

This is Duffing's formula.[1]

[1] Duffing, Funk, Pflanz [2].

**10.3 Example.**

$$y' = -2ty^2, \qquad y(0) = 1, \qquad h = 0.1, \qquad \theta_1 = 1/2.$$

| $t$ | $y_i$ | $y$ exact |
|---|---|---|
| 0 | 1 | 1 |
| 0.1 | 0.990,007 | 0.990,099 |
| 0.2 | 0.961,487 | 0.961,538 |
| 0.3 | 0.917,383 | 0.917,431 |
| 0.4 | 0.862,044 | 0.862,069 |
| 0.5 | 0.800,007 | 0.8 |
| 1.0 | 0.500,063 | 0.5 |
| 1.5 | 0.307,713 | 0.307,692 |
| 2.0 | 0.200,001 | 0.2 |
| 2.5 | 0.137,928 | 0.137,931 |
| 3.0 | 0.099,965 | 0.1 |
| 3.5 | 0.075,469 | 0.075,472 |
| 4.0 | 0.058,821 | 0.058,823 |

### 11.1  One additional derivative with $q = 3$.

In order to obtain the fourth order with four horners it suffices to take $\theta_1$ and $\theta_2$ arbitrarily.

$$A_1' = \theta_1^2/2, \qquad A_2' = \theta_2^2/2 - A_{21}\theta_1, \qquad 1/2 = A_{32}\theta_2 + A_{31}\theta_1 + A_3',$$
$$A_{32}\theta_2^2 + A_{31}\theta_1^2 = 1/3,$$
$$A_{32}\theta_2^3 + A_{31}\theta_1^3 = 1/4, \qquad A_{32}A_{21}\theta_1^2 = 1/12.$$

We will call this formula RKT 3, 4, 4. For example, for $\theta_1 = 1/2$ and $\theta_2 = 1$:

| 1/2 | $A$ | |
|---|---|---|
| $-2$ | 2 | |
| 1/6 | 2/3 | 1/6 |

| 1/8 | $A'$ |
|---|---|
| $-1/2$ | |
| 0 | |

One will notice that $x_{i,1}$ and $x_{i,2}$ are exact up to order 2. Likewise, in formula (10.1) $x_{i,1}$ was exact up to this order.

### 11.2  Examples.

1. 
$$y' = ty, \qquad y(0) = 1, \qquad h = 0.1.$$

| $t$ | $y_i$ | $y$ exact |
|---|---|---|
| 0 | 1 | 1 |
| 0.1 | 0.995,012,48 | 0.995,012,47 |
| 0.2 | 0.980,198,65 | 0.980,198,67 |

| $t$ | $y_i$ | $y$ exact |
|-----|-------|-----------|
| 0.3 | 0.955,997,41 | 0.955,997,48 |
| 0.4 | 0.923,116,21 | 0.923,116,34 |
| 0.5 | 0.882,496,68 | 0.882,496,90 |
| 1.0 | 0.606,529,78 | 0.606,530,65 |
| 1.5 | 0.324,651,25 | 0.324,652,46 |
| 2.0 | 0.135,334,69 | 0.135,335,28 |
| 2.5 | 0.043,937,27 | 0.043,936,93 |
| 3.0 | 0.011,109,65 | 0.011,108,99 |
| 3.5 | 0.002,187,94 | 0.002,187,49 |
| 4.0 | 0.000,335,64 | 0.000,335,46 |
| 4.5 | 0.000,040,11 | 0.000,040,06 |
| 5.0 | 0.000,003,74 | 0.000,003,73 |

2.        $y' = -2ty^2, \qquad y(0) = 1, \qquad h = 0.1.$

| $t$ | $y_i$ | $y$ exact |
|-----|-------|-----------|
| 0 | 1 | 1 |
| 0.1 | 0.990,098,9 | 0.990,099,0 |
| 0.2 | 0.961,549,3 | 0.961,538,4 |
| 0.3 | 0.917,458,4 | 0.917,431,1 |
| 0.4 | 0.862,111,6 | 0.862,068,9 |
| 0.5 | 0.800,052,2 | 0.800,000,0 |
| 1.0 | 0.500,014,0 | 0.500,000,0 |
| 1.5 | 0.307,672,0 | 0.307,692,3 |
| 2.0 | 0.199,978,8 | 0.200,000,0 |
| 2.5 | 0.137,915,9 | 0.137,931,0 |
| 3.0 | 0.099,989,9 | 0.100,000,0 |
| 3.5 | 0.075,465,0 | 0.075,471,6 |
| 4.0 | 0.058,819,0 | 0.058,823,5 |
| 4.5 | 0.047,055,7 | 0.047,058,8 |
| 5.0 | 0.038,459,3 | 0.038,461,5 |

## 12. Two additional derivatives with $q = 2$.

By writing the exact terms up to the order 4, we obtain

$$1/2 = A_{2,1}\theta_1 + A'_{2,C_1}, \qquad A_{2,0} + A_{2,1} = 1,$$
$$1/3 = A_{2,1}\theta_1^2 + 2A'_{2,C_2} \qquad\qquad A_{1,0} = \theta_1,$$
$$1/6 = A_{2,1}A'_{1,C_1} + A'_{2,J_1C_1},$$

$$1/4 = A_{2,1}\theta_1^3,$$
$$1/8 = A_{2,1}A'_{1,C_1}\theta_1,$$
$$1/24 = A_{2,1}A'_{1,J_1C_1},$$
$$1/24 = A_{2,1}A_{1,C_2}.$$

We can satisfy these conditions for arbitrary $\theta_1$ and with only four horners by calculating the combination $x''' = C_2 + J_1C_1$ and not these two terms separately.

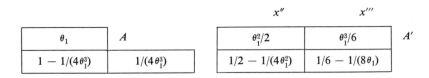

| $\theta_1$ | | $A$ | | $\theta_1^2/2$ | $\theta_1^3/6$ | $A'$ |
|---|---|---|---|---|---|---|
| $1 - 1/(4\theta_1^3)$ | | $1/(4\theta_1^3)$ | | $1/2 - 1/(4\theta_1^2)$ | $1/6 - 1/(8\theta_1)$ | |

We will call this formula RKT 2, 4, 4.

### 13.1 Simplifying hypothesis.

We have noted that the intermediary values were exact up to an order corresponding to the number of additional derivatives introduced at the beginning. This situation seems natural, and we will try to profit from it in order to simplify the formulas.

### 13.2 Investigation for $q = 3$ in the preceding particular case ($p = 1$).

As indicated above, we will consider the case where one has

$$A_{\alpha,C_2}' = A'_{\alpha,J_1C_1},$$
$$\sum_\beta A_{\alpha,\beta}\theta_\beta + A'_{\alpha,C_1} = \theta_\alpha^2/2!,$$
$$\sum_\beta A_{\alpha,\beta}\theta_\beta^2/2! + A'_{\alpha,C_2} = \theta_\alpha^3/3!$$

We obtain then the following simplifications:

$$X_{0,\alpha} - X_0 = h\theta_\alpha C_1 + h^2 \frac{\theta_\alpha^2}{2!}x_0''' + \frac{h^3\theta_\alpha^3}{3!}x_0'''' + h^4\frac{\theta_\alpha^4}{4!}P_1 + h^4\frac{\sum A_{\alpha,\beta}\theta_\beta^3}{3!}P_2$$

with

$$P_1 = C_4 + 6L_1C_1 + 4K_1C_2 + 4K_1J_1C_1 + 3R,$$
$$P_2 = J_1C_3 + J_1^2C_2 + 3J_1K_1C_1 + J_1^3C_1,$$

which gives the following table:

| | Taylor | Runge-Kutta |
|---|---|---|
| $\frac{h^2}{1!}C_1$ | $1/2$ | $\sum A_{q,\alpha}\theta_\alpha + A'_{q,C_1}$ |

| | Taylor | Runge-Kutta |
|---|---|---|
| $\dfrac{h^3}{1!}\, x''$ | 1/6 | $1/2 \sum A_{q,\alpha}\theta_\alpha^2 + A'_{q,c_2}$ |
| $\dfrac{h^4}{1!}\, x'''$ | 1/24 | $1/6 \sum A_{q,\alpha}\theta_\alpha^3$ |
| $\dfrac{h^5}{1!}\, P_1$ | 1/120 | $1/24 \sum A_{q,\alpha}\theta_\alpha^4$ |
| $P_2$ | 1/120 | $1/6 \sum A_{q,\alpha}A_{\alpha,\beta}\theta_\beta^3$ |

### 14.1  Two additional derivatives with $q = 3$.

The preceding formulas reduce themselves to:

$$A_{31}\theta_1^3 + A_{32}\theta_2^3 = 1/4,$$
$$A_{31}\theta_1^4 + A_{32}\theta_2^4 = 1/5,$$
$$A_{32}A_{21}\theta_1^3 = 1/20,$$
$$\theta_2^2/2 - A_{21}\theta_1 = \theta_1/4,$$

which implies the relation

$$\theta_2^4 + \theta_2^2\theta_1^2\,\frac{(5\theta_1 - 4)}{2} + \theta_1^3(4 - 5\theta_1) = 0,$$

to which it is necessary to add the three relations given at the beginning of 13.2.

### 14.2  Proposed formula.

One could take, for example, $\theta_1 = 4/5$, $\theta_2 = 0$. The preceding relations determine neither $A_{32}$ nor $A_{21}$, but only their product. We are going to prescribe one of these quantities arbitrarily. It is easy to see that all the other ones are then determined.

| | | | | $x''$ | | $x'''$ |
|---|---|---|---|---|---|---|
| 4/5 | $A$ | | | 8/25 | | 32/375 |
| 1/4 | $-1/4$ | | | 1/5 | | 2/25 |
| 231/256 | 125/256 | $-100/256$ | | 7/64 | | 1/96 |

We will call this formula RKT 3, 5, 5, since it costs five horners per step and is of order 5.

*Remark.* Such formulas, by reason of the indeterminacies which they contain, lend themselves to optimization.

## III  RUNGE-KUTTA METHOD UTILIZING THE SUBSEQUENT DERIVATIVE

### 15.1  Principle.[1]

Let the system be

$$x^{(p)} = X(x, x', \ldots, x^{(p-1)}).$$

Generalizing the Runge-Kutta formulas, we can write

$$x_{0,\alpha}^{(p-k)} = x_0^{(p-k)} + \frac{h\theta_\alpha}{1!} x_0^{(p-k-1)} + \cdots + \frac{h^{k-1}}{(k-1)!} \theta_\alpha^{k-1} x_0^{(p-1)}$$

$$+ \frac{h^k}{k!} \sum_\beta K_{\alpha,\beta} X_{0,\beta} + \frac{h^{k+1}}{(k+1)!} \sum_\beta K'_{\alpha,\beta} DX_{0,\beta}.$$

We will still assume the reasonable condition:[2]

$$\sum_\beta K_{\alpha,\beta} = \theta_\alpha^k,$$

and we will set

$$\sum_\beta K'_{\alpha,\beta} = K'_\alpha.$$

One can then write

$$x_{0,\alpha}^{(p-k)} = x_0^{(p-k)} + \frac{h\theta_\alpha}{1!} x_0^{(p-k+1)} + \cdots + \frac{h^{k-1}}{(k-1)!} \theta_\alpha^{k-1} x_0^{(p-1)}$$

$$+ \frac{h^k \theta_\alpha^k}{k!} X_0 + \frac{h^{k+1}}{(k+1)!} K'_\alpha DX_0 + \frac{h^k}{k!} \sum_\beta K_{\alpha,\beta}(X_{0,\beta} - X_0)$$

$$+ \frac{h^{k+1}}{(k+1)!} \sum_\beta K'_{\alpha,\beta}(DX_{0,\beta} - DX_0).$$

### 15.2  Expansions of $X_{0,\alpha} - X_0$ and of $DX_{0,\alpha} - DX_0$.

By a calculation analogous to that of Chapter 3, paragraph 10.1, one finds

$$X_{0,\alpha} - X_0 = h\theta_\alpha C_1 + h^2 \left\{ \frac{\theta_\alpha^2}{2} C_2 + \sum A_{\alpha,\beta}\theta_\beta J_1 C_1 + 1/2 A'_\alpha J_1 C_1 \right\}$$

$$+ h^3 \left\{ \frac{\theta_\alpha^3}{6} C_3 + 1/2 \sum B_{\alpha,\beta}\theta_\beta J_2 C_1 + 1/6 B'_\alpha J_2 C_1 + 1/2 \sum A'_{\alpha,\beta}\theta_\beta J_1^2 C_1 \right.$$

$$+ \sum A_{\alpha,\beta}\theta_\alpha\theta_\beta K_1 C_1 + 1/2 A'_\alpha \theta_\alpha K_1 C_1 + 1/2 \sum A_{\alpha,\beta}\theta_\beta^2 J_1 C_2$$

$$\left. + 1/2 A'_{\alpha\beta}\theta_\beta J_1 C_2 + \sum A_{\alpha,\beta}A_{\beta,\gamma}\theta_\gamma J_1^2 C_1 + 1/2 \sum A_{\alpha,\beta}A'_\beta J_1^2 C_1 \right\}$$

$$+ h^4 \left\{ \frac{\theta_\alpha^4 C_4}{24} + 1/6 \sum C_{\alpha,\beta}\theta_\beta J_3 C_1 + 1/24 C'_\alpha J_3 C_1 \right.$$

$$+ 1/6 \sum B'_{\alpha,\beta}\theta_\beta J_2 C_2 + 1/6 \sum B'_{\alpha,\beta}\theta_\beta J_2 J_1 C_1$$

[1]Bard. For another principle, see Vlasov and Carnyi.

[2]We do not use here the simplifying remark of paragraph 13.1. We will return to it in paragraph 19.

$$+ \ 1/2 \ \sum B_{\alpha,\beta}\theta_\alpha\theta_\beta K_2 C_1 + 1/6 \, B'_\alpha\theta_\alpha K_2 C_1 + 1/2 \ \sum A'_{\alpha,\beta}\theta_\alpha\theta_\beta K_1 C_2$$

$$+ \ 1/2 \ \sum A'_{\alpha,\beta}\theta_\alpha\theta_\beta K_1 J_1 C_1 + 1/2 \ \sum A_{\alpha,\beta}\theta_\alpha^2\theta_\beta L_1 C_1$$

$$+ \ 1/4 \ A'_\alpha\theta_\alpha^2 L_1 C_1 + 1/2 \ \sum A_{\alpha,\beta}A_{\alpha,\gamma}\theta_\beta\theta_\gamma R + 1/4 \ \sum A_{\alpha,\beta}A'_\alpha\theta_\beta R$$

$$+ \ 1/8 \, A_\alpha'^2 R + 1/6 \ \sum A_{\alpha,\beta}\theta_\beta^3 J_1 C_3 + 1/2 \ \sum A_{\alpha,\beta}B_{\beta,\gamma}\theta_\gamma J_1 J_2 C_1$$

$$+ \ 1/6 \ \sum A_{\alpha,\beta}B'_\beta J_1 J_2 C_1 + 1/2 \ \sum A_{\alpha,\beta}A'_{\beta,\gamma}\theta_\gamma J_1^2 C_2$$

$$+ \ 1/2 \ \sum A_{\alpha,\beta}A'_{\beta,\gamma}\theta_\gamma J_1^3 C_1 + \sum A_{\alpha,\beta}A_{\beta,\gamma}\theta_\beta\theta_\gamma J_1 K_1 C_1$$

$$+ \ 1/2 \ \sum A_{\alpha,\beta}A'_\beta\theta_\beta J_1 K_1 C_1 + 1/2 \ \sum A_{\alpha,\beta}A_{\beta,\gamma}\theta_\gamma^2 J_1^2 C_2$$

$$+ \ \sum A_{\alpha,\beta}A_{\beta,\gamma}A_{\gamma,\delta}\theta_\delta J_1^3 C_1 + 1/2 \ \sum A_{\alpha,\beta}A_{\beta,\gamma}A'_\gamma J_1^3 C_1$$

$$+ \ 1/4 \ \sum B_{\alpha,\beta}\theta_\beta^2 J_2 C_2 + 1/2 \ \sum B_{\alpha,\beta}A_{\beta,\gamma}\theta_\gamma J_2 J_1 C_1$$

$$+ \ 1/4 \ \sum B_{\alpha,\beta}A'_\beta J_2 J_1 C_1 + 1/4 \ \sum A'_{\alpha,\beta}\theta_\beta^2 J_1 C_3$$

$$+ \ 1/4 \ \sum A'_{\alpha,\beta}\theta_\beta^2 J_1^2 C_2 + 1/2 \ \sum A'_{\alpha,\beta}\theta_\beta^2 J_1 K_1 C_1$$

$$+ \ 1/2 \ \sum A'_{\alpha,\beta}A_{\beta,\gamma}\theta_\gamma J_1 J_2 C_1 + 1/2 \ \sum A'_{\alpha,\beta}A_{\beta,\gamma}\theta_\gamma J_1 K_1 C_1$$

$$+ \ 1/2 \ \sum A'_{\alpha,\beta}A_{\beta,\gamma}\theta_\gamma J_1^3 C_1 + 1/4 \ \sum A'_{\alpha,\beta}A'_\beta J_1 J_2 C_1$$

$$+ \ 1/4 \ \sum A'_{\alpha,\beta}A'_\beta J_1 K_1 C_1 + 1/4 \ \sum A'_{\alpha,\beta}A'_\beta J_1^3 C_1$$

$$+ \ 1/2 \ \sum A_{\alpha,\beta}\theta_\alpha\theta_\beta^2 K_1 C_2 + \sum A_{\alpha,\beta}A_{\beta,\gamma}\theta_\alpha\theta_\gamma K_1 J_1 C_1$$

$$+ \ 1/2 \ \sum A_{\alpha,\beta}A'_\beta\theta_\alpha K_1 J_1 C_1 \Big\}$$

$$DX_{0,\alpha} - DX_0 = h \left\{ \theta_\alpha C_2 + \theta_\alpha J_1 C_1 \right\} + h^2 \left\{ \frac{\theta_\alpha^2}{2} C_3 + \frac{\theta_\alpha^2}{2} J_1 C_2 \right.$$

$$+ \ \theta_\alpha^2 K_1 C_1 + \sum A_{\alpha,\beta}\theta_\beta J_2 C_1 + \sum A_{\alpha,\beta}\theta_\beta K_1 C_1$$

$$+ \ \sum A_{\alpha,\beta}\theta_\beta J_1^2 C_1 + 1/2 \, A'_\alpha J_2 C_1 + 1/2 \, A'_\alpha K_1 C_1$$

$$+ \ \left. 1/2 \ A'_\alpha J_1^2 C_1 \right\} + h^3 \left\{ \frac{\theta_\alpha^3}{6} C_4 + \frac{\theta_\alpha^3}{6} J_1 C_3 + \frac{\theta_\alpha^3}{2} K_1 C_2 \right.$$

$$+ \ \frac{\theta_\alpha^3}{2} L_1 C_1 + 1/2 \ \sum B_{\alpha,\beta}\theta_\beta J_3 C_1 + 1/2 \ \sum B_{\alpha,\beta}\theta_\beta K_2 C_1$$

$$+ \ 1/2 \ \sum B_{\alpha,\beta}\theta_\beta J_1 J_2 C_1 + 1/6 \, B'_\alpha J_3 C_1 + 1/6 \, B'_\alpha K_2 C_1$$

$$+ \ 1/6 \, B'_\alpha J_1 J_2 C_1 + 1/2 \ \sum A'_{\alpha,\beta}\theta_\beta J_2 C_2 + 1/2 \ \sum A'_{\alpha,\beta}\theta_\beta J_2 J_1 C_1$$

$$+ \ 1/2 \ \sum A'_{\alpha,\beta}\theta_\beta K_1 C_2 + 1/2 \ \sum A'_{\alpha,\beta}\theta_\beta K_1 J_1 C_1$$

$$+ \ 1/2 \ \sum A'_{\alpha,\beta}\theta_\beta J_1^2 C_2 + 1/2 \ \sum A'_{\alpha,\beta}\theta_\beta J_1^3 C_1$$

$$+ \ \sum A_{\alpha,\beta}\theta_\alpha\theta_\beta K_2 C_1 + \sum A_{\alpha,\beta}\theta_\alpha\theta_\beta L_1 C_1 + \sum A_{\alpha,\beta}\theta_\alpha\theta_\beta R$$

$$+ \ \sum A_{\alpha,\beta}\theta_\alpha\theta_\beta K_1 J_1 C_1 + \sum A_{\alpha,\beta}\theta_\alpha\theta_\beta J_1 K_1 C_1 + 1/2 \, A'_\alpha\theta_\alpha K_2 C_1$$

$$+ \ 1/2 \, A'_\alpha\theta_\alpha L_1 C_1 + 1/2 \, A'_\alpha\theta_\alpha R + 1/2 \, A'_\alpha\theta_\alpha K_1 J_1 C_1$$

$$+ \ 1/2 \, A'_\alpha\theta_\alpha J_1 K_1 C_1 + 1/2 \ \sum A_{\alpha,\beta}\theta_\beta^2 J_2 C_2$$

$$+ \ \sum A_{\alpha,\beta}A_{\beta,\gamma}\theta_\gamma J_2 J_1 C_1 + 1/2 \ \sum A_{\alpha,\beta}A'_\beta J_2 J_1 C_1$$

$$+ \ 1/2 \ \sum A_{\alpha,\beta}\theta_\beta^2 K_1 C_2 + \sum A_{\alpha,\beta}A_{\beta,\gamma}\theta_\gamma K_1 J_1 C_1$$

$$+ \ 1/2 \ \sum A_{\alpha,\beta}A'_\beta K_1 J_1 C_1 + 1/2 \ \sum A_{\alpha,\beta}\theta_\beta^2 J_1^2 C_2$$

$$+ \ \sum A_{\alpha,\beta}A_{\beta,\gamma}\theta_\gamma J_1^3 C_1 + 1/2 \ \sum A_{\alpha,\beta}A'_\beta J_1^3 C_1 \Big\}$$

## 16. Fundamental table.

One arrives at the fundamental table:

| | Taylor | Runge-Kutta $\quad$ with $\sum K_{\alpha,\beta} = \theta_\alpha^k$ and $\sum K'_{\alpha,\beta} = K'_\alpha$ |
|---|---|---|
| $\dfrac{h^{k+1}}{k!} \cdot C_1$ | $\dfrac{1}{k+1}$ | $\sum K_{q,\alpha}\theta_\alpha + \dfrac{1}{k+1} K'_q$ |
| $\dfrac{h^{k+2}}{k!} \cdot C_2$ | $\dfrac{1}{(k+1)(k+2)}$ | $1/2 \sum K_{q,\alpha}\theta_\alpha^2 + \dfrac{1}{k+1} K'_{q,\alpha}\theta_\alpha$ |
| $\cdot J_1 C_1$ | $\dfrac{1}{(k+1)(k+2)}$ | $\sum K_{q,\alpha}A_{\alpha,\beta}\theta_\beta + 1/2 \sum K_{q,\alpha}A'_\alpha$ $\quad + \dfrac{1}{k+1} \sum K'_{q,\alpha}\theta_\alpha$ |
| $\dfrac{k^{k+3}}{h!} \cdot C_3$ | $\dfrac{1}{(k+1)(k+2)(k+3)}$ | $1/6 \sum K_{q,\alpha}\theta_\alpha^3 + \dfrac{1}{2(k+1)} \sum K'_{q,\alpha}\theta_\alpha^2$ |
| $\cdot J_2 C_1$ | $\dfrac{1}{(k+1)(k+2)(k+3)}$ | $1/2 \sum K_{q,\alpha}B_{\alpha,\beta}\theta_\beta + 1/6 \sum K_{q,\alpha}B'_\alpha$ $\quad + \dfrac{1}{k+1} \sum K'_{q,\alpha}A_{\alpha,\beta}\theta_\beta$ $\quad + \dfrac{1}{2(k+1)} \sum K'_{q,\alpha}A'_\alpha$ |
| $\cdot K_1 C_1$ | $\dfrac{3}{(k+1)(k+2)(k+3)}$ | $\sum K_{q,\alpha}A_{\alpha,\beta}\theta_\alpha\theta_\beta + 1/2 \sum K_{q,\alpha}A'_\alpha\theta_\alpha$ $\quad + \dfrac{1}{k+1} \sum K'_{q,\alpha}\theta_\alpha^2$ $\quad + \dfrac{1}{k+1} \sum K'_{q,\alpha}A_{\alpha,\beta}\theta_\beta$ $\quad + \dfrac{1}{2(k+1)} \sum K'_{q,\alpha}A'_\alpha$ |
| $\cdot J_1^2 C_1$ | $\dfrac{1}{(k+1)(k+2)(k+3)}$ | $1/2 \sum K_{q,\alpha}A'_{\alpha,\beta}\theta_\beta + \sum K_{q,\alpha}A_{\alpha,\beta}A_{\beta,\gamma}\theta_\gamma$ $\quad + 1/2 \sum K_{q,\alpha}A_{\alpha,\beta}A'_\beta$ $\quad + \dfrac{1}{k+1} \sum K'_{q,\alpha}A_{\alpha,\beta}\theta_\beta$ $\quad + \dfrac{1}{2(k+1)} \sum K'_{q,\alpha}A'_\alpha$ |
| $\cdot J_1 C_2$ | $\dfrac{1}{(k+1)(k+2)(k+3)}$ | $1/2 \sum K_{q,\alpha}A'_{\alpha,\beta}\theta_\beta + 1/2 \sum K_{q,\alpha}A_{\alpha,\beta}\theta_\beta^2$ $\quad + \dfrac{1}{2(k+1)} K'_{q,\alpha}\theta_\alpha^2$ |
| $\dfrac{h^{k+4}}{k!} \cdot C_4$ | $\dfrac{1}{(k+1)(k+2)(k+3)(k+4)}$ | $1/24 \sum K_{q,\alpha}\theta_\alpha^4 + \dfrac{1}{6(k+1)} K'_{q,\alpha}\theta_\alpha^3$ |
| $\cdot J_3 C_1$ | $\dfrac{1}{(k+1)(k+2)(k+3)(k+4)}$ | $1/6 \sum K_{q,\alpha}C_{\alpha,\beta}\theta_\beta + 1/24 \sum K_{q,\alpha}C'_\alpha$ $\quad + \dfrac{1}{2(k+1)} \sum K'_{q,\alpha}B_{\alpha,\beta}\theta_\beta$ $\quad + \dfrac{1}{6(k+1)} \sum K'_{q,\alpha}B'_\alpha$ |

| | Taylor | Runge-Kutta | with $\sum K_{\alpha,\beta'} = \theta_\alpha^k$ and $\sum K'_{\alpha,\beta} = K'_\alpha$ |
|---|---|---|---|

$\cdot K_2 C_1$    $\dfrac{4}{(k+1)(k+2)(k+3)(k+4)}$    $1/2 \sum K_{q,\alpha} B_{\alpha,\beta} \theta_\alpha \theta_\beta + 1/6 \sum K_{q,\alpha} B'_\alpha \theta_\alpha$

$$+ \frac{1}{2(k+1)} \sum K'_{q,\alpha} B_{\alpha\beta} \theta_\beta$$

$$+ \frac{1}{6(k+1)} \sum K'_{q,\alpha} B'_\alpha$$

$$+ \frac{1}{k+1} \sum K'_{q,\alpha} A_{\alpha,\beta} \theta_\alpha \theta_\beta$$

$$+ \frac{1}{2(k+1)} \sum K'_{q,\alpha} A'_\alpha \theta_\alpha$$

$\cdot L_1 C_1$    $\dfrac{6}{(k+1)(k+2)(k+3)(k+4)}$    $1/2 \sum K_{q,\alpha} A_{\alpha,\beta} \theta_\alpha^2 \theta_\beta + 1/4 \sum K_{q,\alpha} A'_\alpha \theta_\alpha^2$

$$+ \frac{1}{2(k+1)} \sum K'_{q,\alpha} \theta_\alpha^3$$

$$+ \frac{1}{k+1} \sum K'_{q,\alpha} A_{\alpha,\beta} \theta_\alpha \theta_\beta$$

$$+ \frac{1}{2(k+1)} \sum K'_{q,\alpha} A'_\alpha \theta_\alpha$$

$\cdot R$    $\dfrac{3}{(k+1)(k+2)(k+3)(k+4)}$    $1/4 \sum K_{q,\alpha} A_{\alpha,\beta} A'_\alpha \theta_\beta + 1/8 \sum K_{q,\alpha} A'^2_\alpha$

$$+ 1/2 \sum K_{q,\alpha} A_{\alpha,\beta} A_{\alpha,\gamma} \theta_\beta \theta_\gamma$$

$$+ \frac{1}{k+1} \sum K'_{q,\alpha} A_{\alpha,\beta} \theta_\alpha \theta_\beta$$

$$+ \frac{1}{2(k+1)} \sum K'_{q,\alpha} A'_\alpha \theta_\alpha$$

$\cdot J_2 C_2$    $\dfrac{1}{(k+1)(k+2)(k+3)(k+4)}$    $1/6 \sum K_{q,\alpha} B'_{\alpha,\beta} \theta_\beta + 1/4 \sum K_{q,\alpha} B_{\alpha,\beta} \theta_\beta^2$

$$+ \frac{1}{2(k+1)} \sum K'_{q,\alpha} A'_{\alpha,\beta} \theta_\beta$$

$$+ \frac{1}{2(k+1)} \sum K'_{q,\alpha} A_{\alpha,\beta} \theta_\beta^2$$

$J_2 \cdot J_1 C_1$    $\dfrac{1}{(k+1)(k+2)(k+3)(k+4)}$    $1/6 \sum K_{q,\alpha} B'_{\alpha,\beta} \theta_\beta + 1/2 \sum K_{q,\alpha} B_{\alpha,\beta} A_{\beta,\gamma} \theta_\gamma$

$$+ 1/4 \sum K_{q,\alpha} B_{\alpha,\beta} A'_\beta$$

$$+ \frac{1}{2(k+1)} \sum K'_{q,\alpha} A'_{\alpha,\beta} \theta_\beta$$

$$+ \frac{1}{k+1} \sum K_{q,\alpha} A_{\alpha,\beta} A_{\beta,\gamma} \theta_\gamma$$

$$+ \frac{1}{2(k+1)} \sum K'_{q,\alpha} A_{\alpha,\beta} A'_\beta$$

$\cdot K_1 C_2$    $\dfrac{4}{(k+1)(k+2)(k+3)(k+4)}$    $1/2 \sum K_{q,\alpha} A'_{\alpha,\beta} \theta_\alpha \theta_\beta + 1/2 \sum K_{q,\alpha} A_{\alpha,\beta} \theta_\alpha \theta_\beta^2$

$$+ \frac{1}{2(k+1)} \sum K'_{q,\alpha} \theta_\alpha^3$$

$$+ \frac{1}{2(k+1)} \sum K'_{q,\alpha} A'_{\alpha,\beta} \theta_\beta$$

$$+ \frac{1}{2(k+1)} \sum K'_{q,\alpha} A_{\alpha,\beta} \theta_\beta^2$$

| | Taylor | Runge-Kutta with $\sum K_{\alpha,\beta} = \theta_\alpha^k$ and $\sum K'_{\alpha,\beta} = K'_\alpha$ |
|---|---|---|
| $\cdot K_1 J_1 C_1$ | $\dfrac{4}{(k+1)(k+2)(k+3)(k+4)}$ | $1/2 \sum K_{q,\alpha} A'_{\alpha,\beta} \theta_\alpha \theta_\beta + \sum K_{q,\alpha} A_{\alpha,\beta} A_{\beta,\gamma} \theta_\alpha \theta_\gamma$ $+ 1/2 \sum K_{q,\alpha} A_{\alpha,\beta} A'_\beta \theta_\alpha$ $+ \dfrac{1}{2(k+1)} \sum K'_{q,\alpha} A'_{\alpha,\beta} \theta_\beta$ $+ \dfrac{1}{k+1} \sum K'_{q,\alpha} A_{\alpha,\beta} \theta_\alpha \theta_\beta$ $+ \dfrac{1}{2(k+1)} \sum K'_{q,\alpha} A'_\alpha \theta_\alpha$ $+ \dfrac{1}{k+1} \sum K'_{q,\alpha} A_{\alpha,\beta} A_{\beta,\gamma} \theta_\gamma$ $+ \dfrac{1}{2(k+1)} \sum K'_{q,\alpha} A_{\alpha,\beta} A'_\beta$ |
| $\cdot J_1 C_3$ | $\dfrac{1}{(k+1)(k+2)(k+3)(k+4)}$ | $1/6 \sum K_{q,\alpha} A_{\alpha,\beta} \theta_\beta^3 + 1/4 \sum K_{q,\alpha} A'_{\alpha,\beta} \theta_\beta^2$ $+ \dfrac{1}{6(k+1)} \sum K'_{q,\alpha} \theta_\alpha^3$ |
| $\cdot J_1 J_2 C_1$ | $\dfrac{1}{(k+1)(k+2)(k+3)(k+4)}$ | $1/2 \sum K_{q,\alpha} A_{\alpha,\beta} B_{\beta,\gamma} \theta_\gamma + 1/6 \sum K_{q,\alpha} A_{\alpha,\beta} B'_\beta$ $+ 1/2 \sum K_{q,\alpha} A'_{\alpha,\beta} A_\beta \theta_\gamma$ $+ 1/4 \sum K_{q,\alpha} A'_{\alpha,\beta} A'_\beta$ $+ \dfrac{1}{2(k+1)} \sum K'_{q,\alpha} B_{\alpha,\beta} \theta_\beta$ $+ \dfrac{1}{6(k+1)} \sum K'_{q,\alpha} B'_\alpha$ |
| $\cdot J_1 K_1 C_1$ | $\dfrac{3}{(k+1)(k+2)(k+3)(k+4)}$ | $\sum K_{q,\alpha} A_{\alpha,\beta} A_{\beta,\gamma} \theta_\beta \theta_\gamma$ $+ 1/2 \sum K_{q,\alpha} A_{\alpha,\beta} A'_\beta \theta_\beta$ $+ 1/2 \sum K_{q,\alpha} A'_{\alpha,\beta} \theta_\beta^2$ $+ 1/2 \sum K_{q,\alpha} A'_{\alpha,\beta} A_{\beta,\gamma} \theta_\gamma$ $+ 1/4 \sum K_{q,\alpha} A'_{\alpha,\beta} A'_\beta$ $+ \dfrac{1}{k+1} \sum K'_{q,\alpha} A_{\alpha,\beta} \theta_\alpha \theta_\beta$ $+ \dfrac{1}{2(k+1)} \sum K'_{q,\alpha} A'_\alpha \theta_\alpha$ |
| $\cdot J_1^3 C_1$ | $\dfrac{1}{(k+1)(k+2)(k+3)(k+4)}$ | $\sum K_{q,\alpha} A_{\alpha,\beta} A_{\beta,\gamma} A_{\gamma,\delta} \theta_\delta$ $+ 1/2 \sum K_{q,\alpha} A_{\alpha,\beta} A_{\beta,\gamma} A'_\gamma$ $+ 1/2 \sum K_{q,\alpha} A_{\alpha,\beta} A'_{\beta,\gamma} \theta_\gamma$ $+ 1/2 \sum K_{q,\alpha} A'_{\alpha,\beta} A_{\gamma,\beta} \theta_\gamma$ $+ 1/4 \sum K_{q,\alpha} A_{\alpha,\beta} A'_\beta$ $+ \dfrac{1}{2(k+1)} \sum K'_{q,\alpha} A'_{\alpha,\beta} \theta_\beta$ $+ \dfrac{1}{k+1} \sum K'_{q,\alpha} A_{\alpha,\beta} A_{\beta,\gamma} \theta_\gamma$ $+ \dfrac{1}{2(k+1)} \sum K'_{q,\alpha} A_{\alpha,\beta} A'_\beta$ |

| Taylor | Runge-Kutta | with $\sum K_{\alpha,\beta} = \theta_\alpha^k$ and $\sum K'_{\alpha,\beta} = K'_\alpha$ |
|---|---|---|
| $\cdot J_1^2 C_2 \quad \dfrac{1}{(k+1)(k+2)(k+3)(k+4)}$ | $1/2 \sum K_{q,\alpha} A_{\alpha,\beta} A_{\beta,\gamma} \theta_\gamma^2$ $+ 1/2 \sum K_{q,\alpha} A_{\alpha,\beta} A_{\beta,\gamma} \theta_\gamma$ $+ 1/4 \sum K_{q,\alpha} A_{\alpha,\beta} \theta_\beta^2$ $+ \dfrac{1}{2(k+1)} \sum K'_{q,\alpha} A'_{\alpha,\beta} \theta_\beta$ $+ \dfrac{1}{2(k+1)} K'_{q,\alpha} A_{\alpha,\beta} \theta_\beta^2$ | |

### 17.1 Preliminary remark.

Before beginning a detailed study, we note that the formulas derived previously are actually a particular case of this type. They consist of utilizing

$$X_0, \quad DX_0, \quad DX_1, \quad \ldots$$

At first, we will confine ourselves to formulas utilizing to an equal extent a number of horners less than or equal to those of the previous methods of derivation, i.e., giving the order 3 with at most two horners, giving the order 4 with at most three horners, giving the order 5 with at most four horners, giving the order 6 with at most five horners. This can be realized only because of the vanishing of certain coefficients.

### 17.2 Formula of order 3 for $p = 1$.

We are going to show that there exists such a formula costing only two horners per step. For $q = 1$, the only possible formula is

$$x_{i+1} = x_i + hX_i + \frac{h^2}{2} DX_i;$$

which is only of order 2.

Let us take $p = 2$. One is led to the conditions:

$$A_{10} = \theta_1, \qquad A_{20} + A_{21} = 1, \qquad A'_{20} + A'_{21} = A'_2,$$
$$A_{21}\theta_1 + 1/2\, A'_2 = 1/2, \qquad 1/2\, A_{21}\theta_1^2 + 1/2\, A'_{21}\theta_1 = 1/6,$$
$$1/2\, A_{21}\, A'_1 + 1/2\, A'_{21}\theta_1 = 1/6,$$

whence $A'_1 = \theta_1^2$. Among the coefficients, $A_{10} \neq 0$, hence one uses $X_0$; one can only use one of the other quantities:

$$DX_0, \quad X_1, \quad DX_1.$$

This cannot be $DX_0$, unless $q = 1$, nor $X_1$, unless one has a Runge-Kutta method; therefore, it is $DX_1$; hence

$$A_{21} = 0, \qquad A'_2 = 1, \qquad \theta_1 = 1/3,$$

i.e., the formula $\theta_1 = 1/3$.

*Remark.* This formula is not a previously derived formula (more precisely, by reason of the shortcomings of the order to be attained, the computation of $DX_0$ is futile).

### 17.3 Investigation for $p > 1$.

In taking

one obtains for two horners the order $(3, 3, 4, \ldots)$. We will call this formula RKK2, 2, 3, 3, 4, . . . .

### 17.4 Example.

$$y' = y - 1.5e^{-0.5t}, \qquad y(0) = 1, \qquad h = 0.1.$$

| $t$ | RK K2, 2, 3 | RK2 (improved tangent) | RK3 | $y$ exact |
|---|---|---|---|---|
| 0 | 1 | 1 | 1 | 1 |
| 0.1 | 0.951,229 | 0.951,204 | 0.951,228 | 0.951,229 |
| 0.2 | 0.904,835 | 0.904,784 | 0.904,835 | 0.904,837 |
| 0.3 | 0.860,706 | 0.860,626 | 0.860,705 | 0.860,708 |
| 0.4 | 0.818,727 | 0.818,617 | 0.818,726 | 0.818,731 |
| 0.5 | 0.778,796 | 0.778,654 | 0.778,795 | 0.778,801 |
| 1.0 | 0.606,520 | 0.606,176 | 0.606,516 | 0.606,531 |
| 1.5 | 0.472,346 | 0.471,693 | 0.472,340 | 0.472,367 |
| 2.0 | 0.367,844 | 0.366,700 | 0.367,832 | 0.367,879 |

### 18.1 Formulas of order 4 for $p = 1$.

One formula of order 4 for $p = 1$ in competition costs only three horners. Let us write the conditions:

$$A_{21}\theta_1 + 1/2\, A'_2 = 1/2,$$
$$1/2\, A_{21}\theta_1^2 + 1/2\, A'_{21}\theta_1 = 1/6,$$
$$1/2\, A_{21}A'_1 + 1/2 A'_{21}\theta_1 = 1/6,$$
$$\text{whence} \qquad A'_1 = \theta_1^2,$$

$$1/6\, A_{21}\theta_1^3 + 1/4\, A'_{21}\theta_1^2 = 1/24,$$
$$1/2\, A_{21}A'_1\theta_1 + 1/2\, A'_{21}\theta_1^2 + 1/4\, A'_{21}A'_1 = 3/24,$$
$$1/4\, A'_{21}A'_1 = 1/24,$$
$$1/4\, A'_{21}\theta_1^2 = 1/24.$$

In order to gain one horner, it is necessary that $A_{21} = 0$ or $A'_{21} = 0$. This latter condition is impossible to realize; on the other hand, the other one leads to a previously derived formula of Chapter 5, paragraph 3: RKD1, 2, 3, 4, Zurmühl.

### 18.2 Case $p > 1$.

By taking, always with $\theta_1 = 1/2$:

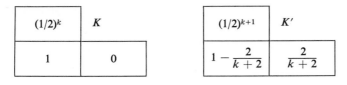

| $(1/2)^k$ | $K$ |
|---|---|
| 1 | 0 |

| $(1/2)^{k+1}$ | $K'$ |
|---|---|
| $1 - \dfrac{2}{k+2}$ | $\dfrac{2}{k+2}$ |

one can make the terms $h^{k+2}$ disappear. It is impossible to make the next terms disappear, except for $k = 1$. The order is thus (4, 4, 5, ...). One obtains a situation which was already given for the Runge-Kutta method. We will call this formula RKK2, 3, 4, 4, 5, . . . .

### 19. Formulas of order 5 for $p = 1$.

We will use the simplifying hypothesis of paragraph 13.1, which is given here:

$$A'_{10} = \theta_1^2, \qquad 2A_{21}\theta_1 + A'_2 = \theta_2^2.$$

One arrives at the equations:

$$A_{10} = \theta_1, \qquad\qquad A'_{20} + A'_{21} = A'_2,$$
$$A_{20} + A_{21} = \theta_2, \qquad A'_{32} + A'_{31} + A'_{30} = A'_3,$$
$$A_{30} + A_{31} + A_{32} = 1,$$

$$1/2 = A_{32}\theta_2 + A_{31}\theta_1 + 1/2\, A'_3, \qquad\qquad\qquad\qquad C_1 \quad (1)$$
$$1/6 = 1/2(A_{32}\theta_2^2 + A_{31}\theta_1^2 + A'_{32}\theta_2 + A'_{31}\theta_1), \qquad\qquad C_2 \quad (2)$$
$$1/24 = 1/6(A_{32}\theta_2^3 + A_{31}\theta_1^3) + 1/4(A'_{32}\theta_2^2 + A'_{31}\theta_1^2), \qquad C_3 \quad (3)$$
$$1/24 = 1/4(A'_{32}\theta_2^2 + A'_{31}\theta_1^2) + 1/2(A_{32}A'_{21}\theta_1 + A_{32}A_{21}\theta_1^2), \quad K_1C_1 \ (4)$$
$$1/120 = 1/24(A_{32}\theta_2^4 + A_{31}\theta_1^4) + 1/12(A'_{32}\theta_2^3 + A'_{31}\theta_1^3), \qquad C_4 \quad (5)$$
$$4/120 = 1/4(A'_{32}\theta_2^3 + A'_{31}\theta_1^3) + 1/2\, A_{32}A'_{21}\theta_2\theta_1 + 1/2\, A_{32}A_{21}\theta_2\theta_1^2$$
$$+ 1/4\, A'_{32}A'_{21}\theta_1 + 1/4\, A'_{32}A_{21}\theta_1^2 K_1 C_2, \quad (6)$$
$$1/120 = 1/12\, A'_{32}\theta_2^3 + 1/12\, A'_{31}\theta_1^3 + 1/6\, A_{32}A_{21}\theta_1^3 + 1/4\, A_{32}A'_{21}\theta_1^2 J_1 K_1 C_1, \quad (7)$$
$$1/120 = 1/4\, A_{32}A'_{21}\theta_1^2 + 1/4\, A'_{32}A'_{21}\theta_1 + 1/4\, A'_{32}A_{21}\theta_1^2 J_1^3 C_1. \quad (8)$$

The previously derived formulas correspond to the nonutilization of $X_{i,1}$ and $X_{i,2}$, which gives a gain of two horners per step. Let us look for other possibilities. We use $X_0$ and $DX_0$. We can use two of the four quantities:

$$X_1, \qquad DX_1,$$
$$X_2, \qquad DX_2,$$

without these being the two of the first column (only higher derivatives at the beginning of the step), or the two of the second column (previous derivation). Thus, there are only the possibilities:

a. $\qquad\qquad\qquad\qquad X_1, \; DX_2.$

b. $\qquad\qquad\qquad\qquad X_2, \; DX_1.$

Let us study a: We must have $A_{32} = 0$, $A'_{21} = A'_{31} = 0$. In subtracting (3) and (4), we find $A_{31} = 0$. Then (2), (3), and (5) give

$$A'_{32}\theta_2 = 1/3, \qquad A'_{32}\theta_2^2 = 1/6, \qquad A'_{32}\theta_2^3 = 1/10,$$

which are incompatible.

b. $\qquad\qquad\qquad A_{31} = A_{21} = 0, \qquad A'_{32} = 0.$

In subtracting (7) and (8), we find $A'_{31} = 0$, then

$$A_{32}\theta_2^2 = 1/3,$$
$$A_{32}\theta_2^3 = 1/4,$$
$$A_{32}\theta_2^4 = 1/5,$$

which are incompatible. Therefore, there is no formula of order 5 costing four horners per step besides the previously derived formulas.


## IV   METHODS UTILIZING $J$[1]

### 20. Principle.

For a system in canonical form containing $n$ unknown functions the square matrix $J$ contains $n^2$ elements. The methods of this section are thus practically useful only for $n = 1$. Let the first order equation be

$$y' = Y(y, t).$$

The matrix $J$ reduces itself to $Y'_y$. We can use this quantity in numerous ways. For $q = 2, 3$, we will use formulas of the type

$$y_{0,\alpha} = y_0 + h\theta_\alpha Y_0 + h \sum_\beta A_{\alpha,\beta}(Y_{0,\beta} - Y_0) + \frac{h^2}{2} Y'_{y,\varphi} \sum A'_{\alpha,\beta}(Y_{0,\beta} - Y_0)$$

$$+ \frac{h^3}{3!}(Y'_{y,\varphi})^2 \sum A''_{\alpha,\beta}(Y_{0,\beta} - Y_0),$$

where we have set

$$Y'_{y,\varphi} = Y'_y(t_0 + \varphi h, y_0 + \varphi h Y_0).$$

### 21. Fundamental table.

After a calculation, which we will not show in detail, one finds

[1]Frey [2].

|  | Taylor | Method utilizing $J$ |
|---|---|---|
| $h^2 C_1$ | 1/2 | $\sum A_{q,\alpha}\theta_\alpha$ |
| $h^3 C_2$ | 1/6 | $1/2 \sum A_{q,\alpha}\theta_\alpha^2$ |
| $J_1 C_1$ | 1/6 | $\sum A_{q,\alpha}A_{\alpha,\beta}\theta_\beta + \frac{1}{2}A'_{q,\alpha}\theta_\alpha$ |
| $h^4 C_3$ | 1/24 | $1/6 \sum A_{q,\alpha}\theta_\alpha^3$ |
| $J_1 C_2$ | 1/24 | $1/2 \sum A_{q,\alpha}A_{\alpha,\beta}\theta_\beta^2 + 1/4\, A'_{q,\alpha}\theta_\alpha^2$ |
| $K_1 C_1$ | 3/24 | $\sum A_{q,\alpha}A_{\alpha,\beta}\theta_\alpha\theta_\beta + \frac{\varphi}{2}\sum A'_{q,\alpha}\theta_\alpha$ |
| $J_1^2 C_1$ | 1/24 | $\sum A_{q,\alpha}A_{\alpha,\beta}A_{\beta,\gamma}\theta_\gamma + 1/2 \sum A_{q,\alpha}A'_{\alpha,\beta}\theta_\beta$ <br> $+ 1/2 \sum A'_{q,\alpha}A_{\alpha,\beta}\theta_\beta + 1/6 \sum A''_{q,\alpha}\theta_\alpha$ |
| $h^5 C_4$ | 1/120 | $1/24 \sum A_{q,\alpha}\theta_\alpha^4$ |
| $J_1 C_3$ | 1/120 | $1/6 \sum A_{q,\alpha}A_{\alpha,\beta}\theta_\beta^3 + 1/2 \sum A'_{q,\alpha}\theta_\alpha^3$ |
| $K_1 C_2$ | 4/120 | $1/2 \sum A_{q,\alpha}A_{\alpha,\beta}\theta_\alpha\theta_\beta^2 + \frac{\varphi}{4}\sum A'_{q,\alpha}\theta_\alpha^2$ |
| $J_1^2 C_2$ | 1/120 | $1/2 \sum A_{q,\alpha}A_{\alpha,\beta}A_{\beta,\gamma}\theta_\gamma^2 + 1/4 \sum A_{q,\alpha}A'_{\alpha,\beta}\theta_\beta^2$ <br> $+ 1/4 \sum A'_{q,\alpha}A_{\alpha,\beta}\theta_\beta^2 + 1/12 \sum A''_{q,\alpha}\theta_\alpha^2$ |
| $L_1 C_1$ | 6/120 | $1/2 \sum A_{q,\alpha}A_{\alpha,\beta}\theta_\alpha^2\theta_\beta + \frac{\varphi^2}{4}\sum A'_{q,\alpha}\theta_\alpha$ |
| $R$ | 3/120 | $1/2 \sum A_{q,\alpha}(\sum A_{\alpha,\beta}\theta_\beta)^2$ |
| $\left.\begin{array}{l}K_1 J_1 C_1\\ J_1 K_1 C_1\end{array}\right\}$ | 7/120 | $\sum A_{q,\alpha}A_{\alpha,\beta}A_{\beta,\gamma}\theta_\beta\theta_\gamma + \sum A_{q,\alpha}A_{\alpha,\beta}A_{\beta,\gamma}\theta_\alpha\theta_\gamma$ <br> $+ 1/2 \sum A_{q,\alpha}A'_{\alpha,\beta}\theta_\alpha\theta_\beta + \frac{\varphi}{2}\sum A_{q,\alpha}A'_{\alpha,\beta}\theta_\beta$ <br> $+ 1/2 \sum A'_{q,\alpha}A_{\alpha,\beta}\theta_\alpha\theta_\beta + \frac{2\varphi}{6}\sum A''_{q,\alpha}\theta_\alpha$ <br> $+ \frac{\varphi}{2}\sum A'_{q,\alpha}A_{\alpha,\beta}\theta_\beta$ |
| $J_1^3 C_1$ | 1/120 | $\sum A_{q,\alpha}A_{\alpha,\beta}A_{\beta,\gamma}A_{\gamma,\delta}\theta_\delta + 1/2 \sum A_{q,\alpha}A_{\alpha,\beta}A'_{\beta,\gamma}\theta_\gamma$ <br> $+ 1/2 \sum A_{q,\alpha}A'_{\alpha,\beta}A_{\beta,\gamma}\theta_\gamma + 1/2 \sum A'_{q,\alpha}A_{\alpha,\beta}A_{\beta,\gamma}\theta_\gamma$ <br> $+ 1/4 \sum A'_{q,\alpha}A'_{\alpha,\beta}\theta_\beta + 1/6 \sum A''_{q,\alpha}A_{\alpha,\beta}\theta_\beta$ <br> $+ 1/6 \sum A_{q,\alpha}A''_{\alpha,\beta}\theta_\beta$ |

## 22. Formulas for $q = 2$.

Let us seek to obtain a formula of order 3. We have

$$A_{2,1}\theta_1 = 1/2,$$
$$A_{2,1}\theta_1^2 = 1/3$$
$$1/2\, A'_{2,1}\theta_1 = 1/6,$$

whence we find: $\theta_1 = 2/3$, $A_{2,1} = 3/4$, $A'_{2,1} = 1/2$. Since $\varphi$ does not occur, we can take it to be zero. In taking it to be equal to 3/4, we can make one error term disappear. $A''_{2,1}$ does not occur, so we can take it to be zero. In taking it to be equal to 3/8, we can suppress one error term.

### 23. Formulas for $q = 3$.

We can obtain a formula of order 4 by the system of seven equations which are taken from the fundamental table. There still remain three arbitrary quantities. We ean take

$$\varphi = A''_{3,2} = A''_{3,1} = 0, \qquad \theta_1 = 1/2.$$

We find then

$$\theta_2 = 1,$$

$$A_{3,1} = 2/3, \qquad A_{3,2} = 1/6, \qquad A_{2,1} = 3/2,$$

$$A'_{3,1} = 1/6, \qquad A'_{3,2} = 0, \qquad A'_{2,1} = 1.$$

We could have used the arbitrary quantities to suppress the error terms.

### 24. Formulas for $q = 4$.

It is impossible to make the $h^5$ terms disappear with the preceding scheme. Let us content ourselves by giving an example due to Frey of a formula of order 5:

$$\theta_1 = 4/5, \qquad \theta_2 = 0, \qquad \theta_3 = 1/3, \qquad \theta_4 = 1,$$

$$y_1 = y_0 + 4/5\,h\,Y_0,$$

$$y_2 = y_0 + 3h(Y_1 - Y_0).$$

We calculate $Y'_y(t_0, y_2)$

$$y_3 = y_0 + \frac{h}{24}(7Y_1 + Y_0),$$

$$y_4 = y_0 + \frac{h}{56}(288\,Y_3 + 27\,Y_1 - 259\,Y_0) - \frac{h^2}{2}\,Y'_y(Y_1 - Y_0),$$

$$y_5 = y_0 + \frac{h}{336}(35\,Y_0 + 125\,Y_1 + 162\,Y_3 + 14\,Y_4)$$

$$- \frac{h^2}{336}[29(Y_1 - Y_0) - 12(Y_2 - Y_0)]\,Y'_y$$

$$- \frac{h^3}{336}[25(Y_1 - Y_0) + 36(Y_2 - Y_0)]\,Y''_y{}^2$$

$$- \frac{h^4}{48}(Y_1 - Y_0)\,Y'_y{}^3.$$

## Problems

Repeat the problems of Chapter 3, using
1. RKDP 2, 3, 4, Zurmühl.
2. RKDP 3, 4, 5, Laurent.
3. RKDP 3, 4, 5, Bard.
4. RK 4 Classic.

Estimate the error of each method. What are the relative merits of each method?

For problems 1, 2, and 4 of Chapter 3 repeat the calculation, using the method utilizing $J$ (see section IV). How does this method compare with the Runge—Kutta method?

PART **II**

# MULTISTEP METHODS

# 6 ADAMS METHOD AND ANALOGUES[1]

The preceding chapters have shown us the scope of the Runge-Kutta principle. Now, we are going to present a different principle which, as remains to be seen later, it is possible to insert into the current of the Runge-Kutta ideas.

## 1. Generalities.

Although the single-step methods do give good results, one notes that they do not use the information furnished by the points already computed (other than the last one). Indeed, in view of the customary regularity of the curves, one can obtain, at little expense, information which the single-step methods furnish only at a considerable amount of calculation. Therefore other methods have been conceived which are called the "multistep methods." On the other hand, these methods have the inconvenience that they no longer adhere to the second fundamental property of the solution of an initial value problem; the values found for $t > t_i$ no longer depend uniquely upon the values for $t = t_i$. This is paid for by the constraining parasitic phenomena, such as the difficulty of varying the length of the step in the course of integration, the necessity of starting formulas (31), and finally the instability (Chapter 7, section II).

One will equally note that the hypotheses of regularity are stronger in these methods than in the single-step methods. This results in inconveniences in the case when the curve has a singularity (corner points in particular). The calculations being simpler than those of the Runge-Kutta method, we will treat separately:

[1]Bashforth and Adams, Chadaja [2], Collatz-Zurmühl [1], Golcov, Mathieu [1], Mikeladze [1, 2], von Mises, Schulz [1], Shue, Stohler.

—systems in canonical form.

—systems containing higher order derivatives.

## I  GENERAL THEORY FOR SYSTEMS IN CANONICAL FORM

### 2. Principle of the methods of this chapter for a system in canonical form.

Let us consider the system

$$x' = X(x, t),$$

where $x$ and $X$ represent columns of functions. Rigorously, we have

$$x(t_{i+1}) = x(t_{i-l}) + \int_{t_{i-l}}^{t_{i+1}} X(x(t), t)dt$$

A very natural idea (Adams-Bashforth) consists of representing the quantity under the summation sign by an interpolation polynomial using a certain number of abscissa points:

$$t_{i-\mu}, \quad t_{i-\mu-1}, \quad \ldots, \quad t_{i-\nu},$$

whose ordinates are supposed to be exactly known. This representation can be done in several ways, which we are going to study successively (Lagrange, Newton.)[1]

### 3.1 The use of the interpolation formula of Lagrange.

For the interpolation polynomial we will use Lagrange's form at $r + 1$ points:

$$X(t) = \sum_{j=\mu}^{\nu} X(t_{i-j}) L_{i-j}^{(r)}(t), \qquad \mu - \nu = r \geqslant 0, \tag{1}$$

with

$$L_{i-j}^{(r)}(t) = \frac{(t - t_{i-\mu})(t - t_{i-\mu-1}) \ldots (t - t_{i-\nu})}{(t_{i-j} - t_{i-\mu})(t_{i-j} - t_{i-\mu-1}) \ldots (t_{i-j} - t_{i-\nu})}$$

One naturally excludes the factor $t - t_{i-j}$ from the numerator. Let us replace $X(t)$ by the expression (1) in the integral. We have

$$x(t_{i+1}) = x(t_{i-l}) + \sum_{j=\mu}^{\nu} X(t_{i-j}) \int_{t_{i-l}}^{t_{i+1}} L_{i-j}^{(r)}(t)dt.$$

We will define the approximate integration method by setting

$$x_{i+1} = x_{i-l} + \sum_{j=\mu}^{\nu} A_j X_{i-j},$$

with

$$A_j = \frac{1}{h} \int_{t_{i-l}}^{t_{i+1}} L_{i-j}^{(r)}(t)dt.$$

[1] We will study other interpolation forms in Chapter 7.

The method is said to be of order $s$ if it uses one interpolation at $s$ points (hence of degree $s - 1$).

### 3.2 Effect of a change of the variable.

It is immediately verifiable that a change of the variable leaves the coefficients which we just defined invariant.

### 3.3 Another way of obtaining the coefficients.

We will proceed as with the establishing of the Runge-Kutta formulas by developing into a Taylor series each of the terms of the two members of the equality

$$x_{i+1} = x_{i-l} + h \sum_{j=\mu}^{v} A_j X(t_{i-j}) \tag{1}$$

and by identifying the terms of the same degree $h$. The coefficients are determined so as to make the two developments coincide as far as possible, which leads to a linear system. Besides, one verifies immediately that one can replace the calculation by a yet simpler calculation which consists of writing that formula (1) is exact for

$$\begin{array}{ll} X(t) = 0, & x(t) = 1, \\ X(t) = 1, & x(t) = t, \\ X(t) = t, & x(t) = t^2/2, \\ \cdots & \cdots \\ X(t) = t^{r-1}, & x(t) = t^r/r. \end{array}$$

### 3.4 Example.

Let $l = 2$, $\mu = 0$, $v = 3$:

$$x_{i+1} = x_{i-2} + h \sum_{j=0}^{3} A_j X_{i-j}.$$

One has the conditions:

$$\begin{array}{ll} 3 \quad = A_0 + A_1 + A_2 + A_3, & \\ 3^2/2 = 2A_0 + A_1 - A_3, & \text{(here } i = 2\text{)} \\ 3^3/3 = 2^2 A_0 + A_1 + A_3, & \\ 3^4/4 = 2^3 A_0 + A_1 - A_3, & \end{array}$$

whence one finds

$$A_0 = 21/8, \quad A_1 = -9/8, \quad A_2 = 15/8, \quad A_3 = -3/8,$$

and the formula

$$x_{i+1} = x_{i-2} + \frac{h}{8}(21 X_i - 9 X_{i-1} + 15 X_{i-2} - 3 X_{i-3}).$$

*Remark.* The above-mentioned procedure is equivalent to one of the handier ones for rapidly verifying that the coefficients of a proposed formula are correct.

### 4. Common cases.

Usually, one takes $\mu = 0$ or $\mu = -1$. We will denote, if $\mu = 0$ (explicit formulas), the $A_j$ by:

$$\alpha_{r,j} \qquad \text{if } l = 0 \text{ (Adams formulas).}$$
$$\beta_{r,j}, \qquad \text{if } l = 1 \text{ (Nyström formulas).}$$
$$\gamma_{r,j}, \qquad \text{if } l = 2.$$
$$\lambda_{r,j}, \qquad \text{if } l \text{ is arbitrary.}$$

Likewise, if $\mu = -1$ (implicit formulas), we will take for $A_j$:

$$\alpha^*_{r,j}, \qquad \text{if } l = 1 \text{ (implicit Adams formulas).}$$
$$\beta^*_{r,j}, \qquad \text{if } l = 1 \text{ (implicit Nyström formulas).}$$
$$\gamma^*_{r,j}, \qquad \text{if } l \text{ is arbitrary.}$$

### 5. Use of Newton's interpolation formula.

Instead of using Lagrange's interpolation formula, one can use that of Newton which appeals to the backward differences $\nabla$. The result obtained is in a different form, but has the same numerical value. For $\mu = 0$, one can write:

$$X(t) = \sum_{j=0}^{\nu} N_j(t) \nabla^j X(t_i), \qquad \nabla X(t_i) = X(t_i) - X(t_{i-1}),$$

$$\nabla^j = \nabla^{j-1} X(t_i) - \nabla^{j-1} X(t_{i-1}),$$

with

$$N_j(t) = \frac{(t - t_i) \ldots (t - t_{i-j+1})}{h^j j!}.$$

By integrating between $t_{i-l}$ and $t_{i+1}$, one can deduce the approximate formula

$$x_{i+1} = x_{i-l} + h \sum_{j=0}^{\nu} K_j \nabla^j X_i,$$

with

$$K_j = \frac{1}{h} \int_{t_{i-l}}^{t_{i+1}} N_j(t) dt.$$

Likewise, for $\mu = -1$, one would write

$$X(t) = \sum_{j=0}^{\nu} N^*_j(t) \nabla^j X(t_{i+1}),$$

with

$$N^*_j(t) = \frac{(t - t_{i+1}) \ldots (t - t_{i-j+2})}{h^j j!}$$

and deduce by integrating between $t_{i-l}$ and $t_{i+1}$:

$$x_{i+1} = x_{i-l} + h \sum_{j=0}^{\nu} K^*_j \nabla^j X_{i+1}$$

with

$$K^*_j = \frac{1}{h} \int_{t_{i-l}}^{t_{i+1}} N^*_j(t) dt.$$

We mark the coefficients $K_j$: $a_j$, if $l = 0$; $b_j$, if $l = 1$; and $l_j$ if $l$ is arbitrary; and the coefficients $K_j^*$: $a_j^*$, if $l = 0$; $b_j^*$, if $l = 1$; and $l_j^*$ if $l$ is arbitrary. We note that this time the coefficients have only a single index. By eliminating the backward differences in these formulas, we recover exactly the formulas of paragraph 4.

### 6.1 Calculation of the coefficients $l_j$.

By changing the variable $t - t_i = uh$, Newton's formula leads us to the expression

$$l_j = \frac{1}{j!} \int_{-l}^{1} u(u + 1) \ldots (u + j - 1)du, \qquad l_0 = l + 1.$$

We can easily obtain a formula giving the $l_j$ recursively. In addition to the operator $\nabla$, let us introduce the translation operator

$$E = (1 - \nabla)^{-1}$$

and the differentiation operator

$$E = e^{hD},$$

from which we derive

$$D^{-1} = h/\ln E = -h/\ln(1 - \nabla) = h\nabla^{-1}(1 + \nabla/2 + \nabla^2/3 + \cdots)^{-1}.$$

If we apply the result to the equality $Dx_i = X_i$, we obtain

$$x_i = h\nabla^{-1}(1 + \nabla/2 + \nabla^2/3 + \cdots)^{-1}X_i,$$

from which

$$x_i - x_{i-1} = h(1 + \nabla/2 + \nabla^2/3 + \cdots)^{-1}X_i.$$

Applying the operator $E$ to the two members of this equality, we arrive at

$$x_{i+1} - x_i = h(1 - \nabla)^{-1}(1 + \nabla/2 + \nabla^2/3 + \cdots)^{-1}X_i$$

and, more generally, at

$$x_{i-l+1} - x_{i-l} = h(1 - \nabla)^{l-1}(1 + \nabla/2 + \nabla^2/3 + \cdots)^{-1}X_i.$$

Adding both these equalities term by term, we obtain:

$$x_{i+1} - x_{i-l}$$
$$= h[(1 - \nabla)^{-1} + 1 + (1 - \nabla) + \cdots + (1 - \nabla)^{l-1}][1 + \nabla/2 + \nabla^2/3 + \cdots]^{-1}X_i.$$

Replacing $x_{i+1} - x_{i-l}$ by this expression in the approximate integration formula, we find

$$(l_0 + l_1\nabla + l_2\nabla^2 + \cdots)(1 + \nabla/2 + \nabla^2/3 + \cdots) = (1 - \nabla)^{-1} + 1$$
$$+ (1 - \nabla) + \cdots + (1 - \nabla)^{l-1},$$

from which, identifying the terms of $\nabla^q$, we find

$$\sum_{j=0}^{q} \frac{l_j}{q + 1 - j} = 1 + (-1)^q C_l^{q+1} \text{ §.}$$

§ This formula is exact even if $q \geqslant l$, assuming $C_i^j = 0$ if $j > i$.

This is the formula, announced previously, which permits us to calculate the $l_j$ recursively.

### 6.2 Properties of the $\lambda_{r,j}$.

If, in Lagrange's interpolation formula, we make the change of variable

$$t - t_i = uh,$$

the coefficients of the Lagrange polynomial are written as

$$L^{(r)}_{i-j}(u) = \frac{(-1)^j C^j_r}{r!} \frac{u(u+1) \dots (u+r-1)}{u+j},$$

which gives

$$h\lambda_{r,j} = \int^{t_{i+1}}_{t_{i-l}} L^{(r)}_{i-j}(t)\,dt = \frac{(-1)^j C^j_r h}{r!} \int^1_{-l} \frac{u(u+1) \dots (u+r)}{u+j}\,du.$$

From the known relation

$$\sum_{j=0}^{r} L^{(r)}_{i-j}(t) = 1,$$

we deduce

$$\sum_{j=0}^{r} \alpha_{r,j} = 1, \qquad \text{for} \qquad l = 0,$$

and, more generally,

$$\sum_{j=0}^{r} \lambda_{r,j} = l + 1, \qquad \text{for} \qquad l \text{ whatsoever.}$$

### 6.3 Recursive calculation of the $\lambda_{r,j}$.

One can write

$$\begin{aligned}
\lambda_{r,j} &= \frac{(-1)^j C^j_r}{r!} \int^1_{-l} \frac{u(u+1) \dots (u+r)}{u+j}\,du \\
&= \frac{(-1)^j C^j_r}{r!} \int^1_{-l} \frac{u(u+1) \dots (u+r-1)(u+j)}{u+j}\,du \\
&\quad + \frac{(-1)^j C^j_r (r-j)}{r!} \int^1_{-l} \frac{u(u+1) \dots (u+r-1)}{u+j}\,du,
\end{aligned}$$

from which:

$$\lambda_{r,j} = (-1)^{j+r} C^j_r \lambda_{r,r} + \lambda_{r-1,j}.$$

### 6.4 Relation with the $l_j$.

In order to use the preceding relation conveniently, it will be necessary to know $\lambda_{r,r}$. Let us remark that $X_{i-r}$ occur in the formula truncated after $\nabla^r$ only in $\nabla^r$ itself. This results in $\lambda_{r,r} = (-1)^r l_r$.

### 7.1 Calculation of the coefficients $l_j^*$.

Starting from Newton's formula, we find:

$$l_j^* = \frac{1}{j!} \int_{-(l+1)}^{0} u(u+1) \ldots (u+j-1)\, du = (-1)^j \lambda_{j,j}^*.$$

We can equally give a formula which permits the recursive calculation of $l_j^*$. Let us return to paragraph 6.1, the formula which immediately precedes the introduction of the $l_i$. We can write it as

$$x_{i+1} - x_{i-l} = h[1 + (1-\nabla) + \cdots + (1-\nabla)^l][1 + \nabla/2 + \nabla^2/3 + \cdots]^{-1} X_{i+1},$$

from which one can find, by replacing $x_{i+1} - x_{i-l}$ by its expression derived from the approximate integration formula,

$$(l_0^* + l_1^* \nabla + l_2^* \nabla^2 + \cdots)(1 + \nabla/2 + \nabla^2/3 + \cdots)$$
$$= 1 + (1-\nabla) + \cdots + (1-\nabla)^l.$$

In identifying the corresponding terms $\nabla^q$ in the two members, we deduce

$$\sum_{j=0}^{q} \frac{l_j^*}{q+1-j} = (-1)^q C_{l+1}^{q+1}, \S$$

which permits the recursive calculation of the $l_j^*$.

### 7.2 Relations between the $l_j$ and the $l_j^*$.

After the preceding, one sees immediately that

$$(l_0 + l_1 \nabla + l_2 \nabla^2 + \cdots)(1 - \nabla) = l_0^* + l_1^* \nabla + l_2^* \nabla^2 + \cdots,$$

from which, by identifying the powers of $\nabla$ in the two members, one has

$$l_j - l_{j-1} = l_j^*,$$

or

$$l_r = \sum_{j=0}^{r} l_j^*,$$

since

$$l_0 = l_0^* = l + 1.$$

### 7.3 Investigation of the coefficients $\lambda_{r,j}^*$.

Setting $t - t_i = uh$ in Lagrange's interpolation formula, the polynomials $L_{i+1-j}^{(r)}$ become

$$L_{i+1-j}^{(r)}(u) = \frac{(-1)^j C_r^j u(u+1) \ldots (u+r)}{r!} \cdot \frac{1}{u+j}.$$

from which

$$h\lambda_{r,j}^* = \int_{t_{i-l}}^{t_{i+1}} L_{i+1-j}^{(r)}(t)\, dt = \frac{(-1)^j C_r^j h}{r!} \int_{-l-1}^{0} \frac{u(u+1) \ldots (u+r)}{u+j}\, du.$$

§ See footnote 1, p. 133.

Proceeding as in paragraph 6.3, one finds

$$\lambda^*_{r,j} = (-1)^{j+r} C^j_r \lambda^*_{r,r} + \lambda^*_{r-1,j},$$

with

$$\lambda^*_{r,r} = (-1)^r l^*_r.$$

The collection of these formulas permits the recursive calculation of the $\lambda^*_{r,j}$.


## II  EXPLICIT FORMULAS FOR SYSTEMS IN CANONICAL FORM

### 8.1 Explicit Adams formulas or the Adams-Bashforth formulas ($l = 0$).

We have written the explicit Adams formulas

$$x_{i+1} = x_i + h \sum_{j=0}^{r} a_{r,j} X_{i-j}.$$

The table on p. 137 gives the first $a_{r,j}$.

### 8.2 Expression in terms of differences.

We have written the formula

$$x_{i+1} = x_i + h \sum_{j=0}^{r} a_j \nabla^j X_i,$$

or, by replacing the coefficients by their values,

$$x_{i+1} = x_i + h(X_i + 1/2 \nabla X_i + 5/12 \nabla^2 X_i + 3/8 \nabla^3 X_i + 251/720 \nabla^4 X_i$$
$$+ 475/1440 \nabla^5 X_i + 19{,}087/60{,}480 \nabla^6 X_i + \cdots).$$

In order to have a formula of order $r$, it suffices to take the terms in the parentheses up to $\nabla^{r-1} X_i$ inclusive.

### 8.3 Examples.

*Example* 1. Let

$$y' = 0.1 y^2 - ty, \qquad y(0) = 1, \qquad h = 0.1,$$

with the formula

$$y_{i+1} = y_i + \frac{h}{12}(23 Y_i - 16 Y_{i-1} + 5 Y_{i-2}).$$

| $t$ | $y$ approximate | $y$ exact |
|---|---|---|
| 0 | | 1.0000 |
| 0.1 | | 1.0050 |
| 0.2 | | 1.0001 |
| 0.3 | 0.9850 | 0.9851 |
| 0.4 | 0.9603 | 0.9605 |
| 0.5 | 0.9267 | 0.9270 |
| 1.0 | 0.6629 | 0.6633 |

| r \ j | 0 | 1 | 2 | 3 | 4 | 5 | 6 | 7 | 8 | 9 |
|---|---|---|---|---|---|---|---|---|---|---|
| 0 | 1 | | | | | | | | | |
| 1 | $3/2$ | $-1/2$ | | | | | | | | |
| 2 | $23/12$ | $-16/12$ | $5/12$ | | | | | | | |
| 3 | $55/24$ | $-59/24$ | $37/24$ | $-9/24$ | | | | | | |
| 4 | $\dfrac{1,901}{720}$ | $\dfrac{-2,774}{720}$ | $\dfrac{2,616}{720}$ | $\dfrac{-1,274}{720}$ | $\dfrac{251}{720}$ | | | | | |
| 5 | $\dfrac{4,277}{1,440}$ | $\dfrac{-7,923}{1,440}$ | $\dfrac{9,982}{1,440}$ | $\dfrac{-7,298}{1,440}$ | $\dfrac{2,877}{1,440}$ | $\dfrac{-475}{1,440}$ | | | | |
| 6 | $\dfrac{198,721}{60,480}$ | $\dfrac{-447,288}{60,480}$ | $\dfrac{705,549}{60,480}$ | $\dfrac{-688,256}{60,480}$ | $\dfrac{407,139}{60,480}$ | $\dfrac{-134,472}{60,480}$ | $\dfrac{19,087}{60,480}$ | | | |
| 7 | $\dfrac{434,241}{120,960}$ | $\dfrac{-1,152,169}{120,960}$ | $\dfrac{2,183,877}{120,960}$ | $\dfrac{-2,664,477}{120,960}$ | $\dfrac{2,102,243}{120,960}$ | $\dfrac{-1,041,723}{120,960}$ | $\dfrac{295,767}{120,960}$ | $\dfrac{-36,799}{120,960}$ | | |
| 8 | $\dfrac{14,097,247}{3,628,800}$ | $\dfrac{-43,125,206}{3,628,800}$ | $\dfrac{95,476,786}{3,628,800}$ | $\dfrac{-139,855,262}{3,628,800}$ | $\dfrac{137,968,480}{3,628,800}$ | $\dfrac{-91,172,642}{3,628,800}$ | $\dfrac{38,833,486}{3,628,800}$ | $\dfrac{-9,664,106}{3,628,800}$ | $\dfrac{1,070,017}{3,628,800}$ | |
| 9 | $\dfrac{30,277,247}{7,257,600}$ | $\dfrac{-104,995,189}{7,257,600}$ | $\dfrac{265,932,680}{7,257,600}$ | $\dfrac{-454,661,776}{7,257,600}$ | $\dfrac{538,363,838}{7,257,600}$ | $\dfrac{-444,772,162}{7,257,600}$ | $\dfrac{252,618,224}{7,257,600}$ | $\dfrac{-94,307,320}{7,257,600}$ | $\dfrac{20,884,811}{7,257,600}$ | $\dfrac{-2,082,753}{7,257,600}$ |

137

The first three values have been taken to be equal to the exact values.

*Example* 2. Let us integrate

$$y' = t + y, \qquad y(0) = 0$$

by the fifth order formula, using the difference equation

$$y_{i+1} = y_i + h(Y_i + 1/2 \nabla Y_i + 5/12 \nabla^2 Y_i + 3/8 \nabla^3 Y_i + 251/720 \nabla^4 Y_i).$$

The values of the above relation have been determined by an approximate procedure, different from the integration method itself.

| $t$ | $y_i$ | $Y_i$ | $\Delta Y_i$ | $\Delta^2 Y_i$ | $\Delta^3 Y_i$ | $\Delta^4 Y_i$ | $y$ exact |
|-----|-------|-------|--------------|----------------|----------------|----------------|-----------|
| 0 | 0 | 0 | | | | | |
| 0.1 | 0.0051 | 0.1051 | 1051 | | | | 2 |
| 0.2 | 0.0213 | 0.2213 | 1162 | 111 | | | 4 |
| 0.3 | 0.0498 | 0.3498 | 1285 | 123 | 12 | | 9 |
| 0.4 | 0.0916 | 0.4916 | 1418 | 133 | 10 | −2 | 8 |
| 0.5 | 0.1484 | 0.6484 | 1568 | 150 | 17 | 7 | 7 |
| 0.6 | 0.2218 | 0.8218 | 1734 | 166 | 16 | −1 | 21 |
| 0.7 | 0.3134 | 1.0134 | 1916 | 182 | 16 | 0 | 8 |
| 0.8 | 0.4251 | 1.2251 | 2117 | 201 | 19 | 3 | 5 |
| 0.9 | 0.5590 | 1.4590 | 2339 | 222 | 21 | 2 | 6 |
| 1.0 | 0.7176 | | | | | | 83 |

In manual computation, the practical interest of the differences is three-fold:

—it is agreeable because the size of the numbers becomes rapidly small.

—the majority of the round-off errors are translated in an abnormal manner into the differences.

—the order of size of the first neglected difference gives information about the error (paragraph 12).

In automatic calculation, the first two advantages disappear and the program, on the contrary, turns out to be slightly complicated because of the calculation of the differences.

*Remark.* The incoherent appearance of the fourth order differences in the preceding example is due to the amplification of the round-off errors in the formation of the differences (see, for example, Kuntzmann [4]).

*Example* 3.

$$y' = z, \qquad z' = -y, \qquad y(0) = 0, \qquad z(0) = 1, \qquad h = 0.1$$

and the formula of order 3. One finds

| $t$ | $y_i$ | $y$ exact | $z_i$ | $z$ exact |
|---|---|---|---|---|
| 0 | 0 | 0 | 1 | 1 |
| 0.1 | 0.099,833 | 0.099,833 | 0.995,004 | 0.995,004 |
| 0.2 | 0.198,669 | 0.198,669 | 0.980,067 | 0.980,067 |
| 0.3 | 0.295,515 | 0.295,520 | 0.955,300 | 0.955,336 |
| 0.4 | 0.389,397 | 0.389,418 | 0.920,989 | 0.921,061 |
| 0.5 | 0.479,383 | 0.479,426 | 0.877,479 | 0.877,583 |
| 1.0 | 0.841,237 | 0.841,471 | 0.540,114 | 0.540,302 |
| 1.5 | 0.997,015 | 0.997,495 | 0.070,651 | 0.070,737 |
| 2.0 | 0.908,657 | 0.909,297 | $-0.415,933$ | $-0.416,147$ |
| 2.5 | 0.597,885 | 0.598,472 | $-0.800,511$ | $-0.801,144$ |
| 3.0 | 0.140,861 | 0.141,120 | $-0.988,975$ | $-0.989,993$ |

### 8.4 Cowell's method.[1]

Certain authors use a slightly different approach. Let us return to the formula

$$x_{i+1} - x_i = h(X_i + 1/2 \nabla X_i + 5/12 \nabla^2 X_i + 3/8 \nabla^3 X_i + 251/720 \nabla^4 X_i).$$

Applying to both members of this relation the operator $\nabla^{-1}$, we can write

$$x_{i+1} = h(\nabla^{-1} X_i + 1/2 X_i + 5/12 \nabla X_i + 3/8 \nabla^2 X_i + 251/720 \nabla^3 X_i). \quad (1)$$

$\nabla^{-1} X_i$ is a known quantity:

$$\nabla^{-1} X_i = \nabla^{-1} X_{i-1} + X_i.$$

In order to begin with the calculation, we naturally have to know the same quantities as in the usual presentation, i.e., for the formula below:

$$x_0, \quad x_1, \quad x_2, \quad x_3, \quad x_4.$$

We then deduce

$$X_3, \quad \nabla X_3, \quad \nabla^2 X_3, \quad \nabla^3 X_3.$$

Taking $i = 3$ in formula (1), we find $\nabla^{-1} X_3$.

We note that this variant uses one subtraction less per step (one does not calculate $\nabla^4$). On the other hand, it causes larger numbers to appear (in particular, $\nabla^{-1} X$), whereas the goal of the introduction of the differences was to have small numbers. This presentation does not modify the truncation error. On the contrary, the computation error is presented in a slightly different manner and may be more favorable.

[1]Cowell and Crommelin [1, 2], Florinsky, Herrick.

### 8.5 Example.

Let us return to example 2 of 8.3. We find

| $t$ | $y$ | $\nabla^{-1}Y_i \times 10^4$ | $Y_i \times 10^4$ | $\nabla Y_i \times 10^4$ | $\nabla^2 Y_i \times 10^4$ | $\nabla^3 Y_i \times 10^4$ |
|---|---|---|---|---|---|---|
| 0   | 0      |        | 0      |        |     |    |
| 0.1 | 0.0051 |        | 1,051  | 1,051  |     |    |
| 0.2 | 0.0213 |        | 2,213  | 1,162  | 111 |    |
| 0.3 | 0.0498 | 6,826  | 3,498  | 1,285  | 123 | 12 |
| 0.4 | 0.0916 | 11,742 | 4,916  | 1,418  | 133 | 10 |
| 0.5 | 0.1484 | 18,226 | 6,484  | 1,568  | 150 | 17 |
| 0.6 | 0.2218 | 26,444 | 8,218  | 1,734  | 166 | 16 |
| 0.7 | 0.3134 | 36,578 | 10,134 | 1,916  | 182 | 16 |
| 0.8 | 0.4252 | 48,830 | 12,252 | 2,118  | 202 | 20 |
| 0.9 | 0.5592 | 63,422 | 14,592 | 2,340  | 222 | 20 |
| 1.0 | 0.7178 |        |        |        |     |    |

We can state that the results are a little better.

### 9.1 Nyström's formulas ($l = 1$).

These are Nyström's formulas ($l = 1$):

$$x_{i+1} = x_{i-1} + h \sum_{j=0}^{r} \beta_{r,j} X_{i-j}$$

Here are the first coefficients of these formulas:

| r \ j | 0 | 1 | 2 | 3 | 4 |
|---|---|---|---|---|---|
| 0 | 2      |         |        |         |       |
| 1 | 2      | 0       |        |         |       |
| 2 | 7/3    | −2/3    | 1/3    |         |       |
| 3 | 8/3    | −5/3    | 4/3    | −1/3    |       |
| 4 | 269/90 | −266/90 | 294/90 | −146/90 | 29/90 |

We can equally write these formulas by means of backward differences:

$$x_{i+1} = x_{i-1} + h \sum_{j=0}^{r} b_j \nabla^j X_i.$$

Thus

$$x_{i+1} = x_{i-1} + h(2 X_i + 1/3 \nabla^2 X_i + 1/3 \nabla^3 X_i + 29/90 \nabla^4 X_i$$
$$+ 14/45 \nabla^5 X_i + 1139/3780 \nabla^5 X_i + \cdots).$$

In order to obtain the formula of order $r$, we retain the terms in the parentheses up to $\nabla^r X_i$ inclusive.

## 9.2 Example.

1.
$$y' = -y, \qquad y(0) = 1, \qquad h = 0.1,$$
$$y_{i+1} = y_{i-1} + \frac{h}{3}(7\,Y_i - 2\,Y_{i-1} + Y_{i-2}).$$

| $t$ | $y_i$ | $y$ exact |
|---|---|---|
| 0 | 1 | 1 |
| 0.1 | 0.904,84 | 0.904,84 |
| 0.2 | 0.818,73 | 0.818,73 |
| 0.3 | 0.740,79 | 0.740,82 |
| 0.4 | 0.670,30 | 0.670,32 |
| 0.5 | 0.606,48 | 0.606,53 |
| 1.0 | 0.367,84 | 0.367,88 |
| 1.5 | 0.223,02 | 0.223,13 |
| 2.0 | 0.135,39 | 0.135,33 |

The three starting values were taken to be exact.

2.
$$y' = t + y, \qquad y(0) = 0,$$
$$y_{i+1} = y_{i-1} + 2h\,Y_i, \qquad h = 0.1.$$

| $t$ | $10^4 y_i$ | $10^4 y$ exact |
|---|---|---|
| 0 | 0 | 0 |
| 0.1 | 51.64 | 52 |
| 0.2 | 213.28 | 214 |
| 0.3 | 494.29 | 499 |
| 0.4 | 912.14 | 918 |
| 0.5 | 1476.72 | 1487 |
| 1.0 | 7143.89 | 7183 |

## 10. Formulas for $l = 2$.

We can write

$$x_{i+1} = x_{i-2} + h \sum_{j=0}^{r} \gamma_{r,j} X_{i-j}.$$

Here is a table which gives the values of the first $\gamma_{r,j}$:

| r \ j | 0 | 1 | 2 | 3 | 4 |
|---|---|---|---|---|---|
| 1 | 3/2 | 3/2 | | | |
| 2 | 9/4 | 0 | 3/4 | | |
| 3 | 63/24 | −27/24 | 45/24 | −9/24 | |
| 4 | 237/80 | −198/80 | 312/80 | −138/80 | 27/80 |

### 11. General formulas using the differences.

We can write, in a general way,

$$x_{i+1} = x_{i-l} + h \sum_{j=0}^{r} l_j \nabla^j X_i.$$

Here is a table which gives the values of the first $l_j$:

| j \ l | 0 | 1 | 2 | 3 | 4 |
|---|---|---|---|---|---|
| 0 | 1 | $\dfrac{1}{2}$ | $\dfrac{5}{12}$ | $\dfrac{9}{24}$ | $\dfrac{251}{720}$ |
| 1 | 2 | 0 | 4 | 8 | 232 |
| 2 | 3 | −3 | 9 | 9 | 243 |
| 3 | 4 | −8 | 32 | 0 | 224 |
| 4 | 5 | −15 | 85 | −55 | 475 |
| 5 | 6 | −24 | 180 | −216 | 376 |
| 6 | 7 | −35 | 329 | −567 | 9,107 |
| 7 | 8 | −48 | 544 | −1216 | 26,368 |

| j \ l | 5 | 6 | 7 | 8 | 9 |
|---|---|---|---|---|---|
| 0 | $\dfrac{475}{1,440}$ | $\dfrac{19,087}{60,480}$ | $\dfrac{36,799}{120,960}$ | $\dfrac{1,070,017}{3,628,800}$ | $\dfrac{2,082,753}{7,257,600}$ |
| 1 | 448 | 18,224 | 35,424 | 1,036,064 | 2,025,472 |
| 2 | 459 | 18,495 | 35,775 | 1,043,361 | 2,036,097 |
| 3 | 448 | 18,304 | 35,584 | 1,040,128 | 2,032,128 |
| 4 | 475 | 18,575 | 35,775 | 1,042,625 | 2,034,625 |
| 5 | 0 | 17,712 | 35,424 | 1,039,392 | 2,032,128 |
| 6 | −4,277 | 36,799 | 36,799 | 1,046,689 | 2,036,097 |
| 7 | −22,016 | 235,520 | 0 | 1,012,736 | 2,025,472 |

The denominators, which are the same for all the coefficients of the same column, are indicated only in the first line.

### 12.1 Local error. Quadrature error.

We will postpone a more elaborate study of the errors to Chapter 9. Let us only remark here that one commits an error by replacing

$$\int_{t_{i-l}}^{t_{i+1}} X(x, t)\, dt \quad \text{by} \quad h \sum_{j=0}^{r} \lambda_{r,j} X(t_{i-j}).$$

This error is called local error. It is composed of

—a *quadrature error* due to the use of an approximate quadrature formula.

—a *local round-off error* due to the loss of digits in the various arithmetic operations.

It is easy to give an approximate expression for the quadrature error by supposing that the round-off error is negligible before the former. Actually, the formulas using the differences can be developed up to any order. We can consider their successive terms as infinitesimals of a higher and higher order. The principal part of the quadrature error (often we will call it the quadrature error for short) is then the first of these terms which has been neglected and which is not zero. In the actual case, this term is

$$hl_{r+1}\nabla^{r+1}X(x, t) \approx l_{r+1}h^{r+2}x^{(r+2)}(t).$$

## 12.2 Example.

For the formula

$$x_{i+1} = x_i + h/12(23\,X_i - 16\,X_{i-1} + 5\,X_{i-2})$$
$$= x_i + h(X_i + 1/2\nabla X_i + 5/12\nabla^2 X_i)$$

the quadrature error has for a principal part

$$3/8\,h\nabla^3 X_i = 3/8\,h^4 x^{(4)}(\xi) \quad \text{with} \quad t_{i-3} \leqslant \xi \leqslant t_i.$$

## III  IMPLICIT FORMULAS FOR SYSTEMS IN CANONICAL FORM

### 13.1 Implicit method of Adams or of Adams-Moulton ($l = 0$.)

For a system in canonical form, we write

$$X_{i+1} = x_i + h\sum_{j=0}^{r} \alpha^*_{r,j} X_{i+1-j},$$

where $r$ is the degree of the interpolation and $r + 1$ is the order of the method. We give the values of the first coefficients $a^*_{j,r}$ on p. 144.

### 13.2 Example.

$$y' = -y, \qquad y(0) = 1, \qquad h = 0.1.$$

By the third order formula:

$$y_{i+1} = y_i + \frac{h}{12}(5\,Y_{i+1} + 8\,Y_i - Y_{i-1}).$$

$y_1$ is taken to be equal to the exact value.

| $t$ | $y_i$ | Error |
|-----|-------|-------|
| 0   | 1.000,000,0 | 0 |
| 0.1 | 0.904,837,4 | 0 |
| 0.2 | 0.818,734,3 | $-35$ |
| 0.3 | 0.740,824,6 | $-64$ |
| 0.4 | 0.670,328,7 | $-87$ |
| 0.5 | 0.606,541,1 | $-104$ |
| 1.0 | 0.367,893,7 | $-143$ |
| 1.5 | 0.223,143,6 | $-134$ |
| 2.0 | 0.135,346,4 | $-111$ |
| 2.5 | 0.082,093,5 | $-85$ |
| 3.0 | 0.049,793,3 | $-62$ |

| j \ r | 0 | 1 | 2 | 3 | 4 | 5 | 6 | 7 | 8 | 9 |
|---|---|---|---|---|---|---|---|---|---|---|
| 0 | $1$ | | | | | | | | | |
| 1 | $\frac{1}{2}$ | $\frac{1}{2}$ | | | | | | | | |
| 2 | $\frac{5}{12}$ | $\frac{8}{12}$ | $-\frac{1}{12}$ | | | | | | | |
| 3 | $\frac{9}{24}$ | $\frac{19}{24}$ | $-\frac{5}{24}$ | $\frac{1}{24}$ | | | | | | |
| 4 | $\frac{251}{720}$ | $\frac{646}{720}$ | $-\frac{264}{720}$ | $\frac{106}{720}$ | $-\frac{19}{720}$ | | | | | |
| 5 | $\frac{475}{1,440}$ | $\frac{1427}{1,440}$ | $-\frac{798}{1,440}$ | $\frac{482}{1,440}$ | $-\frac{173}{1,440}$ | $\frac{27}{1,440}$ | | | | |
| 6 | $\frac{19,087}{60,480}$ | $\frac{65,112}{60,480}$ | $-\frac{46,461}{60,480}$ | $\frac{37,504}{60,480}$ | $-\frac{20,211}{60,480}$ | $\frac{6,312}{60,480}$ | $-\frac{863}{60,480}$ | | | |
| 7 | $\frac{36,799}{120,960}$ | $\frac{139,849}{120,960}$ | $-\frac{121,797}{120,960}$ | $\frac{123,133}{120,960}$ | $-\frac{88,547}{120,960}$ | $\frac{41,499}{120,960}$ | $-\frac{1,1351}{120,960}$ | $\frac{1,375}{120,960}$ | | |
| 8 | $\frac{1,070,017}{3,628,800}$ | $\frac{4,467,094}{3,628,800}$ | $-\frac{4,604,594}{3,628,800}$ | $\frac{5,593,358}{3,628,800}$ | $-\frac{5,033,120}{3,628,800}$ | $\frac{3,146,338}{3,628,800}$ | $-\frac{1,291,214}{3,628,800}$ | $\frac{312,874}{3,628,800}$ | $-\frac{339,533}{3,628,800}$ | |
| 9 | $\frac{2,082,753}{7,257,600}$ | $\frac{2,449,717}{7,257,600}$ | $-\frac{11,271,304}{7,257,600}$ | $\frac{16,002,320}{7,257,600}$ | $-\frac{17,283,646}{7,257,600}$ | $\frac{13,510,082}{7,257,600}$ | $-\frac{7,394,032}{7,257,600}$ | $\frac{2,687,864}{7,257,600}$ | $-\frac{583,435}{7,257,600}$ | $\frac{57,281}{7,257,600}$ |

### 14.1  Other formulas.

Here are some other formulas which can be used ($l \neq 0$):

$$x_{i+1} - x_{i-1} = \frac{h}{3}(X_{i+1} + 4X_i + X_{i-1})$$

(formula with central differences),

$$x_{i+1} - x_{i-1} = \frac{h}{90}(29X_{i+1} + 124X_i + 24X_{i-1} + 4X_{i-2} - X_{i-3}),$$

$$x_{i+1} - x_{i-1} = \frac{h}{90}(28X_{i+1} + 129X_i + 14X_{i-1} + 14X_{i-2} - 6X_{i-3} + X_{i-4}),$$

$$x_{i+1} - x_{i-2} = \frac{3h}{8}(X_{i+1} + 3X_i + 3X_{i-1} + X_{i-2}),$$

$$x_{i+1} - x_{i-2} = \frac{h}{80}(27X_{i+1} + 102X_i + 72X_{i-1} + 42X_{i-2} - 3X_{i-3}),$$

$$x_{i+1} - x_{i-2} = \frac{3h}{160}(17X_{i+1} + 73X_i + 38X_{i-1} + 38X_{i-2} - 7X_{i-3} + X_{i-4}),$$

$$x_{i+1} - x_{i-3} = \frac{4h}{90}(7X_{i+1} + 32X_i + 12X_{i-1} + 32X_{i-2} + 7X_{i-3}),$$

$$x_{i+1} - x_{i-4} = \frac{5h}{288}(19X_{i+1} + 75X_i + 50X_{i-1} + 50X_{i-2} + 75X_{i-3} + 19X_{i-4}).$$

### 14.2  Example of the formula with central differences.

$$y' = -y, \qquad y(0) = 1, \qquad h = 0.1.$$

| $t$ | $y_i$ | $y$ exact |
|---|---|---|
| 0 | 1 | |
| 0.1 | 0.904,837,418 | |
| 0.2 | 0.818,730,655 | 0.818,730,753 |
| 0.3 | 0.740,818,145 | 0.740,818,220 |
| 0.4 | 0.670,319,885 | 0.670,320,046 |
| 0.5 | 0.606,530,537 | 0.606,530,659 |
| 1.0 | 0.367,879,210 | 0.367,879,441 |
| 1.5 | 0.223,130,022 | 0.223,130,160 |
| 2.0 | 0.135,335,086 | 0.135,335,283 |
| 2.5 | 0.082,084,950 | 0.082,084,998 |
| 3.0 | 0.049,786,914 | 0.049,787,068 |

### 15.  Use of the differences.

We write

$$x_{i+1} = x_{i-l} + h \sum_{j=0}^{r} l_j^* \nabla^j X_{i+1}.$$

The first $l_j^*$ are given by the table below (the denominators are the same for an entire column).

| $l$ \\ $j$ | 0 | 1 | 2 | 3 | 4 |
|---|---|---|---|---|---|
| 0 | 1 | $\dfrac{-1}{2}$ | $\dfrac{-1}{12}$ | $\dfrac{-1}{24}$ | $\dfrac{-19}{720}$ |
| 1 | 2 | $-4$ | 4 | 0 | $-8$ |
| 2 | 3 | $-9$ | 27 | $-9$ | $-27$ |
| 3 | 4 | $-16$ | 80 | $-64$ | 224 |
| 4 | 5 | $-25$ | 175 | $-225$ | 2,125 |
| 5 | 6 | $-36$ | 324 | $-576$ | 8,856 |
| 6 | 7 | $-49$ | 539 | $-1,255$ | 26,117 |
| 7 | 8 | $-64$ | 832 | $-2,304$ | 62,848 |

| $l$ \\ $j$ | 5 | 6 | 7 | 8 | 9 |
|---|---|---|---|---|---|
| 0 | $\dfrac{-27}{1,440}$ | $\dfrac{-863}{60,480}$ | $\dfrac{-1,375}{120,960}$ | $\dfrac{-33,953}{3,628,800}$ | $\dfrac{-57,281}{7,257,600}$ |
| 1 | $-16$ | $-592$ | $-1,024$ | $-26,656$ | $-46,656$ |
| 2 | $-27$ | $-783$ | $-1,215$ | $-29,889$ | $-51,138$ |
| 3 | 0 | $-512$ | $-1,024$ | $-27,392$ | $-48,128$ |
| 4 | $-475$ | $-1,375$ | $-1,375$ | $-30,625$ | $-51,138$ |
| 5 | $-4,752$ | 17,712 | 0 | $-23,328$ | $-46,656$ |
| 6 | $-22,491$ | 216,433 | $-36,799$ | $-57,281$ | $-57,281$ |
| 7 | $-74,752$ | 1,160,192 | $-471,040$ | 1,012,736 | 0 |

## 16. Quadrature error.

Quadrature error for implicit formulas is defined and computed in the same way as for the explicit formulas (paragraph 12).

### 17.1 Comparison from the point of view of precision, equal cost of the various explicit methods being assumed.

Here is a table giving for the various orders the relation of the quadrature error of an explicit formula to the corresponding Adams formula:

| | $r = 1$ | $r = 2$ | $r = 3$ | $r = 4$ |
|---|---|---|---|---|
| $l = 1$ | 0 | 4/5 | 8/9 | 232/251 |
| $l = 2$ | 3 | 9/5 | 1 | 243/251 |
| $l = 3$ | 8 | 32/5 | 0 | 224/251 |
| $l = 4$ | 15 | 85/5 | 55/9 | 475/251 |

We note:

—that the usual convention $r \geqslant l$ is entirely justified.

—that the use of explicit formulas corresponding to $l \neq 0$ is of little advantage. Since, furthermore, the formulas with $l \neq 0$ are only weakly stable (Chapter 7, paragraph 6.1), which entails inconveniences in certain cases, it is preferable to abstain from using them. A sole exception can be made in favor of the formula

$$x_{i+1} = x_{i-1} + 2hX_i$$

because of its extreme simplicity.

### 17.2 Comparison from the viewpoint of precision, equal cost between the implicit and explicit methods being assumed.

In order to make this comparison, we will consider that we put the implicit formulas to work by means of a predictor and of a corrector (21). This means that the computation of one step costs two horners (instead of one horner for the explicit formulas). Hence, for the explicit formulas, we take one step $h$, doubling the error in order to obtain the error over an interval of $2h$, for the implicit formulas one step of length $2h$. Here are the results of this comparison:

|  | Explicit Adams' method | Implicit methods | | |
|---|---|---|---|---|
|  |  | $l = 0$ (Implicit Adams' method) | $l = 1$ | $l = 2$ |
| Two values | $10\ h^3/12$ | Trapezoidal $8\ h^3/12$ |  |  |
| Three values | $18\ h^4/24$ | $16\ h^4/24$ | As below |  |
| Four values | $502\ h^5/720$ | $19 \times 32\ h^5/720$ | Central differences $8 \times 32\ h^5/720$ | $27 \times 32\ h^5/720$ |
| Five values | $950\ h^6/1440$ | $27 \times 64\ h^6/1440$ | $16 \times 64\ h^6/1440$ | $27 \times 64\ h^6/1440$ |

We see that the only formulas which are better at equal cost than the corresponding explicit Adams formulas are as follows:
*Two values*—the trapezoidal formula

$$x_{i+1} = x_i + \frac{h}{2}(X_i + X_{i+1}).$$

*Three values*—the formula

$$x_{i+1} = x_i + \frac{h}{12}(5X_{i+1} + 8X_i - X_{i-1}).$$

*Four values*—the central difference formula

$$x_{i+1} = x_{i-1} + \frac{h}{3}(X_{i+1} + 4X_i + X_{i-1}).$$

Outside of these few formulas (the last one is only weakly stable) it is preferable to use an explicit Adams formula.

## IV    UTILIZATION OF THE IMPLICIT FORMULAS

### 18.1 Iteration in the case of a single equation.

In the examples treated above, the question of the implicit form of the approximate relation obtained was not posed, because it was a question of linear equations, which were treated by formulas not using differences. In the general case, we can have recourse to one iteration.

Let us consider a single equation and the relation

$$y_{i+1} = y_{i-l} + h(A_0 Y_{i+1} + A_1 Y_i + \cdots + A_r Y_{i-r+1}).$$

We start from a value $y_{i+1}^{[0]}$ and, by iteration, we determine

$$y_{i+1}^{[m]} = y_{i-l} + h(A_0 Y_{i+1}^{[m-1]} + A_1 Y_i + \cdots + A_r Y_{i-r+1}).$$

This iteration converges, provided that

$$|h A_0 Y_y'|_{i+1} < 1.$$

The convergence is rapid when

$$|h A_0 Y_y'|_{i+1}$$

is of order 0.1.

Since it is necessary to recalculate $Y$ at each step, these methods are, in general, tedious and costly. We can shorten them by resorting to the usual procedures of accelerating convergence. By subtracting, let us write, for example,

$$y_{i+1}^{[m+2]} - y_{i+1}^{[m+1]} = h A_0 Y_y'(y_{i+1}^{[m+1]} - y_{i+1}^{[m]}).$$

The convergence of $y_{i+1}^{[m]}$ tends towards the limit and is that of a geometric progression by virtue of $h A_0 Y_y'$, if one can suppose that, in a neighborhood of the point under consideration, $Y_y'$ is constant. Writing the sum of this geometric progression, we find

$$y_{i+1} = \frac{y_{i+1}^{[m+1]} - h A_0 Y_y' y_{i+1}^{[m]}}{1 - h A_0 Y_y'}.$$

### 18.2 Example of an iteration.

Let

$$y' = -2ty^2, \qquad y(0) = 1, \qquad h = 0.1.$$

By the trapezoidal method, we have

$$y_{i+1} = y_i + \frac{h}{2}(Y_{i+1} + Y_i).$$

We find

| $t$ | $y$ | $Y$ | $y$ exact |
|-----|-----|-----|-----------|
| 0 | 1 | 0 | 1 |
| 0.1 | 1 | −0.2 | 0.990,099 |
|  | 0.99 | −0.196,020 |  |
|  | 0.990,199 | −0.196,098 |  |
|  | 0.990,195 | −0.196,098 |  |
| 0.2 | 0.970,585 | −0.376,814 | 0.961,538 |
|  | 0.961,549 | −0.369,830 |  |
|  | 0.961,899 | −0.370,100 |  |
|  | 0.961,885 | −0.370,090 |  |
| 0.3 | 0.924,876 | −0.513,238 | 0.917,431 |
|  | 0.917,718 | −0.505,324 |  |
|  | 0.918,114 | −0.505,760 |  |
|  | 0.918,092 | −0.505,736 |  |
|  | 0.918,093 | −0.505,736 |  |
| 0.4 | 0.867,519 | −0.602,072 | 0.862,069 |
|  | 0.862,702 | −0.595,404 |  |
|  | 0.863,036 | −0.595,864 |  |
|  | 0.863,013 | −0.595,832 |  |
|  | 0.863,014 | −0.595,834 |  |
| 0.5 | 0.803,430 | −0.645,500 | 0.800,000 |
|  | 0.800,947 | −0.641,516 |  |
|  | 0.801,146 | −0.641,834 |  |
|  | 0.801,130 | −0.641,808 |  |
|  | 0.801,132 | −0.641,812 |  |

In order to start, we have taken in each case the iteration

$$y_{i+1}^{[0]} = y_i + h Y_i.$$

### 18.3 Termination of the iteration.

We will suppose that we have fixed:
—the formula to be utilized.
—the step.
—the number of digits to be retained in the operations.
The termination of the iteration creates an additional error which will be added to the quadrature error and to the round-off error at one step. We can take into account this error by estimating its order of magnitude. It is useless and dangerous to continue the iteration until it has been established that two consecutive results are identical. It can very well be that this phenomenon will never present itself. Here is an example:

$$x^{[m+1]} = (1 - x^{[m]^2})/2,$$

$$x^{[1]} = 0.41, \qquad \text{with two figures,}$$

$$x^{[2]} = 0.42, \qquad \text{with two figures,}$$

$$x^{[3]} = 0.41, \qquad \text{with two figures.}$$

We can continue indefinitely going back and forth between the above-mentioned two values. In order to avoid this, it is necessary to stop the iteration at the moment where the difference between two consecutive iterates is less than or equal to twice the round-off error at one cycle of the iteration (in the example cited above, $2 \times 5.10^{-3}$). Sometimes it is possible to have a reasonable bound of the round-off error over one cycle of the iteration. Moreover, in general the quadrature error will be much larger than the round-off error. Thus it will suffice to stop the iteration when the difference between two successive iterates has become small compared to the quadrature error.

Let us return to the example of 18.2. We have admitted that the round-off error over one iteration cycle is smaller than $0.5 \cdot 10^{-6}$, and we have stopped the iteration when

$$\left| \frac{h}{2} (Y^{[r]}_{i+1} - Y^{[r-1]}_{i+1}) \right| < 10^{-6},$$

i.e., when

$$Y^{[r]}_{i+1} - Y^{[r-1]}_{i+1} < 2.10^{-5}.$$

Moreover, we could have suppressed the iteration cycles, the quadrature error being greater than $10^{-6}$.

### 18.4  Case of a system.

Once more, we have the same relations, but now with columns:

$$X_{i+1} = hA_0 X_{i+1} + \text{columns depending on}$$

$$X_{i-k}, \qquad X_{i-k}, \qquad k \geqslant 0.$$

We start from the values $x^{[0]}_{i+1}$:

$$x^{[r]}_{i+1} = hA_0 X^{[r-1]}_{i+1} + \text{columns depending on}$$

$$X_{i-k}, \qquad X_{i-k}, \qquad k \geqslant 0.$$

Such an iteration converges provided that the Jacobian matrix

$$\| X'_x \|$$

has eigenvalues whose magnitude is smaller than $|1/(hA_0)|$. This will certainly occur if $h$ is sufficiently small.

### 19.  Choice of a starting value.

The number of iterations necessary to obtain a given precision depends on the starting value of the iteration. One will be interested in taking a starting value as close as possible to the limiting value of the iteration. This is what we are going to take up in the following paragraphs.

### 20.1 Choice of a proper starting value in the case of a difference formula.

The utilization of the method requires the formation of a table of differences. As in the case of the explicit methods, this table permits us
— to manipulate small numbers.
— to compute the quadrature error.
— to discover the computation error.
Furthermore, it permits us to anticipate a proper starting value in extrapolating the differences. We are going to show this in an example.

### 20.2 Example.

Let

$$y' = -2ty^2, \qquad y(0) = 1, \qquad h = 0.1.$$

We take the formula

$$y_{i+1} = y_i + h(Y_{i+1} - 1/2\nabla Y_{i+1} - 1/12\nabla^2 Y_{i+1}).$$

| $t$ | $y$ | $Y$ | $\nabla Y$ | $\nabla^2 Y$ | $y$ exact |
|---|---|---|---|---|---|
| 0 | 1 | 0 | | | |
| 0.1 | 0.990,099 | −0.196,059 | −0.196,059 | | |
| 0.2 | 0.961,538 | −0.369,822 | −0.173,763 | +0.022,296 | |
| 0.3 | | −0.521,289 | −0.151,467 | 0.022,296 | 0.917,431 |
| | 0.916,797 | −0.504,310 | −0.134,488 | 0.039,275 | |
| | 0.917,504 | −0.505,088 | −0.135,266 | 0.038,497 | |
| | 0.917,472 | −0.505,053 | −0.135,231 | 0.038,532 | |
| 0.3 | 0.917,473 | −0.505,054 | −0.135,232 | 0.038,531 | |
| 0.4 | | −0.601,755 | −0.096,701 | 0.038,531 | 0.862,069,0 |
| | 0.861,811 | −0.594,175 | −0.089,121 | 0.046,111 | |
| | 0.862,127 | −0.594,611 | −0.089,557 | 0.045,675 | |
| | 0.862,109 | −0.594,586 | −0.089,532 | 0.045,700 | |
| 0.4 | 0.862,110 | −0.594,587 | −0.089,533 | 0.045,699 | |
| 0.5 | | −0.638,421 | −0.043,834 | 0.045,699 | 0.800,000 |
| | 0.800,079 | −0.640,126 | −0.045,539 | 0.043,994 | |
| | 0.800,008 | −0.640,012 | −0.045,425 | 0.044,108 | |
| 0.5 | 0.800,012 | −0.640,019 | −0.045,432 | 0.044,101 | |
| 0.6 | | −0.641,350 | −0.001,331 | 0.044,101 | 0.735,294 |
| | 0.735,576 | −0.649,286 | −0.009,267 | 0.036,165 | |
| | 0.735,245 | −0.648,703 | −0.008,684 | 0.036,748 | |
| | 0.735,270 | −0.648,746 | −0.008,727 | 0.036,705 | |
| 0.6 | 0.735,268 | −0.648,743 | −0.008,724 | 0.036,708 | |
| 0.7 | | −0.620,750 | 0.027,984 | 0.036,708 | 0.671,141 |
| | 0.671,487 | −0.631,253 | 0.017,490 | 0.026,214 | |
| | 0.671,050 | −0.630,431 | 0.018,312 | 0.027,036 | |
| | 0.671,084 | −0.630,495 | 0.018,248 | 0.026,972 | |
| 0.7 | 0.671,081 | −0.630,490 | 0.018,253 | 0.026,977 | |

| $t$ | $y$ | $Y$ | $\nabla Y$ | $\nabla^2 Y$ | $\nabla^3 Y$ | $\nabla^4 Y$ |
|-----|-----|-----|------------|--------------|--------------|--------------|
| 0.4 | 0.862,110 | −0.594,587 | −0.089,533 | 0.045,699 | 0.007,168 | −0.009,067 |
| 0.5 | | −0.640,320 | −0.045,733 | 0.043,800 | −0.001,899 | −0.009,067 |
| | 0.800,000 | −0.64 | −0.045,413 | 0.044,120 | | |
| 0.5 | 0.800,013 | −0.640,021 | −0.045,434 | 0.044,099 | −0.001,600 | −0.008,768 |
| 0.6 | | −0.651,724 | −0.011,703 | 0.033,731 | −0.010,368 | −0.008,768 |
| | 0.735,145 | −0.648,525 | −0.008,504 | 0.036,930 | | |
| | 0.735,278 | −0.648,760 | −0.008,749 | 0.036,685 | | |
| 0.6 | 0.735,269 | −0.648,745 | −0.008,724 | 0.036,710 | −0.007,389 | −0.005,789 |
| 0.7 | | −0.633,937 | −0.014,808 | 0.023,532 | −0.013,178 | −0.005,789 |
| | 0.670,939 | −0.630,223 | 0.018,522 | 0.027,246 | | |
| | 0.671,094 | −0.630,514 | 0.018,231 | 0.026,955 | | |
| 0.7 | 0.671,081 | −0.630,490 | 0.018,255 | 0.026,979 | | |

The values for 0.1 and 0.2 have been taken to be exact. We form the corresponding differences $\nabla Y$ and $\nabla^2 Y$. For each step, we start again with $\nabla^2 Y$, which was just found, for example, 0.022296 for $t = 0.3$. We deduce thus the provisional values

$$\nabla Y_{0.3} = -0.151,467, \qquad Y_{0.3} = -0.521,289$$

which permit the calculation of

$$y_{0.3}^{[0]} = y_{0.2} + h(Y_{0.3} - 1/2\nabla Y_{0.3} - 1/12\nabla^2 Y_{0.3}) = 0.916,797.$$

We find, brought forward into the differential equation,

$$Y_{0.3}^{[0]} = -0.504,310, \quad \text{hence} \quad \nabla Y_{0.3}^{[0]} \quad \text{and} \quad \nabla^2 Y_{0.3}^{[0]}.$$

A new iteration cycle gives $y_{0.3}^{[1]} = 0.917,504$, and so forth. The iteration has been halted whenever two consecutive iterates differ by at least $1.5 \times 10^{-5}$.

We can ask if it would be possible to accelerate the convergence by trying to evaluate the future value of $\nabla^2 Y_{i+1}$. The simplest way seems to be to extend the difference table (without, however, using these in the approximate integration formula). Let us return in this fashion to the preceding calculation with two additional differences (see the table on page 154).

We have taken for $\nabla^4 Y$ the value found at the preceding step. Thus we suppress one iteration at each step.

### 21.1 Milne's method.[1]

The procedure which we are now going to indicate aims to reduce the iteration to only one cycle in the case where one uses formulas without differences. It consists of starting with a sufficiently precise initial value of the iteration. This value is given by a formula, called the predictor, which furnishes a value $x_{i+1}^*$. The implicit formula, where one introduces $X_{i+1}^*$, is called the corrector. The two formulas are, in general, of the same order.

[1]Booth [1], Milne [1, 3], Wall, Southard, and Yowell.

### 21.2 Examples of pairs of formulas.

One could use, for example, the pair:

$$x^*_{i+1} = x_i + \frac{h}{12}(23X_i - 16X_{i-1} + 5X_{i-2}),$$

$$x_{i+1} = x_i + \frac{h}{12}(5X^*_{i+1} + 8X - X_{i-1}),$$

or, also, the following pair proposed by Milne himself:

$$x^*_{i+1} = x_{i-3} + \frac{h}{3}(8X_i - 4X_{i-1} + 8X_{i-2}),$$

$$x_{i+1} = x_{i-1} + \frac{h}{3}(X^*_{i+1} + 4X_i + X_{i-1}).$$

### 21.3 Examples.

1. Let the equation be

$$y' = -\frac{5y}{5 - t}, \qquad y(-1.2) = 18.322{,}65.$$

We are going to integrate this equation by means of the following pair:

$$\begin{cases} y^*_{i+1} = y_i + \frac{h}{24}(55Y_i - 59Y_{i-1} + 37Y_{i-2} - 9Y_{i-3}), \\ y_{i+1} = y_i + \frac{h}{24}(9Y^*_{i+1} + 19Y_i - 5Y_{i-1} + Y_{i-2}), \end{cases}$$

$$h = 0.2.$$

The first four values are determined by another procedure:

| $t$ | $y^*_i$ | $y_i$ |
|---|---|---|
| −1.2 | | 18.322,65 |
| −1 | 15.552,03 | 15.551,99 |
| −0.8 | 13.127,16 | 13.127,13 |
| −0.6 | 11.014,66 | 11.014,63 |
| | | |
| −0.4 | 9.183,32 | 9.183,29 |
| −0.2 | 7.604,10 | 7.604,07 |

2.       $y' = -y + \cos t, \qquad y(0) = 1/2, \qquad h = 0.1,$

with

$$y^*_{i+1} = y_i + \frac{h}{12}(23Y_i - 16Y_{i-1} + 5Y_{i-2}),$$

$$y_{i+1} = y_i + \frac{h}{12}(5Y^*_{i+1} + 8Y_i - Y_{i-1})$$

| $t$ | $y^*_i$ | $y_i$ | $y(t)$ |
|---|---|---|---|
| 0 | 0.5 | 0.5 | 0.5 |
| 0.1 | 0.547,40 | 0.547,42 | 0.547,42 |
| 0.2 | 0.589,35 | 0.589,37 | 0.589,37 |
| 0.3 | 0.625,41 | 0.625,44 | 0.625,43 |
| 0.4 | 0.655,22 | 0.655,25 | 0.655,24 |
| 0.5 | 0.678,49 | 0.678,51 | 0.678,50 |
| 1.0 | 0.690,88 | 0.690,91 | 0.690,89 |
| 1.5 | 0.534,12 | 0.534,14 | 0.534,12 |
| 2.0 | 0.246,59 | 0.246,60 | 0.246,58 |
| 2.5 | −0.101,32 | −0.101,32 | −0.101,34 |
| 3.0 | −0.424,42 | −0.424,43 | −0.424,44 |
| 3.5 | −0.643,60 | −0.643,62 | −0.643,62 |
| 4.0 | −0.705,21 | −0.705,24 | −0.705,22 |
| 4.5 | −0.594,16 | −0.594,19 | −0.594,16 |
| 5.0 | −0.337,64 | −0.337,66 | −0.337,63 |
| 5.5 | +0.001,55 | 0.001,54 | +0.001,56 |
| 6.0 | 0.340,36 | 0.340,37 | 0.340,38 |
| 6.5 | 0.598,84 | 0.595,86 | 0.595,85 |
| 7.0 | 0.705,43 | 0.705,46 | 0.705,44 |
| 7.5 | 0.642,32 | 0.642,35 | 0.642,32 |
| 8.0 | 0.421,94 | 0.421,96 | 0.421,93 |
| 8.5 | 0.098,25 | 0.098,26 | 0.098,24 |
| 9.0 | −0.249,49 | −0.249,49 | −0.249,51 |
| 9.5 | −0.536,14 | −0.536,16 | −0.536,16 |
| 10.0 | −0.691,53 | −0.691,56 | −0.691,55 |

## 22. Investigation of the quadrature errors and of the noniteration error if the predictor and corrector formulas are of the same order.

Let us suppose that the predictor formula has a quadrature error $Ph^{q+1}$, the corrector formula a quadrature error $Qh^{q+1}$, and the iteration a convergence factor $Ch$. Let $y_i(t_{i+1})$ be the value which would be furnished by the formulas if the quadrature error did not exist, and $\Omega$ the limit which would be attained if the iteration were to be continued indefinitely. We have

$$y^*_{i+1} = y_i(t_{i+1}) + Ph^{q+1},$$
$$\Omega = y_i(t_{i+1}) + Qh^{q+1},$$

whence

$$y^*_{i+1} - \Omega = (P - Q)h^{q+1},$$
$$y_{i+1} - \Omega = C(P - Q)h^{q+2}.$$

We will neglect this term in favor of the terms $h^{q+1}$, and consequently

$$y_{i+1} - y^*_{i+1} \approx (Q - P)h^{q+1}.$$

The difference between the predicted value and the corrected value gives information on the quadrature error of the corrector formula:

$$Qh^{q+1} \approx \frac{Q}{P-Q}(P-Q)h^{q+1} \approx \frac{Q}{P-Q}(y_{i+1}^* - y_{i+1}).$$

One notes that, if the iteration approaches $\Omega$, it does not necessarily approach $y_i(t_{i+1})$. An intermediate iterate can very well be much better than the final iterated value. This is particularly the case for the example of 18.2.

### 23. Investigation of the case where the two formulas are not of the same order.

We will study an example. We have
*Predictor*
$$y_{i+1}^* = y_i + h\,Y_i.$$

*Corrector*
$$y_{i+1} = y_i + \frac{h}{2}(Y_i + Y_{i+1}^*)$$

(actually, this is the Euler-Cauchy method). For the predictor formula, the quadrature error is
$$-\frac{h^2}{2}y'',$$

and for the corrector formula:
$$+\frac{h^3}{12}y'''.$$

This results in
$$y_{i+1}^* - \Omega \approx -\frac{h^3}{2}y'',$$

$$y_{i+1} - \Omega \approx -\frac{h^3}{4}Y_y'y''.$$

(The iteration converges like a geometric progression of ratio $hY_y'/2$.)

We see

—that the noniteration error is no longer negligible in favor of the quadrature error, as it was in the preceding paragraph.

—that one loses the possibility of evaluating the quadrature error easily.

## V SYSTEMS CONTAINING HIGHER ORDER DERIVATIVES[1]

We suppose these systems to be written in the equilibrated resolved form.

### 24.1 Explicit Adams formulas for higher orders.

Let the system, which we write in vector form, be
$$x^{(p)} = X(t, x, x', \ldots, x^{(p-1)})$$

[1]Collatz [3], Collatz-Zurmühl [1].

with

$$x(t_0) = x_0, \qquad x'(t_0) = x'_0, \; \ldots, \; x^{(p-1)}(t_0) = x_0^{(p-1)}.$$

We start from the exact formula:

$$x^{(p-k)}(t_{i+1}) = \sum_{j=0}^{k-1} \frac{h^j}{j!} x^{(p-k+j)}(t_i) + \underbrace{\int_{t_i}^{t_{i+1}} \ldots \int_{t_i}^{t} X(t)\,dt \; \ldots \; dt}_{k \text{ times}},$$

where $k = 1, 2, \ldots, p$.

Taking up what was said in paragraph 2, we arrive at the formula

$$x_{i+1}^{(p-k)} = \sum_{j=0}^{k-1} \frac{h^j x^{(p-k+j)}}{j!} + h^k \sum_{j=0}^{r} \alpha_{rj}^{(k)} X_{i-j},$$

with

$$\alpha_{rj}^{(k)} = \frac{(-1)^j C_r^j}{r!} \underbrace{\int_0^1 \ldots \int_0^u}_{k \text{ times}} \frac{u(u+1) \ldots (u+r)}{u+j}\,du \; \ldots \; du.$$

We can easily verify the relation

$$\sum_{j=0}^{r} \alpha_{r,j}^{(k)} = \frac{1}{k!}.$$

*Remark.* The developments are stopped at different infinitesimal orders, but the rule of the conservation of orders is satisfied.

**24.2 Table of $\alpha_{r,j}^{(k)}$.**

$$k = 2.$$

| $r$ \ $j$ | 0 | 1 | 2 | 3 | 4 |
|---|---|---|---|---|---|
| 1 | 4/6 | −1/6 | | | |
| 2 | 19/24 | −10/24 | 3/24 | | |
| 3 | 323/360 | −264/360 | 159/360 | −38/360 | |
| 4 | 1427/1440 | −1596/1440 | 1446/1440 | −692/1440 | 135/1440 |

$$k = 3.$$

| $r$ \ $j$ | 0 | 1 | 2 | 3 | 4 |
|---|---|---|---|---|---|
| 1 | 5/24 | −1/24 | | | |
| 2 | 57/240 | −24/240 | 7/240 | | |
| 3 | 188/720 | −123/720 | 72/720 | −17/720 | |
| 4 | 2837/10,080 | −2542/10,080 | 2238/10,080 | −1058/10,080 | 205/10,080 |

### 24.3 Example.

$$y'' + 1.5y' + 0.5y = 0, \qquad y(0) = 1, \qquad y'(0) = -1, \qquad h = 0.1.$$

We will use the formulas:

$$y'_{i+1} = y'_i + \frac{h}{12}(23\,Y_i - 16\,Y_{i-1} + 5\,Y_{i-2}),$$

$$y_{i+1} = y_i + hy'_i + \frac{h^2}{24}(19\,Y_i - 10\,Y_{i-1} + 3\,Y_{i-2}).$$

The first two values have been taken exact.

| $t$ | $y_i$ | $y'_i$ | $y$ exact |
|---|---|---|---|
| 0 | 1 | −1 | |
| 0.1 | 0.904,837 | −0.904,837 | |
| 0.2 | 0.818,731 | −0.818,731 | |
| 0.3 | 0.740,819 | −0.740,786 | 0.740,818 |
| 0.4 | 0.670,325 | −0.670,267 | 0.670,320 |
| 0.5 | 0.606,541 | −0.606,460 | 0.606,531 |
| 0.6 | 0.548,829 | −0.548,730 | 0.548,812 |
| 0.7 | 0.496,611 | −0.496,495 | 0.496,585 |
| 0.8 | 0.449,363 | −0.449,235 | 0.449,329 |
| 0.9 | 0.406,613 | −0.406,474 | 0.406,570 |
| 1.0 | 0.367,932 | −0.367,784 | 0.367,879 |

### 25.1 Utilization of differences (Falkner's formulas).

The representation of $X$ by Newton's interpolation formula gives

$$X_{i+1}^{(p-k)} = \sum_{j=0}^{k-1} \frac{h^j x^{(p-k+j)}}{j!} + h^k \sum_{j=0}^{r} a_j^{(k)} \nabla^j X_{i+1},$$

with

$$a_j^{(k)} = \frac{1}{j!} \underbrace{\int_0^1 \dots \int_0^u}_{k \text{ times}} u(u+1) \dots (u+j-1)\, du \dots du, \qquad j = 1, 2, \dots,$$

$$a_0^{(k)} = 1/k!$$

### 25.2 Table of values of the $a_j^{(k)}$.

| $k$ \ $j$ | 0 | 1 | 2 | 3 | 4 | 5 |
|---|---|---|---|---|---|---|
| 2 | 1/2 | 1/6 | 1/8 | 19/180 | 45/480 | 863/10,080 |
| 3 | 1/6 | 1/24 | 7/240 | 17/720 | 41/2016 | 731/40,320 |
| 4 | 1/24 | 1/120 | 1/180 | 11/2520 | 89/24,192 | 5849/1,814,400 |

### 25.3 Example.

Let us return to the example of paragraph 24.3 with the formulas:

$$y'_{i+1} = y'_i + h(Y_i + 1/2 \nabla Y_1 + 5/12 \nabla^2 Y_i),$$
$$y_{i+1} = y_i + hy'_i + h^2 (1/2 Y_i + 1/6 \nabla Y_i + 1/8 \nabla^2 Y_i).$$

| $t$ | $y$ | $y'$ | $Y$ | $\nabla Y$ | $\nabla^2 Y$ |
|---|---|---|---|---|---|
| 0 | 1 | −1 | 1 | | |
| 0.1 | 0.904,837 | −0.904,837 | 0.904,837 | −95,163 | |
| 0.2 | 0.818,731 | −0.818,731 | 0.818,731 | −86,106 | 9057 |
| 0.3 | 0.740,819 | −0.740,786 | 0.740,769 | −77,962 | 8144 |
| 0.4 | 0.670,324 | −0.670,268 | 0.670,240 | −70,529 | 7433 |
| 0.5 | 0.606,540 | −0.606,461 | 0.606,421 | −63,819 | 6710 |
| 0.6 | 0.548,828 | −0.548,730 | 0.548,681 | −57,740 | 6079 |
| 0.7 | 0.496,610 | −0.496,496 | 0.496,439 | −52,242 | 5498 |
| 0.8 | 0.449,362 | −0.449,235 | 0.449,171 | −47,268 | 4974 |
| 0.9 | 0.406,612 | −0.406,474 | 0.406,405 | −42,766 | 4502 |
| 1.0 | 0.367,931 | −0.367,784 | | | |

### 26.1 Implicit Adams formulas for the higher orders.

Returning to what was done in paragraph 13.1, we will easily find

$$x_{i+1}^{(p-k)} = \sum_{j=0}^{k-1} \frac{h^j x_i^{(p-k+j)}}{j!} + h^k \sum_{j=0}^{r} \alpha_{r,j}^{*(k)} X_{i+1-j},$$

with

$$\alpha_{r,j}^{*(k)} = (-1)^j \frac{C_r^j}{r!} \underbrace{\int_{-1}^{0} \ldots \int_{-1}^{u}}_{k \text{ times}} \frac{u(u+1) \ldots (u+r)}{u+j} du \ldots du$$

and the relation

$$\sum_{j=0}^{r} \alpha_{r,j}^{*(k)} = \frac{1}{k!}.$$

### 26.2 Table of $\alpha_{r,j}^{*(k)}$.

$$k = 2.$$

| r \ j | 0 | 1 | 2 | 3 | 4 |
|---|---|---|---|---|---|
| 1 | 1/6 | 2/6 | | | |
| 2 | 3/24 | 10/24 | −1/24 | | |
| 3 | 38/360 | 171/360 | −36/360 | 7/360 | |
| 4 | 135/1440 | 752/1440 | −246/1440 | 96/1440 | −17/1440 |

$$k = 3.$$

| r \ j | 0 | 1 | 2 | 3 | 4 |
|---|---|---|---|---|---|
| 1 | 1/24 | 3/24 | | | |
| 2 | 7/240 | 36/240 | −3/240 | | |
| 3 | 17/720 | 120/720 | −21/720 | 4/720 | |
| 4 | 205/10,080 | 1812/10,080 | −492/10,080 | 188/10,080 | −33/10,080 |

### 27.1  Utilization of the differences (Falkner's formula).

In the same manner we write

$$x_{i+1}^{(p-k)} = \sum_{j=0}^{k-1} \frac{h^j x_i^{(p-k+j)}}{j!} + h^k \sum_{j=0}^{r} a_j^{*(k)} \nabla^j X_{i+1},$$

with

$$a_j^{*(k)} = \frac{1}{j!} \underbrace{\int_{-1}^{0} \ldots \int_{-1}^{u}}_{k \text{ times}} u(u+1) \ldots (u+j-1) \mathrm{d}u \ldots \mathrm{d}u.$$

### 27.2  Table of $a_j^{*(k)}$.

| k \ j | 0 | 1 | 2 | 3 | 4 |
|---|---|---|---|---|---|
| 2 | 1/2 | −1/3 | −1/24 | −7/360 | −17/1440 |
| 3 | 1/6 | −1/8 | −1/80 | −1/180 | −11/3360 |
| 4 | 1/24 | −1/30 | −1/360 | −1/840 | −83/120,960 |

### 28.  Utilization through iteration.

As for the systems in canonical form, where we use an implicit formula, we generally utilize it through iteration. Let us study, for example, the case of the equation

$$y^{(p)} = Y(t, yy', \ldots, y^{(p-1)}).$$

We have to solve for

$$y_{i+1}^{(p-k)}, \qquad k = 1, \ldots, p$$

the system

$$y_{i+1}^{(p-k)} = \sum_{j=0}^{k-1} \frac{h^j y_i^{(p-k+j)}}{j!} + h^k \sum_{j=0}^{r} \alpha_{r,j}^{*(k)} Y_{i+1-j},$$

which we will do by writing the Gauss-Seidel formula:

$$y_{i+1}^{(p-k)\,[s+1]} = \sum_{j=0}^{k-1} \frac{h^j}{j!}\, y_i^{(p-k+j)}$$

$$+ h^k \Big\{ \alpha_{r,0}^{*k}\, Y(t_{i+1};\, y_{i+1}^{[s]};\, \ldots;\, y_{i+1}^{(p-k+1)\,[s]},\, y_{i+1}^{(p-k)\,[s]},\, y_{i+1}^{(p-k+1)\,[s+1]},\, \ldots$$

$$\ldots,\, y_{i+1}^{(p-1)\,[s+1]} + \sum_{j=1}^{r} \alpha_{r,j}^{*\,(k)}\, Y_{i+1-j} \Big\},$$

where $k = 1, 2, \ldots, p-1$, unless we prefer to write

$$y_{i+1}^{(p-k)\,[s+1]} = \sum_{j=0}^{k-1} \frac{h^j}{j!}\, y_i^{(p-k+j)} + h^k \Big\{ \alpha_{r,0}^{*k}\, Y(t_{i+1}, y_{i+1}^{[s]}, \ldots, y_{i+1}^{(p-1)\,[s]})$$

$$+ \sum_{j=1}^{r} \alpha_{r,j}^{*\,(k)}\, Y_{i+1-j} \Big\}.$$

All these formulas certainly converge if $h$ is sufficiently small.

The number of iteration cycles necessary to obtain a given precision will be even fewer if one has taken a starting value closer to the limit of the iteration. In practice, one utilizes either difference extrapolation, or a predictor formula.

### 29.1  Utilization through the difference table.

As in the case of a system in canonical form, we can use these formulas by attempting to predict the values for the differences of the highest order of $Y$.

### 29.2  Example

Let the equation be

$$y'' + 1.5y' + 0.5y = 0, \qquad y(0) = -y'(0) = 1, \qquad h = 0.1$$

and the formulas:

$$y'_{i+1} = y'_i + h(Y_{i+1} - 1/2 \nabla Y_{i+1} - 1/12 \nabla^2 Y_{i+1}),$$

$$y_{i+1} = y_i + hy'_i + h^2(1/2\, Y_{i+1} - 1/3 \nabla Y_{i+1} - 1/24 \nabla^2 Y_{i+1}).$$

| $t$ | $y_i$ | $y'_i$ | $Y_i$ | $\nabla Y_i$ | $\nabla^2 Y_i$ | $y(t) = -y'(t)$ |
|---|---|---|---|---|---|---|
| 0 | 1 | −1 | 1 | | | |
| 0.1 | 0.904,837,4 | −0.904,837,4 | 0.904,837,4 | −9 516 26 | | |
| 0.2 | 0.818,730,7 | −0.818,730,7 | 0.818,730,7 | −8 610 67 | 9 055 9 | |
| | | | 0.741,679,9 | −7 705 08 | 9 055 9 | |
| | 0.740,819,1 | −0.740,785,6 | 0.740,768,8 | −7 796 19 | 8 144 8 | |
| | 0.740,817,5 | −0.740,823,6 | 0.740,826,6 | −7 790 41 | 8 202 6 | |
| | 0.740,818,0 | −0.740,821,2 | 0.740,822,8 | −7 790 79 | 8 198 8 | 0.740,818,2 |
| 0.3 | 0.740,818,0 | −0.740,821,4 | 0.740,823,1 | −7 790 76 | 8 199 1 | |
| | | | 0.670,337,6 | −7 048 55 | 7 422 1 | |
| | 0.670,319,4 | −0.670,325,2 | 0.670,328,1 | −7 049 50 | 7 413 6 | |
| 0.4 | 0.670,319,3 | −0.670,325,6 | 0.670,328,2 | −7 049 49 | 7 413 5 | 0.670,320,0 |

| $t$ | $y_i$ | $y_i'$ | $Y_i$ | $\nabla Y_i$ | $\nabla^2 Y_i$ | $y(t) = -y'(t)$ |
|---|---|---|---|---|---|---|
|  |  |  | 0.606,545,2 | −6 378 30 | 6 711 6 |  |
|  | 0.606,529,3 | −0.606,537,8 | 0.606,542,0 | −6 378 62 | 6 708 4 | 0.606,530,7 |
| 0.5 | 0.606,529,3 | −0.606,538,0 | 0.606,542,3 | −6 378 59 | 6 708 7 |  |
|  |  |  | 0.548,821,7 | −577 206 | 6 065 3 |  |
|  | 0.548,809,5 | −0.548,820,4 | 0.548,825,8 | −577 165 | 6 069 4 |  |
| 0.6 | 0.548,809,5 | −0.548,820,2 | 0.548,825,5 | −577 168 | 6 069 1 | 0.548,811,6 |
|  |  |  | 0.496,596,9 | −522 286 | 5 488 2 |  |
|  | 0.496,582,3 | −0.496,594,8 | 0.496,601,0 | −522 245 | 5 492 3 |  |
| 0.7 | 0.496,582,3 | −0.496,594,7 | 0.496,600,9 | −522 246 | 5 492 2 | 0.496,585,3 |
|  |  |  | 0.449,342,3 | −472 586 | 4 966 0 |  |
|  | 0.449,325,0 | −0.449,338,9 | 0.449,345,9 | −472 550 | 4 969 6 |  |
| 0.8 | 0.449,325,0 | −0.449,338,8 | 0.449,335,7 | −472 552 | 4 969 4 | 0.449,329,0 |

For the first points, we have conserved the preceding $\nabla^2$. After the second point, we have admitted a decrease of $\nabla^2$ in geometric progression which manifestly hastens the convergence. Starting from 0.6, we have taken

$$\nabla^2 Y_{i+1} \approx -0.01\, Y_i,$$

which is almost exact here.

### 30.1 Utilization of Milne's method.

When we do not use difference formulas and the system is not linear, we have recourse to predictor formulas permitting, in general, a reduction of the iteration to one cycle. We will take, for example,

$$y_{i+1}'^* = y_{i-1}' + 2hY_i,$$

$$y_{i+1}^* = y_i + hy_i' + \frac{h^2}{2} Y_{i+1}^*,$$

$$y_{i+1}' = y_i' + \frac{h}{2}(Y_{i+1i}^* + Y),$$

$$y_{i+1} = y_i + hy_i' + \frac{h^2}{6}(Y_{i+1}^* + 2Y_i).$$

The quadrature error is of order $h^3$ at $y_{i+1}'^*$, $y_{i+1}'^*$, $y_{i+1}'$ and of order $h^4$ at $y_{i+1}$.

### 30.2 Example

$$y'' = -ty, \qquad y(0) = 1, \qquad y'(0) = 0, \qquad h = 0.1.$$

| $t$ | $y_i$ | $y_i'$ | $y(t)$ | $Y$ |
|---|---|---|---|---|
| 0 | 1 | 0 | 1 | 0 |
| 0.1 | 0.999,833 | −0.005,000 |  | −0.099,983 |

| $t$ | $y_i$ | $y_i'$ | $y(t)$ | $Y$ |
|---|---|---|---|---|
| 0.2 { | 0.998,833 | −0.019,997 | | −0.199,767 |
|       | 0.998,667 | −0.019,987 | 0.998,667 | −0.199,733 |
| 0.3 { | 0.995,670 | −0.044,946 | | −0.298,701 |
|       | 0.995,505 | −0.044,909 | 0.995,504 | −0.298,651 |
| 0.4 { | 0.989,521 | −0.079,717 | | −0.395,808 |
|       | 0.989,359 | −0.079,632 | 0.989,356 | −0.395,744 |
| 0.5 { | 0.979,418 | −0.124,057 | | −0.489,709 |
|       | 0.979,261 | −0.123,905 | 0.979,253 | −0.489,630 |
| 0.6 { | 0.964,423 | −0.177,558 | | −0.578,654 |
|       | 0.964,274 | −0.177,319 | 0.964,258 | −0.578,564 |
| 0.7 { | 0.943,649 | −0.239,617 | | −0.660,554 |
|       | 0.943,513 | −0.239,275 | 0.943,484 | −0.660,459 |
| 0.8 { | 0.916,284 | −0.309,411 | | −0.733,027 |
|       | 0.916,163 | −0.308,949 | 0.916,113 | −0.732,930 |
| 0.9 { | 0.881,663 | −0.385,861 | | −0.793,443 |
|       | 0.881,503 | −0.385,268 | 0.881,423 | −0.793,353 |
| 1.0 { | 0.839,009 | −0.467,619 | | −0.839,009 |
|       | 0.838,933 | −0.466,886 | 0.838,812 | |

## VI  PROCEDURES LEADING TO THE MULTISTEP METHODS

### 31.1 Principle.

Multistep formulas make quantities with indices $i, i - 1, \ldots, i - q$ appear in the calculation of $x_{i+1}$. Only the quantities $x_0, x_0', \ldots, x_0^{(p-1)}$ at the initial point are known. It is thus necessary to calculate by a different procedure the unknown values which one needs in order to start.

### 31.2 Use of a single-step method.

One of any of the single-step methods permits us to determine the number of points necessary for the starting of the chosen multi-step formula. The different Runge-Kutta formulas are frequently used for this objective, as well as the Taylor series. In order to diminish the length of the interval in which one expands and thus to limit the number of derivatives to be calculated, we often use the Taylor expansions on both sides of the starting point. For example, instead of calculating

$$x(t_0), x(t_0 + h), \ldots, x(t_0 + 4h)$$

we calculate

$$x(t_0 - 2h), \; x(t_0 - h), \; x(t_0), \; x(t_0 + h), \; x(t_0 + 2h).$$

### 32.1 Successive predictions for three values.

For $x' = X(x, t)$, $x(t_0) = x_0$, let us determine three starting values. According to what was said, let us seek to determine $x$ at the abscissas:

$$t_{-1}, \, t_0, \, t_1.$$

This leads us to solve the implicit system

$$x_{-1} - x_0 = -\frac{h}{12}(5X_{-1} + 8X_0 - X_1),$$

$$x_1 - x_0 = \frac{h}{12}(-X_{-1} + 8X_0 + 5X_1).$$

(The error of each of these formulas is of order $h^4$.) We solve this system iteratively by successive predictors:

$$x_1^* = x_0 + hX_0, \qquad x_1^{**} = x_0 + \frac{h}{2}(X_0 + X_1^*),$$

$$x_{-1}^* = x_0 - hX_0, \qquad x_{-1}^{**} = x_0 - \frac{h}{2}(X_0 + X_{-1}^*).$$

$$\text{Error of order } h^2 \qquad \text{Error of order } h^3$$

We substitute $x_1^{**}$, $x_{-1}^{**}$ in these formulas of three values and we iterate until stabilization.

### 32.2 Successive predictions for five values.

Let us determine five starting values for $x' = X(x, t)$. According to what has been said before, we seek to determine $x$ at the abscissas

$$t_{-2}, \, t_{-1}, \, t_0, \, t_1, \, t_2.$$

This leads us to solve the implicit system:

$$x_{-2} - x_0 = -\frac{h}{90}(29X_{-2} + 124X_{-1} + 24X_0 + 4X_1 - X_2),$$

$$x_{-1} - x_0 = -\frac{h}{720}(-19X_{-2} + 346X_{-1} + 456X_0 - 74X_1 + 11X_2),$$

$$x_1 - x_0 = \frac{h}{720}(11X_{-2} - 74X_{-1} + 456X_0 + 346X_1 - 19X_2),$$

$$x_2 - x_0 = \frac{h}{90}(-X_{-2} + 4X_{-1} + 24X_0 + 124X_1 + 29X_2).$$

The error of each of these formulas is of order $h^6$. We solve this system iteratively by successive predictors:

$$\left.\begin{aligned}x_1^* &= y_0 + hX_0\\ x_{-1} &= y_0 - hX_0\end{aligned}\right\},\qquad \text{error of order } h^2.$$

$$\left.\begin{aligned}x_1^{**} &= y_0 + \frac{h}{2}(X_0 + X_1^*)\\[4pt]x_2^{**} &= y_0 + 2hX_1^*\\[4pt]x_{-1}^{**} &= y_0 - \frac{h}{2}(X_0 + X_{-1}^*)\\[4pt]x_{-2}^{**} &= y_0 - 2hX_{-1}^*\end{aligned}\right\},\qquad \text{error of order } h^3.$$

$$\left.\begin{aligned}x_1^{***} &= y_0 + \frac{h}{12}(5X_0 + 8X_1^{***} - X_2^{**})\\[4pt]x_2^{***} &= y_0 + \frac{h}{3}(X_0 + 4X_1^{**} + X_2^{**})\\[4pt]x_{-1}^{***} &= y_0 - \frac{h}{12}(5X_0 + 8X_{-1}^{**} - X_{-2}^{**})\\[4pt]x_{-2}^{***} &= y_0 - \frac{h}{3}(X_0 + 4X_{-1}^{**} + X_{-2}^{**})\end{aligned}\right\},\qquad \text{error of order } h^4.$$

Consequently, we pass to definite formulas with which we iterate the number of times necessary in order that the values vary no more than the desired precision.

*Remark.* In view of the form of the convergence factor of the iteration, one or at most two cycles of iteration are necessary. The succeeding cycles furnish digits without significance.

### 33.1 Other formulas.

On the same principle, let us determine the values relative to $t_1$ and $t_2$ for $y' = Y(y, t)$. We utilize

$$y_1^* = y_0 + hY_0.$$

The error at $y_1^*$ is of order $h^2$:

$$y_1^{**} = y_0 + \frac{h}{2}(Y_0 + Y_1^*),$$

$$y_2^{**} = y_0 + 2hY_1^*.$$

The errors at $y_1^{**}$ and $y_2^{**}$ are of order $h^3$:

$$y_1^{***} = y_0 + \frac{h}{12}(5Y_0 + 8Y_1^{**} - Y_2^{**}),$$

$$y_2^{***} = y_0 + \frac{h}{3}(Y_0 + 4Y_1^{**} + Y_2^{**}).$$

The errors at $y_1^{***}$ and $y_2^{***}$ are of order $h^4$.

We effect one or more iterations on these formulas until we obtain values which vary no more than the desired precision. The general principle of this calculation is the following: In order to obtain $y_{i+1}$ exact at order 3, it suffices to have $Y_{i+1}$ and $Y_{i+2}$, hence $y_{i+1}$ and $y_{i+2}$ exact at order 2. We deduce these same quantities of provisional values exact at order 1, etc. This is what we can call a method of progressive gradients.

*Remark.* As was already said in Chapter 4, paragraph 1, the principle of the Runge-Kutta method permits one to bring back all these formulas to a unique principle to evaluate the remaining errors and eventually to construct more effective methods.

### 33.2 Example.

Let

$$y' = -2ty^2, \qquad y(0) = 1, \qquad h = 0.1,$$

$$
\begin{aligned}
y(0) &= 1, & Y_0 &= 0, \\
y_1^* &= 1, & Y_1^* &= -0.2, \\
y_1^{**} &= 0.99, & Y_1^{**} &= -0.196{,}02, \\
y_2^{**} &= 0.96, & Y_2^{**} &= -0.368{,}64, \\
y_1^{***} &= 0.990{,}004, & Y_1^{***} &= -0.196{,}021{,}6, \\
y_2^{***} &= 0.961{,}576, & Y_2^{***} &= -0.369{,}851, \\
y_1 &= 0.990{,}014, & Y_1 &= -0.196{,}025{,}5, \\
y_2 &= 0.924{,}550, & Y_2 &= -0.369{,}820{,}1.
\end{aligned}
$$

### 34. Formulas with higher order derivatives.

We can consider using higher order derivatives at the starting point. The following procedure demands only the knowledge of $y_0''$ for integrating:

$$y' = Y(y, t).$$

$$y_1^{[n+1]} = y_0 + \frac{h}{24}(7Y_1^{[n]} + 16Y_0 + Y_{-1}^{[n]}) + \frac{h^2}{4}y_0'' + O(h^5),$$

$$y_{-1}^{[n+1]} = y_0 - \frac{h}{24}(Y_1^{[n]} + 16Y_0 + 7Y_{-1}^{[n]}) + \frac{h^2}{4}y_0'' - O(h^5).$$

We begin the iteration with

$$Y_1^{[0]} = Y_0 + hy_0'',$$
$$Y_{-1}^{[0]} = Y_0 - hy_0''.$$

In the actual case,

$$O(h^5) \approx -1/180\,h^5 y^{(v)}.$$

*Remark.* On the choice of starting values, see Chapter 7, paragraphs 12.3 and 12.4.

## Problems

By applying a combination of the Runge-Kutta and Adams' methods or Runge-Kutta and Milne's methods, calculate to two decimal places the solutions to the following differential equations and systems at the given values of $x$.

1. $y' = x + y$,      $y(0) = 1$,      $y$ at $x = 0.5$.
2. $y' = x^2 + y$,      $y(0) = 1$,      $y$ at $x = 1$.
3. $y' = 2y - 3$,      $y(0) = 1$,      $y$ at $x = 0.5$.
4. $y' = -x + 2y + z$,      $y(0) = 2$,      $y$ and $z$ at $x = 0.5$.
    $z' = x + 2y + 3z$,      $z(0) = -2$.
5. $y^3 y'' + 1 = 0$,      $y(1) = 1$,      $y'(1) = 0$,      $y$ at $x = 1.5$.
6. $y'' + \frac{1}{2} y \cos 2x = 0$,      $y(0) = 0$,      $y'(0) = 1$.
   What are $y(\pi)$ and $y'(\pi)$?

# 7 DIFFERENT MULTISTEP FORMULAS[1]

## I GENERAL CONSIDERATIONS

We can try to obtain by different procedures other multistep formulas than those of the preceding chapter. Below, we indicate some of them.

### 1. Formulas utilizing central differences.[2]

The formulas of the preceding chapter were based on the use of backward differences. The use of central differences, i.e., points placed symmetrically in relation to the interval of integration, will give a smaller quadrature error. The central difference formula

$$x_{i+1} = x_{i-1} + \frac{h}{3}(X_{i+1} + 4X_i + X_{i-1})$$

gives an example of this situation. Here is another example:

$$x_{i+1} = x_i + \frac{h}{24}(-X_{i+2} + 13X_{i+1} + 13X_i - X_{i-1}).$$

The application of such a formula is rather laborious. It necessitates, in effect, a prior evaluation of the provisional values, either by iteration, or by using differences, or by a predictor formula: $x_{i+1}^*$, $x_{i+2}^*$.

### 2. Multiple predictor formulas.[3]

The preceding situation is only a particular case of a more general situation where the application of a formula requires the provisional evaluation of several quantities. For example, we can propose to integrate

[1]Lotkin [2].
[2]Dahlquist [1, 2], Urabe and Tsushima, Löwdin.
[3]Wilf [1, 2], Dimsdale and Clippinger (in Grabbe, Ramo, Woolridge, pp. 14–60).

167

$$x' = X(x, t)$$

by the formula

$$x_{i+1} = x_i + \frac{h}{12}(5X_i + 8X_{i+1} - X_{i+2}).$$

The advantage of such a formula is that it does not require the knowledge of starting values other than the initial value. It can thus serve as a vehicle of a multistep method. We have shown in Chapter 6, paragraph 25.2, how to use it. Let us cite Lindelöff's formula:

$$x_{i+1} = x_{i-1} + h[2X_i + 1/3\,(\nabla^2 X_i + \nabla^3 X_i)] + \delta,$$

with

$$\delta = h/3\,(\nabla^4 X_{i+1} - 1/30\,\nabla^4 X_{i+2}).$$

The correction term $\delta$ is obtained by using the formula without this term, in order to calculate $x_{i+1}$ and $x_{i+2}$, which permits the approximate evaluation of the $\nabla^4 X$. The use of such formulas for an integration itself is very difficult and can only be discouraging.

### 3. Formulas containing several $x_{i-1}$.[1]

We can imagine more general multistep formulas than those of the preceding chapter. It suffices to write:

$$x_{i+1} = \sum_{j=-\mu}^{\nu} A_j x_{i-j} + h \sum_{k=-\rho}^{\sigma} BX_{i-k}.$$

Such formulas are implicit if one of the two numbers $\mu$ or $\rho$ is positive. They are multiple predictors as soon as one of these two numbers exceeds 1. We obtain such formulas very easily by the method of undetermined coefficients.

### 4.1 Construction of a formula.

Let us look for a formula of as high an order as possible in the form:

$$x_{i+1} = Ax_i + Bx_{i-1} + h(CX_i + DX_{i-1}).$$

Noting that the formula is valid for

$$X = 0, \quad x = 1,$$
$$X = 1, \quad x = t,$$
$$X = t, \quad x = t^2/2,$$
$$X = t^2, \quad x = t^3/3,$$

we find

$$1 = A + B, \quad 2 = A + C + D, \quad 2 = C + A/2, \quad 8/3 = C + A/3.$$

[1]Hamming.

whence

$$A = -4, \quad B = 5, \quad C = 4, \quad D = 2,$$

and

$$x_{i+1} = -4x_i + 5x_{i-1} + 2h(2X_i + X_{i-1}).$$

### 4.2 Example.

Let us apply this formula to the equation

$$y' = y, \quad y(0) = 1, \quad h = 0.1.$$

We find

| $x$ | $y$ | $x$ | $y$ |
|-----|-----|-----|-----|
| 0   | 1     | 0.8 | 3.287       |
| 0.1 | 1.105 | 0.9 | -2.941      |
| 0.2 | 1.222 | 1.0 | 27.680      |
| 0.3 | 1.347 | 1.1 | -14.941     |
| 0.4 | 1.505 | 1.2 | 557.724     |
| 0.5 | 1.586 | 1.3 | -2,605.499  |
| 0.6 | 1.816 | 1.4 | 12,279.961  |
| 0.7 | 1.710 | 1.5 | -57,756.454 |

This formula is obviously to be rejected. The investigation of the stability will give us the explanation of the phenomena.

## II   STABILITY[1]

### 5.1 Investigation of a particular equation.

Let the equation be

$$y' = 0, \quad y(t_0) = y_0,$$

to which we shall apply the formula

$$y_{i+1} = \sum_{j=0}^{v} A_j y_{i-j} + h \sum_{k=0}^{\beta} B_k Y_{i-k}.$$

In the actual case, we obtain a difference equation with constant coefficients:

$$y_{i+1} = \sum_{j=0}^{v} A_j y_{i-j},$$

the solution of which is of the form

$$y_i = \sum_{\rho=0}^{v} C_\rho r_\rho^i.$$

The $C_\rho$ are arbitrary constants, and the $r_\rho$ are the roots of the equation

[1]Budak and Gorbunov, Dahlquist [1, 2, 3], Henrici [5], Hull and Luxemburg, Mitchell and Craggs, Quade [3], Rutishauser [1], Skalkina, Todd [1].

$$r^{\nu+1} = \sum_{j=0}^{\nu} A_j\, r^{\nu-j}.$$

This equation is said to be the reduced characteristic equation of the approximate integration formula. For simplicity we suppose that all the $r_\rho$ are distinct.

Theoretically, the $C_\rho$ are given by the solution of the system of equations

$$y_i = \sum_{\rho=0}^{\nu} C_\rho r_\rho^i, \qquad i = 0, 1, \ldots, \nu$$

If we require that the formula give the exact integral of the equation

$$y' = 0,$$

it is necessary that

$$r_0 = 1, \qquad C_0 = y_0, \qquad C_\rho = 0, \qquad \rho \neq 0.$$

Let us suppose that the $y_i$, instead of being all equal to $y_0$, are slightly different from it; then the values of the $C_\rho$ will be found to be nonzero. The behavior of this solution will depend on the order of magnitude of the $r_\rho$.

### 5.2  Parasitic roots.

We will call the principal root of the reduced characteristic equation the root $r_0 = 1$. We will suppose it to be simple. We will call all the other roots of this equation *parasitic roots*. Let us investigate the effect of one such root. It introduces in $y_i$ a term

$$Ar_\rho^i.$$

If $|r_\rho| < 1$, this root is not troublesome, as the corresponding term tends to zero as $i$ increases indefinitely. If $|r_\rho| > 1$, the term $Ar_\rho^i$ grows in modulus. The actual solution is smothered by this parasitic term. If $|r_\rho| = 1$, we have a parasitic term with a constant modulus; it is less troublesome than in the preceding case, but nevertheless it can render the solution useless in certain cases.

The appearance of these parasitic roots is the price which we must pay for not having satisfied the second property of the solution of an initial value problem (Chapter 1, paragraph 12).

### 6.1  Stability.

An approximate integration formula of the type studied in paragraph 5.1 is said to be:

—*strongly stable*, if for all the parasitic roots of the reduced characteristic equation we have $|r| < 1$.

—*weakly stable*, if for all the parasitic roots of the reduced characteristic equation we have $|r| \leqslant 1$.

—*unstable*, if the reduced characteristic equation has at least one root whose modulus is greater than 1.

**6.2 Example.**

Let us return to the formula of paragraph 4.1. The reduced characteristic equation is written as

$$r^2 + 4r - 5 = 0.$$

It has the roots:

$$1 \quad \text{and} \quad -5.$$

It is thus unstable.

**6.3 Investigation of any arbitrary system in canonical form.**

Let the system be

$$x' = X(x, t),$$

to which we will apply the formula of paragraph 5.1. We see easily that, if $h$ is very small, the solution of the expression

$$x_{i+1} = \sum_{j=0}^{\nu} A_j x_{i-j} + h \sum_{k=0}^{\beta} B_k X_{i-k}$$

behaves almost like that of the relation

$$x_{i+1} = \sum_{j=0}^{\nu} A_j x_{i-j}.$$

But, for this relation, the components separate and one recovers the same situation as for the equation $y' = 0$. One unstable formula will thus give the phenomenon evidenced in example 4.2.

**6.4 Investigation of the equation $y' = ay$.**

For the equation $y' = ay$, the formula of 5.1 becomes

$$y_{i+1} = \sum_{j=0}^{\nu} A_j y_{i-j} + \varphi \sum_{j=0}^{\beta} B_k y_{i-k},$$

where $\varphi = ah$. This is again a linear recurrence relation with constant coefficients. For this relation, we call the characteristic equation the equation

$$r^{\gamma+1} = \sum_{j=0}^{\nu} A_j r^{\gamma-j} + \varphi \sum_{k=0}^{\beta} B_k r^{\gamma-k}$$

with $\gamma = \max (\beta, \nu)$. If we set $\varphi = 0$, we recover the reduced characteristic equation multiplied by a power in $r$.

By virtue of the theorem of continuity of the roots, the characteristic equation has for $\varphi$ small:

—a root close to 1. We will call it the principal root; all the others will be called parasitic roots. Among these roots:

—some are close to zero.

—others are close to the parasitic roots of the reduced characteristic equation.

A little later, we will give a limited development of certain of these roots in power of $\varphi$.

### 7. Investigation of the stability of the methods of Chapter 6.

The Adams' methods have as the reduced characteristic equation:

$$r = 1.$$

They are thus strongly stable. The methods with $l \neq 1$ have as the reduced characteristic equation:

$$r^l = 1.$$

They are weakly stable.

For this purpose, let us cite a theorem[1].

*Explicit formulas.* A formula which uses the values $x_{i-j}$ and $X_{i-j}$, where $0 \leqslant j \leqslant q$, and is of a higher order than the Adams formula using the same $X_{i-j}$ is unstable.

*Implicit formulas.* Under analogous conditions, we can construct formulas which are weakly stable.

### 8.1 Example of a weakly stable formula.

Let us return to example 1 of Chapter 6, paragraph 9.2. If one considers only the results, these seem to be very good. Indeed, the error does not exceed

$$2 \times 10^{-4}.$$

Nevertheless, the investigation of the difference between the exact and the approximate solution shows a certain disturbance. This difference has a regrettable tendency to oscillate, as the table below shows.

| $t$ | $y$ exact $- y_i$ | $t$ | $y$ exact $- y_i$ |
|---|---|---|---|
| 0 | 0 | 1.1 | 0.000,087 |
| 0.1 | 0 | 1.2 | 0.000,031 |
| 0.2 | 0 | 1.3 | 0.000,095 |
| 0.3 | 0.000,03 | 1.4 | 0.000,018 |
| 0.4 | 0.000,02 | 1.5 | 0.000,104 |
| 0.5 | 0.000,05 | 1.6 | 0 |
| 0.6 | 0.000,03 | 1.7 | 0.000,118 |
| 0.7 | 0.000,07 | 1.8 | −0.000,025 |
| 0.8 | 0.000,04 | 1.9 | +0.000,137 |
| 0.9 | 0.000,08 | 2.0 | −0.000,058 |
| 1.0 | 0.000,04 | | |

[1]Ceschino-Kuntzmann [1], Dahlquist [2, 3].

This impression is confirmed by the investigation of the differences of the $y_i$:

| $-\nabla^2 y_i$ | $-\nabla^3 y_i$ | $-\nabla^2 y_i$ | $-\nabla^3 y_i$ |
|---|---|---|---|
| 905 | 88 | 344 | 54 |
| 817 | 72 | 290 | 4 |
| 745 | 78 | 286 | 55 |
| 667 | 55 | 231 | −11 |
| 612 | 68 | 242 | 62 |
| 544 | 41 | 180 | −28 |
| 503 | 60 | 208 | 72 |
| 443 | 28 | 136 | −49 |
| 415 | 56 | 185 | |
| 359 | 15 | | |

*Remark.* The parasitic root is close to $-1.167$. It creates slightly ampli-fied oscillations of period 2 steps which can be perceived in the table above. We have an unfavorable case, because the solution tends towards zero while the oscillations tend to amplify themselves.

On the other hand, let us investigate

$$y' = y, \qquad y(0) = 1, \qquad h = 0.1$$

by the formula

$$y_{i+1} = y_{i-1} + 2h Y_i.$$

| $t$ | $y_i$ | $(y_{\text{exact}} - y_i)\,10^5$ | $10^5\,\nabla^3 y$ |
|---|---|---|---|
| 0 | 1.000,00 | 0 | |
| 0.1 | 1.105,17 | 0 | |
| 0.2 | 1.221,03 | 11 | |
| 0.3 | 1.349,37 | 48 | 179 |
| 0.4 | 1.490,90 | 92 | 71 |
| 0.5 | 1.647,55 | 117 | 193 |
| 0.6 | 1.820,41 | 170 | 109 |
| 0.7 | 2.011,63 | 212 | 215 |
| 0.8 | 2.222,73 | 281 | 152 |
| 0.9 | 2.456,17 | 343 | 246 |
| 1.0 | 2.713,96 | 432 | 201 |
| 1.1 | 2.998,96 | 520 | 286 |
| 1.2 | 3.313,75 | 636 | 258 |
| 1.3 | 3.661,71 | 758 | 338 |
| 1.4 | 4.046,09 | 910 | 325 |
| 1.5 | 4.470,92 | 1,076 | 403 |
| 1.6 | 4.940,27 | 1,276 | 407 |
| 1.7 | 5.458,97 | 1,497 | 483 |
| 1.8 | 6.032,06 | 1,758 | 504 |
| 1.9 | 6.665,38 | 2,051 | 584 |
| 2.0 | 7.365,13 | 2,393 | 620 |
| 2.1 | 8.138,40 | 2,777 | 709 |

| $t$ | $y_i$ | $(y_{\text{exact}} - y_i)\, 10^5$ | $10^5\, \nabla^3 y$ |
|---|---|---|---|
| 2.2 | 8.992,81 | 3,220 | 762 |
| 2.3 | 9.936,96 | 3,722 | 860 |
| 2.4 | 10.980,20 | 4,298 | 935 |
| 2.5 | 12.133,00 | 4,949 | 1,047 |
| 2.6 | 13.406,80 | 5,694 | 1,144 |
| 2.7 | 14.814,36 | 6,537 | 1,276 |
| 2.8 | 16.369,67 | 7,497 | 1,399 |
| 2.9 | 18.088,29 | 8,585 | 1,556 |
| 3.0 | 19.987,33 | 9,820 | 1,711 |
| 3.1 | 22.085,76 | 11,219 | 1,897 |
| 3.2 | 24.404,48 | 12,805 | 2,091 |
| 3.3 | 26.966,65 | 14,598 | 2,315 |
| 3.4 | 29.797,81 | 16,629 | 2,554 |
| 3.5 | 32.926,21 | 18,912 | 2,826 |
| 3.6 | 36.383,05 | 21,518 | 3,119 |
| 3.7 | 40.202,82 | 24,448 | 3,449 |
| 3.8 | 44.423,62 | 27,756 | 3,809 |
| 3.9 | 49.087,55 | 31,489 | 4,211 |

The investigation of the third differences reveals the start of oscillation which decreases and finally disappears ahead of the growth of the said differences. Indeed, the parasitic root is close to $-0.9$.

## 8.2 Another example of a weakly stable formula.

Let us take up the example of the central difference method given in Chapter 6, paragraph 14.2. The differences $y(t_i) - y_i$ are equal to:

| $t$ | $y - y_i$ | $t$ | $y - y_i$ |
|---|---|---|---|
| 0.2 | $973 \cdot 10^{-10}$ | 1.7 | 1222 |
| 0.3 | 755 | 1.8 | 2081 |
| 0.4 | 1610 | 1.9 | 1052 |
| 0.5 | 1221 | 2.0 | 1972 |
| 0.6 | 2001 | 2.1 | 876 |
| 0.7 | 1474 | 2.2 | 1865 |
| 0.8 | 2217 | 2.3 | 649 |
| 0.9 | 1577 | 2.4 | 1769 |
| 1.0 | 2308 | 2.5 | 471 |
| 1.1 | 1574 | 2.6 | 1680 |
| 1.2 | 2315 | 2.7 | 312 |
| 1.3 | 1498 | 2.8 | 1600 |
| 1.4 | 2266 | 2.9 | 148 |
| 1.5 | 1375 | 3.0 | 1539 |
| 1.6 | 2183 | | |

Their behavior toward the end is clearly oscillatory.

### 9. Investigation of the stability in the use of a predictor and of a corrector.

Let us consider the formulas

$$y_{i+1}^* = \sum_{j=0}^{\mu} C_j y_{i-j} + h \sum_{j=0}^{r} D_j Y_{i-j}$$

$$y_{i+1} = \sum_{j=0}^{\mu'} C_j' y_{i-j} + h \left( D_{-1}' Y_{i+1} + \sum_{j=0}^{r} D_j' Y_{i-j} \right).$$

Prompted by paragraph 6.3, we understand easily that, for $h$ very small, the solution of this pair of relations will have a behavior similar to that which would correspond to $h = 0$. In this case, we find

$$y_{i+1} = \sum_{j=0}^{\mu} C_j' y_{i-j}.$$

This amounts to saying that the stability questions, when one uses a predictor and a corrector, reduce themselves to the study of the stability of the corrector if the step is assumed to be infinitely small. Without inconvenience one can then use an unstable predictor. For example, Milne's formulas

$$y_{i+1}^* = y_{i-3} + \frac{8h}{3} (Y_i - 1/2\, Y_{i-1} + Y_{i-2}),$$

$$y_{i+1} = y_{i-1} + \frac{h}{3} (Y_{i+1}^* + 4 Y_i + Y_{i-1})$$

are weakly stable, since the correction formula is the central difference formula.

### 10.1 Development of roots of the characteristic equation.

For the various classical methods we are going to give the development of parasitic roots in powers of $\varphi$ as mentioned in paragraph 6.4. So far as the principal root is concerned, we will demonstrate for it an exact theorem in Chapter 9, paragraph 6.1.

### 10.2 Numerical informations on the explicit and implicit methods.

a. *Explicit methods.*

| | $l = 0$ Adams | $l = 1$ Nyström | $l = 2$ | $l = 3$ |
|---|---|---|---|---|
| $r = 0$ | No parasitic root | As below | $\exp(\pm 2j\pi/3) + \varphi$ | $-1 + \varphi$ $\pm j 1 + \varphi/3$ |
| $r = 1$ | | $-1 + \varphi$ | $\exp(\pm 2j\pi/3)(1 - \varphi/2)$ | $-(1 + \varphi)$ $\pm j(1 - \varphi)$ |
| $r = 2$ | | $-1 + 5\varphi/3$ | $\exp(\pm 2j\pi/3)(1 + \varphi/4) + 3\varphi/4$ | $-1 + 5\varphi/3$ $\pm j(1 + \varphi/3)$ |
| $r = 3$ | | $-1 + 3\varphi$ | | |

b. *Implicit methods.*

| $l = 0$ Adams | $l = 1$ | $l = 2$ | $l = 3$ | $l = 4$ |
|---|---|---|---|---|
| $r = 2$ | As below | | | |
| $r = 3$ | $-1 + \varphi/3$ | $\exp(\pm 2j\pi/3)(1 - \varphi/8)$ | | |
| $r = 4$  No para- | $-1 + 38\varphi/90$ | $\exp(\pm 2j\pi/3)$ $[1 - \varphi/480(33 \pm 27j\sqrt{3})]$ | As below | |
| $r = 5$  sitic root | $-1 + 3\varphi/5$ | $\exp(\pm 2j\pi/3)$ $[1 + \varphi/320(7 \pm 25j\sqrt{3})]$ | $-1 + 38\varphi/90$ $\pm j(1 + \varphi/45)$ | $\exp(\pm 2j\pi/5)\cdot$ $(1 + 25.5\varphi/288)$ $\exp(\pm 4j\pi/5)\cdot$ $(1 - 19.3\varphi/288)$ |

In these two tables

$$j^2 = -1,$$

$$\varphi = ah.$$

## 11. Investigation of stability of systems containing second derivatives.

Let us consider the equation $y'' = 0$, and let us apply to it a formula of the type:

$$y'_{i+1} = \sum_{j=0}^{\nu} A_j y'_{i-j} + h \sum_{k=0}^{\beta} B_k Y_{i-k},$$

$$y_{i+1} = \sum_{l=0}^{\gamma} C_l y_{i-l} + h \sum_{m=0}^{\delta} D_m y'_{i-m} + h^2 \sum_{q=0}^{\epsilon} E_q Y_{i-q}. \tag{1}$$

In the present case, we obtain the following difference system with constant coefficients:

$$y'_{i+1} = \sum_{j=0}^{\nu} A_j y'_{i-j}, \tag{2}$$

$$y_{i+1} = \sum_{l=0}^{\gamma} C_l y_{i-l} + h \sum_{m=0}^{\delta} D_m y'_{i-m}. \tag{3}$$

Writing these formulas so that they give for all initial conditions the correct solution of $y'' = 0$, we obtain

$$\sum_{j=0}^{\nu} A_j = 1, \tag{4}$$

$$\sum_{l=0}^{\gamma} C_l = 1, \tag{5}$$

$$\sum_{m=0}^{\delta} D_m - \sum_{l=0}^{\gamma} lC_l = 1. \tag{6}$$

The solution of (2) is of the form

$$y_i' = \sum_{\rho=1}^{\nu} K_\rho r_\rho^i.$$

The $K_\rho$ are arbitrary constants, and the $r_\rho$ are the roots of the equation

$$r^{\nu+1} = \sum_{j=0}^{\nu} A_j r^{\nu-j},$$

which we will call the first reduced characteristic equation of the approximate integration formula (1). Condition (4) shows that this equation possesses the root 1, which corresponds to the correct solution of the problem. All the other roots will be called parasitic roots.

When we have solved (2), (3) becomes a nonhomogeneous linear difference equation with constant coefficients. At first, let us seek to solve the corresponding homogeneous equation:

$$y_{i+1} = \sum_{l=0}^{\gamma} C_l \gamma_{i-l}.$$

Its general solution is given by

$$y_i = \sum_{\sigma} K_\sigma' s_\sigma^i.$$

The $K_\sigma'$ are arbitrary constants, and the $s_\sigma$ are the roots of the equation

$$s^{\gamma+1} = \sum_{l=0}^{\gamma} C_l s^{\gamma-l},$$

which we will call the second reduced characteristic equation of the approximate integration formula (1). Condition (5) shows that this equation has the root 1, which also corresponds to the correct solution of the problem. All the other roots will be called parasitic roots. One will say that formula (1) is:

—strongly stable if all the parasitic roots of the first and second characteristic equation are in modulus smaller than 1.

—weakly stable if all the roots of the first and second characteristic equation are in modulus less than or equal to 1.

—unstable if there exists at least one parasitic root whose modulus is greater than 1.

### 12.1 Investigation of stability of formulas of Chapter 6.

For the Adams formulas with $p = 2$ (Chapter 6, paragraph 24.1), the two reduced characteristic equations are written as

$$r = 1, \qquad r = 1.$$

We thus have strong stability. This is the same for the implicit Adams formulas (Chapter 6, paragraph 26.1).

We will leave to the reader the extension of the considerations of paragraphs 6.3, 6.4, and 6.10 to systems containing second derivatives. Likewise, we will leave it to him to extend the theory to systems containing any derivatives of order $p$.

## 12.2 Other investigations on stability.

In the preceding we have considered $h$ to be infinitesimally small. We can take up again the stability investigation for any arbitrary $h$.[1] We will restrict ourselves to the equation

$$y' = -y,$$

whose general solution tends to zero. We will call the stability boundary of approximate solution formula relative to this equation the largest number $H$, such that for

$$0 \leqslant h \leqslant H,$$

the characteristic roots of the approximate solution method have all their moduli less than or equal to 1. Here are some results on this subject:
*Runge-Kutta method of order* 4

$$H = 2.785.$$

*Explicit Adams method*

| $r$ | 1 | 2 | 3 | 4 |
|-----|---|-----|------|--------|
| $H$ | 1 | 6/11 | 6/20 | 90/551 |

*Implicit Adams method*

| $r$ | 1 | 2 | 3 | 4 |
|-----|----------|---|---|-------|
| $H$ | $\infty$ | 6 | 3 | 90/49 |

## 12.3 Remark on the choice of starting values when a weakly stable formula is used.[2]

Let us return to the equation $y' = -y$, $y(0) = 1$, and integrate it by Nyström's method:

$$y_{i+1} = y_{i-1} + 2hy_i' = y_{i-1} - 2hy_i, \qquad h = 0.1.$$

The characteristic roots are

$$r_1 = 1 - h + h^2/2 \approx e^{-h},$$
$$r_2 = -(1 + h + h^2/2) \approx -e^h.$$

$r_2$ is a parasitic root.

If we start the integration with the initial values

$$y_{-1} = e^h, \qquad y_0 = 1$$

corresponding to two initial points on the exact integral curve, we find in the approximate solution $y_i$ a term $r_2^i$ which produces oscillations of increasing amplitude. If, on the other hand, we take the solution corresponding

[1]Robertson, Quade [3], Lago and Guillou, Liniger, Hamming.
[2]Richardson [2].

to the approximate values

$$z_{-1} = 1/r_1, \qquad z_0 = 1,$$

we find, neglecting the round-off errors,

$$z_i = r_1^i.$$

We do not have the term $r^2$, and hence, no oscillation. This is just what the calculation shows:

| $t$ | $y - e^{-t}$ | $z - e^{-t}$ |
|---|---|---|
| 0 | 0 | 0 |
| 0.1 | 0.000,333,5 | 0.000,150,2 |
| 0.2 | 0.000,235,1 | 0.000,271,8 |
| 0.3 | 0.000,559,4 | 0.000,368,8 |
| 0.4 | 0.000,369,9 | 0.000,444,8 |
| 0.5 | 0.000,709,0 | 0.000,503,4 |
| 0.6 | 0.000,430,6 | 0.000,546,6 |
| 0.7 | 0.000,805,9 | 0.000,577,1 |
| 0.8 | 0.000,435,0 | 0.000,598,7 |
| 0.9 | 0.000,868,4 | 0.000,607,2 |
| 1.0 | 0.000,396,9 | 0.000,610,9 |
| ... | ......... | ......... |
| 2.1 | 0.001,181,0 | 0.000,427,5 |
| 2.2 | −0.000,404,9 | 0.000,405,1 |
| 2.3 | 0.001,298,9 | 0.000,383,4 |
| 2.4 | −0.000,631,3 | 0.000,361,8 |
| 2.5 | 0.001,455,4 | 0.000,341,3 |
| 2.6 | −0.000,895,0 | 0.000,320,9 |
| 2.7 | 0.001,659,2 | 0.000,301,9 |
| 2.8 | −0.001,204,4 | 0.000,282,9 |
| 2.9 | 0.001,920,3 | 0.000,265,5 |
| 3.0 | −0.001,570,1 | 0.000,248,2 |
| ... | ......... | ......... |
| 7.1 | 0.109,27 | 0.000,024,5 |
| 7.2 | −0.120,73 | −0.000,007,3 |
| 7.3 | 0.133,42 | 0.000,026,4 |
| 7.4 | −0.147,41 | −0.000,012,4 |
| 7.5 | 0.162,90 | 0.000,028,9 |
| 7.6 | −0.179,99 | −0.000,018,0 |
| 7.7 | 0.198,90 | 0.000,032,7 |

Finally, oscillations appear in $z$. They are due to the introduction of the terms $r_2$ following the calculation errors.

### 12.4 Possibility of a convenient choice of the starting values.

It seems preferable that the starting values be affected by the same errors as the succeeding values. We can arrive at it in the following manner: Let the formula

$$y_{i+1} = y_i + h(\alpha Y_i + \beta Y_{i-1} + \gamma Y_{i-2} + \delta Y_{i-3}) \tag{1}$$

be used. An approximate value of $y_{-1}$, $y_{-2}$, and $y_{-3}$ having been obtained, we calculate $y^{[0]}$, $y_2^{[0]}$, and $y_3^{[0]}$ by means of formula (1); then $y_{-1}^{[1]}$, $y_{-2}^{[1]}$ and $y_{-3}^{[1]}$ by the same formula and integrating in an inverse sense, then $y_1^{[1]}$, $y_2^{[1]}$, and $y_3^{[1]}$, and so on up to coincidence of the values of $y_{-1}$, $y_{-2}$, and $y_{-3}$ which one will use along the integration. If $h$ is taken to be sufficiently small, the principal part of the error of $y_{-j}$ is hence

$$\tau_{-j} - h\alpha(Y_y')_{-j+1}\tau_{-j+1} - h\beta(Y_y')_{-j+2}\tau_{-j+2} - \cdots - h\delta(Y_y')_{-j+2}\tau_{-j+4},$$

where $\tau_j$ denotes the quadrature error to the point $t_j$ relative to formula (1).

### 12.5 Example.

Let it be required to integrate

$$y' = \frac{4y}{1+t}, \qquad y(0) = 1, \qquad h = 0.05$$

by the formula

$$y_{i+1} = y_i + \frac{h}{12}(23\,Y_i - 16\,Y_{i-1} + 5\,Y_{i-2}).$$

As starting values, one finds

$$y_1 = 1.215,458, \qquad y_2 = 1.463,973,$$

whereas the exact values are

$$1.215,506, \qquad 1.464,100.$$

## III   INTEGRATION OF SYSTEMS IN THE PARTICULAR FORM $x^{(p)} = X(x, t)$ [1]

In order to integrate such systems, we must naturally obtain the successive derivatives. The formulas which we are going to indicate avoid recourse to them. This advantage is compensated by a drop of the order of the approximation of the principal characteristic root (see Chapter 9, paragraph 8.1).

### 13. Explicit difference formulas.

Let us integrate $p$ times $x^{(p)} = X(x, t)$ between $t_{i-r}$ and $t_i$, with $r = -1$, $0, 1, \ldots, p-1$. We obtain

$$x(t_{i-r}) - x(t_i)$$
$$= \sum_{k=1}^{p-1} x^{(k)}(t_i) \cdot \frac{(t_{i-r} - t_i)^k}{k!} + \underbrace{\int_{t_i}^{t_{i-r}} \cdots \int_{t_i}^{t} \int_{t_i}^{t} X(x, t)\, dt\, dt \ldots dt}_{p \text{ times}}. \quad (1)$$

In order to continue we set

$$t - t_i = uh$$

[1]Henrici [7], Herrick, Jackson, and Salzer [1, 2], Urabe and Yanagihara, de Vogelaere [2].

and we replace $X(x, t)$ by

$$X(x_i, t_i) + \frac{u}{1} \nabla X(x_i, t_i) + \frac{u(u+1)}{2!} \cdot \nabla^2 X(x_i, t_i) + \cdots .$$

We obtain thus a certain number of relations between which we can propose to eliminate the

$$x^{(k)}(t_i).$$

For this, it suffices to add the various relations (1) after having multiplied each by

$$(-1)^{r+1} C_p^{r+1}.$$

We find then

$$x_{i+1} - C_p^1 x_i + C_p^2 x_{i-1} + \cdots + (-1)^p C_p^p x_{i-p+1} = h^p (s_0 X_i + s_1 \nabla X_i + \cdots),$$

i.e.,

$$\nabla^p x_{i+1} = h^p \sum_{j=0}^{r} s_j \nabla^j X_i,$$

with

$$s_j = \sum_{k=0}^{p} (-1)^k C_p^k \underbrace{\int_0^{1-k} \cdots \int_0^u \int_0^u \frac{u(u+1) \ldots (u+j-1)}{j!} du \ldots du.}_{p \text{ times}}$$

Here is a table giving the first values of the $s_j$:

| $j$ $\backslash$ $p$ | 0 | 1 | 2 | 3 | 4 | 5 |
|---|---|---|---|---|---|---|
| 2 | 1 | 0 | 1/12 | 1/12 | 19/240 | 3/40 |
| 3 | 1 | −1/2 | 0 | 0 | 1/240 | 1/160 |
| 4 | 1 | −1 | 1/6 | 0 | −1/720 | −1/720 |
| 5 | 1 | −3/2 | 7/12 | −1/24 | 0 | 0 |

## 14. Case $p = 2$. Störmer's formulas.[1]

As is the usage in difference formulas, we can truncate the development given by the preceding table after any term. Thus, for the system

$$x'' = X(x, t),$$

Störmer indicates the formula

$$\nabla^2 X_{i+1} = h^2 [X_i + 1/12 \, (\nabla^2 X_i + \nabla^3 X_i + \nabla^4 X_i - 1/20 \, \nabla^4 X_i)],$$

the following term $(3h^2/40)\nabla^5 X_i$ being of the order $h^7$. If we exclude $(-h^2/240)\nabla^4 X_i$ (of the order $h^6$), there remains a formula of a very simple form.

## 15. Example.

We will discuss the equation

$$y'' = -ty, \qquad y(0) = 1, \qquad y'(0) = 0$$

[1]Dainelli, Schultz [2], Störmer [2], Tamarkine.

by means of the formula

$$y_{i+1} = 2y_i - y_{i-1} + h^2 [Y_i + 1/12 (\nabla^2 Y_i + \nabla^3 Y_i)].$$

| $t$ | $y$ | $Y$ | $\nabla Y$ | $\nabla^2 Y$ | $\nabla^3 Y$ | $y$ exact |
|---|---|---|---|---|---|---|
| 0 | 1 | 0 | | | | |
| 0.1 | 0.999,833,34 | −0.099,983,33 | −99 983 33 | | | |
| 0.2 | 0.998,667,02 | −0.199,733,40 | −99 750 07 | 233 26 | | |
| 0.3 | 0.995,504,05 | −0.298,651,22 | −98 917 82 | 832 25 | 598 99 | |
| ... | ... | ... | ... | ... | ... | ... |
| 0.4 | 0.989,355,76 | −0.395,742,30 | −97 091 08 | 1 826 74 | 994 49 | 6 07 |
| 0.5 | 0.979,252,40 | −0.489,626,20 | −93 883 90 | 3 207 18 | 1 380 44 | 3 23 |
| 0.6 | 0.964,256,60 | −0.578,553,96 | −88 927 76 | 4 956 14 | 1 748 96 | 8 43 |
| 0.7 | 0.943,480 89 | −0.660,436,62 | −81 882 66 | 7 045 10 | 2 088 96 | 3 84 |
| 0.8 | 0.916,108,42 | −0.732,886,74 | −72 450 12 | 9 432 54 | 2 387 44 | 12 71 |
| 0.9 | 0.881,416,93 | −0.793,275,24 | −60 388 50 | 12 061 62 | 2 629 08 | 22 72 |
| 1.0 | 0.838,804,93 | | | | | 12 31 |

The first three values have been obtained by another procedure (we have taken exact values).

### 16.1  Application of Cowell's method.[1]

As for the first order equations, one can appeal to the inverse operator of $\nabla$. One has

$$x_{i+1} = h^2(\nabla^{-2}X_i + 1/12X_i + 1/12\,\nabla X_i + 19/240\,\nabla^2 X_i + 3/40\,\nabla^3 X_i$$
$$+ 863/12096\,\nabla^4 X_i + 275/4032\,\nabla^5 X_i + 33953/518400\,\nabla^6 X_i + \cdots),$$

where one has set:

$$\nabla^{-1} X_i = \nabla^{-1} X_{i-1} + X_i, \qquad \nabla^{-2} X_i = \nabla^{-2} X_{i-1} + \nabla^{-1} X_i.$$

The interest in this manner of attack is that one gains one subtraction per step. On the other hand, the numbers to be handled are a little larger. The round-off errors have a behavior which is different from the one the errors in Störmer's formula have, and this behavior can be more favorable.

### 16.2  Example.

Let us take up again the example of paragraph 15.2, working with the same order but keeping only six decimal figures in the $Y$.

[1]Sheldon, Herrick, Jackson.

| $t$ | $y$ | $\nabla^{-2} Y$ | $\nabla^{-1} Y$ | $Y$ | $\nabla Y$ |
|---|---|---|---|---|---|
| 0 | 1 | | | 0 | |
| 0.1 | 0.999,833,34 | 99.883,366 | | −0.099,983 | −99,983 |
| 0.2 | 0.998,667,02 | 99.575,362 | −0.308,004 | −0.199,733 | −99,750 |
| 0.3 | 0.995,504,05 | 98.968,707 | −0.606,655 | −0.298,651 | −98,918 |
| ... | ... | ... | ... | ... | ... |
| 0.4 | 0.989,335,76 | 97.966,310 | −1.002,397 | −0.395,742 | −97,091 |
| 0.5 | 0.979,852,41 | 96.474,287 | −1.492,023 | −0.489,626 | −93,884 |
| 0.6 | 0.964,256,61 | 94.403,710 | −2.070,577 | −0.578,554 | −88,928 |
| 0.7 | 0.943,480,87 | 91.672,697 | −2.731,013 | −0.660,436 | −81,882 |
| 0.8 | 0.916,108,37 | 88.208,797 | −3.463,900 | −0.732,887 | −72,451 |
| 0.9 | 0.881,416,86 | 83.951,622 | −4.257,175 | −0.793,275 | −60,388 |
| 1.0 | 0.838,804,83 | | | | |

### 17.1 The expressions as functions of the ordinates (second derivatives).

As a function of the ordinates, these formulas are written

$$x_{i+1} = 2x_i - x_{i-1} + h^2(\sigma^*_{r,0} X_i + \sigma^*_{r,1} X_{i-1} + \cdots + \sigma^*_{r,r} X_{i-r}).$$

Here is a table of the first $\sigma^*_{r,j}$:

| $r$ / $j$ | 2 | 3 | 4 | 5 | 6 | 7 | 8 | 9 |
|---|---|---|---|---|---|---|---|---|
| 0 | $\dfrac{13}{12}$ | $\dfrac{14}{12}$ | $\dfrac{299}{240}$ | $\dfrac{317}{240}$ | $\dfrac{168398}{120960}$ | $\dfrac{176648}{120960}$ | $\dfrac{5537111}{3628800}$ | $\dfrac{5766235}{3628800}$ |
| 1 | −2 | −5 | −176 | −266 | −185844 | −243594 | −9209188 | −11271304 |
| 2 | 1 | 4 | 194 | 374 | 317946 | 491196 | 21390668 | 29639132 |
| 3 | | −1 | −96 | −276 | −311704 | −600454 | −31323196 | −50569612 |
| 4 | | | 19 | 109 | 184386 | 473136 | 30831050 | 59700674 |
| 5 | | | | −18 | −60852 | −234102 | −20332636 | −49202260 |
| 6 | | | | | 8630 | 66380 | 8646188 | 27892604 |
| 7 | | | | | | −8250 | −2148868 | −10397332 |
| 8 | | | | | | | 237671 | 2299787 |
| 9 | | | | | | | | −229124 |

The denominator of each of the coefficients of the first line is to be repeated for all the coefficients of the corresponding column.

### 17.2 Example.

Let us take up the example of paragraph 15 with the formula

$$y_{i+1} = 2y_i - y_{i-1} + \frac{h^2}{12}(14 Y_i - 5 Y_{i-1} + 4 Y_{i-2} - Y_{i-3}).$$

| $t$ | $y$ | $Y$ |
|---|---|---|
| 0 | 0 | 1 |
| 0.1 | 0.999,833,34 | −0.099,983,33 |
| 0.2 | 0.998,667,02 | −0.199,733,40 |
| 0.3 | 0.995,504,05 | −0.298,651,22 |
| 0.4 | 0.989,355,76 | −0.395,742,30 |
| 0.5 | 0.979,252,40 | −0.489,626,20 |
| 0.6 | 0.964,256,60 | −0.578,553,93 |
| 0.7 | 0.943,480,85 | −0.660,436,60 |
| 0.8 | 0.916,108,35 | −0.732,886,68 |
| 0.9 | 0.881,416,83 | −0.793,275,15 |
| 1.0 | 0.838,804,80 | |

### 18.1  Difference formulas for $p = 3$ and $p = 4$.

Let us point out only the very simple formulas.
For $p = 3$:

$$x_{i+1} - 3x_i + 3x_{i-1} - x_{i-2} = h^3(X_i - 1/2 \nabla X_i + 1/240 \nabla^4 X_i).$$

For $p = 4$:

$$x_{i+1} - 4x_i + 6x_{i+1} - 4x_{i-2} + x_{i-3} = h^4 \left[ X_i - \nabla X_i + \frac{\nabla^2}{6} X_i - \frac{\nabla^4}{720} X_i \right].$$

### 18.2  Formula as a function of ordinates for $p = 3$.

From the first formula given above, in which we have neglected the term $\nabla^4 X_i$, we deduce immediately the very simple formula relative to $p = 3$:

$$x_{i+1} = 3x_i - 3x_{i-1} + x_{i-2} + h^3(X_i + X_{i-1})/2.$$

### 19.1  Implicit formulas.

By a reasoning analogous to that of paragraph 13, we obtain, for

$$x^{(p)} = X(x, t),$$

the approximate solution formula

$$x_i - C_p^1 x_{i-1} + C_p^2 x_{i-2} + \cdots + (-1)^p C_p^p x_{i-p} = h^p [s_0^* X_i + s_1^* \nabla X_i + \cdots],$$

or

$$\nabla^p x_i = h^p \sum_{j=0}^{r} s_j^* \nabla^j X_i$$

with

$$s_j^* = \sum_{k=1}^{p} C_p^k (-1)^k \underbrace{\int_0^{-k} \int_0^u \cdots \int_0^u}_{p \text{ times}} \frac{u(u+1) \dots (u+j-1)}{j!} \, du \dots du$$

### 19.2  Table of values of the first $s_j^*$.

| $j$<br>$p$ | 0 | 1 | 2 | 3 | 4 | 5 |
|---|---|---|---|---|---|---|
| 2 | 1 | −1 | 1/12 | 0 | −1/240 | −1/24 |
| 3 | 1 | −3/2 | 1/2 | 0 | 1/240 | 1/480 |

### 19.3 Implicit formulas as functions of the ordinates for $p = 2$.

By eliminating the differences in the preceding formulas one obtains for

$$x'' = X(x, t)$$

the approximate solution formula

$$x_{i+1} = 2x_i - x_{i-1} + h^2 \sum_{j=0}^{r} \sigma_{r,j}^* X_{i-j}.$$

Here is a table of the first $\sigma_{r,j}^*$:

| $j$ <br> $r$ | 0 | 1 | 2 | 3 | 4 | 5 |
|---|---|---|---|---|---|---|
| 2 | 1/12 | 10/12 | 1/12 | (Formula is named "royal road") | | |
| 3 | 1/12 | 10/12 | 1/12 | 0 | | |
| 4 | 19/240 | 51/60 | 7/120 | 1/60 | −1/240 | |
| 5 | 3/80 | 127/120 | −43/120 | 13/30 | −17/80 | 1/24 |

The application of these formulas is done as for the general systems.

### 19.4 Example.

Let us return to

$$y'' = -ty, \qquad y(0) = 1, \qquad y'(0) = 0, \qquad h = 0.1$$

through the formula

$$y_{i+1} = 2y_i - y_{i-1} + h^2(Y_{i+1} + 10 Y_i + Y_{i-1})/12.$$

We will avoid the iteration by utilizing the fact that the equation is linear:

$$y_{i+1} = \frac{2y_i - y_{i-1} + h^2(10 Y_i + Y_{i-1})/12}{1 + h^2 t_{i+1}/12}.$$

| $t$ | $y$ | $Y$ |
|---|---|---|
| 0 | 1 | 0 |
| 0.1 | 0.999,833,34 | −0.099,983,33 |
| 0.2 | 0.998,667,05 | −0.199,733,41 |
| 0.3 | 0.995,504,12 | −0.298,651,24 |
| 0.4 | 0.989,356,20 | −0.395,742,48 |
| 0.5 | 0.979,253,53 | −0.489,626,76 |
| 0.6 | 0.964,258,72 | −0.578,555,23 |
| 0.7 | 0.943,484,22 | −0.660,438,95 |
| 0.8 | 0.916,113,19 | −0.732,890,55 |
| 0.9 | 0.881,423,30 | −0.793,280,97 |
| 1.0 | 0.838,812,98 | |

## IV  USE OF CENTRAL DIFFERENCES FOR THE INTEGRATION OF THE SYSTEMS $x^{(2p)} = X(x, t)$.

The use of central differences is particularly well adapted to this case. We are going to present some methods based on this principle.

### 20. Use of Stirling's interpolation.

Let the system be
$$x^{(2p)} = X(x, t).$$

Let us represent $X$ by Stirling's formula and integrate $2p$ times from $t_i$ to $t_{i\pm k}$, with $k = p, p-1, \ldots, 2.1$. Let us multiply the obtained equalities respectively by

$$C_{2p}^0, \qquad -C_{2p}^1, \qquad C_{2p}^2, \qquad \ldots, \qquad (-1)^{p-1} C_{2p}^{p-1}$$

and

$$C_{2p}^{2p}, \qquad -C_{2p}^{2p-1}, \qquad \ldots, \qquad (-1)^{p+1} C_{2p}^{p+1}$$

and add term by term. The terms

$$x_i', x_i'', \ldots, x_i^{(2p-1)}$$

disappear, and we arrive at

$$\delta^{2p} x_i = \sum_{j=0}^{2p} (-1)^j C_{2p}^j x_{i+p-j} = h^{2p}(\eta_0 X_i + \eta_2 \delta^2 X_i + \cdots)$$

with

$$\eta_{2r} = \sum_{j=0}^{2p} (-1)^j C_{2p}^j \underbrace{\int_0^{p-j} \cdots \int_0^u \frac{u^2(u^2 - 1) \ldots (u^2 - (r-1)^2)}{(2r)!} du \ldots du}_{2p \text{ times}}$$

The terms of Stirling's formula containing $\mu$ have disappeared in the summation.

### 21.1 Case $p = 1$.

For the system $x'' = X(x, t)$, the preceding formula gives
$$\delta^2 x_i = h^2(X_i + \delta^2 X_i/12 - \delta^4 X_i/240 + 31/60,480 \, \delta^6 X_i$$
$$- 289/3,628,800 \, \delta^8 X_i + \cdots).$$

One uses frequently the formula
$$\delta^2 x_i = h^2(X_i + \delta^2 X_i/12),$$

in which the first neglected term is

$$h^2 \delta^4 X_i/240$$

a quantity which is of order $h^6$. This formula has been called the "royal road" by the Anglo-Saxon mathematicians. We have already met this formula in paragraph 19.3.

### 21.2 Application in the linear case.

Let the equation be
$$y'' + g(t)y = f(t).$$

It is easy to see that by setting

$$z = \left[\frac{1 + h^2 g(t)}{12}\right] y, \qquad \left[1 + \frac{h^2 g(t)}{12}\right]^{-1} h^2 g(t) = G(t),$$

$$h^2 \left(f(t) + \frac{\delta^2 f(t)}{12}\right) = F(t), \qquad \delta^2 z + G(t)z = F(t),$$

the "royal road" formula can be written as difference equation of the second order.

### 21.3 Application in the general case.

The utilization of differences is conducive to the scheme of Fig. 7-1, for the formula containing fourth differences.

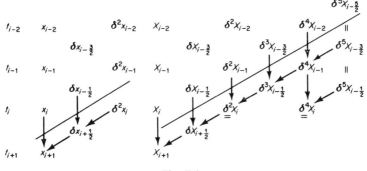

**Fig. 7-1.**

The integration having been performed up to $t_i$, the part of the table situated above the oblique lines is known. Let us suppose that

$$\delta^5 X_{i-1/2} = \delta^5 X_{i-3/2} = \delta^5 X_{i-5/2}.$$

We can then evaluate the provisional values of $\delta^2 X_i$ and of $\delta^4 X_i$. Carrying these values into the approximate integration formula, we deduce from it a provisional value of $\delta^2 x_i$ from which finally we deduce a value of $x_{i+1}$. This value permits the calculation of $X_{i+1}$. The comparison between this value and that found by starting from the differences permits us to decide whether or not to proceed with an iteration. This method is naturally not usable at the beginning of the calculation.

We calculate

$$x(h), \quad x(2h), \quad x(3h)$$

by another procedure. For $x(4h), x(5h)$ we iterate by starting from a provisional value furnished by $\delta^2 x_i = h^2 X_i$.

### 21.4 Example.

Let

$$x'' = -tx, \qquad x(0) = 1, \qquad x'(0) = 0, \qquad h = 0.1.$$

| $t$ | $x$ | $\delta x$ | $\delta^2 x$ | $X$ | $\delta X$ | $\delta^2 X$ | $\delta^3 X$ | $\delta^4 X$ | | $\delta^5 X$ |
|---|---|---|---|---|---|---|---|---|---|---|
| 0 | 1.000,000,00 | | | 0.000,000,00 | | | | | | 0 |
| | | −166,66 | | | −99,983,33 | +233,26 | | 0 | 1 | |
| 0.1 | 0.999,833,34 | | −996,66 | −0.099,983,33 | | | 598,99 | 0 | 3 | |
| | | −1,166,32 | | | −99,750,07 | 832,25 | | 395,50 | 2 | |
| 0.2 | 0.998,667,02 | | −1,996,65 | −0.199,733,40 | | | 994,49 | 395,50 | 3 | |
| | | −3,162,97 | | | −98,917,82 | 1,431,24 | | 395,37 | 2 | −9,36 |
| 0.3 | 0.995,504,05 | | −2,985,32 | −0.298,651,22 | | | 994,36 | 395,37 | 3 | |
| | | −6,148,29 | | | −97,091,08 | 1,826,74 | | 395,37 | 4 | |
| 0.4 | 0.989,355,76 | | −2,985,01 | −0.395,742,30 | | 1,826,61 | 1,389,73 | 386,01 | 3 | |
| | 0.989,356,07 | −6,147,98 | | −0.395,742,43 | −97,091,21 | | 1,380,37 | 376,65 | 4 | −17,52 |
| | | −10,102,74 | −3,954,76 | | −93,884,23 | 3,216,34 | | 367,29 | 5 | |
| 0.5 | 0.979,253,33 | | | −0.489,626,66 | | 3,206,98 | 1,757,02 | 368,49 | 4 | |
| | 0.979,253,32 | −10,102,75 | −3,954,77 | | | | 1,748,86 | 350,97 | 5 | |
| | | | −4,892,15 | | −88,928,39 | 4,964,00 | | 333,45 | 6 | −28,44 |
| | | −14,994,90 | −4,892,15 | | | 4,955,84 | 2,099,83 | 340,05 | 5 | |
| 0.6 | 0.963,258,42 | | | −0.578,555,05 | | 7,055,67 | | | | |

| $t$ | $x$ | $\delta x$ | $\delta^2 x$ | $X$ | $\delta X$ | $\delta^2 X$ | $\delta^3 X$ | $\delta^4 X$ | | $\delta^5 X$ |
|---|---|---|---|---|---|---|---|---|---|---|
| 0.7 | 0.943,483,84 | −20,774,58 | −5,779,68 | −0.660,438,69 | −81,883,64 | 7,044,75 | 2,088,91 | 311,61 | 6 | −28,43 |
| | 0.943,483,83 | −20,774,59 | −5,779,69 | −0.660,438,68 | −81,883,63 | 7,044,76 | 2,088,92 | 340,06 | 5 | |
| 0.8 | 0.916,112,71 | −27,371,12 | −6,596,53 | −0.732,890,17 | −72,451,49 | 9,445,31 | 2,400,55 | 311,63 | 6 | −41,60 |
| | 0.916,112,70 | −27,371,13 | −6,596,54 | −0.732,890,16 | −72,451,48 | 9,432,14 | 2,387,38 | 283,20 | 7 | −41,59 |
| | | | | | | 9,432,15 | 2,387,39 | 298,46 | 6 | |
| | | | | | | | | 256,86 | 7 | |
| | | | | | | | | 298,47 | 6 | |
| 0.9 | 0.881,422,72 | −34,689,98 | −7,318,85 | −0.793,280,45 | −60,390,29 | 12,076,42 | 2,644,27 | 256,88 | 7 | −56,82 |
| | 0.881,422,71 | −34,689,99 | −7,318,86 | −0.793,280,44 | −60,390,28 | 12,061,19 | 2,629,04 | 215,29 | 8 | −56,81 |
| | | | | | | 12,061,20 | 2,629,05 | 241,65 | 7 | |
| | | | | | | | | 184,83 | 8 | |
| | | | | | | | | 241,66 | 7 | |
| 1.0 | 0.838,812,31 | −42,610,40 | −7,920,41 | −0.838,812,31 | −45,531,87 | 14,875,15 | 2,813,95 | 184,85 | 8 | −73,50 |
| | 0.838,812,9 | −42,610,42 | −7,920,43 | −0.838,812,9 | | 14,858,41 | 2,797,21 | 128,04 | 9 | |
| | | | | | | | | 168,16 | 8 | |
| | | | | | | | | 94,66 | 9 | |

The physical implementation of such a calculation is rather cumbersome. In particular, the index, by which the values $\delta^4 X$ are affected, is not present. We have indicated it in a small column between that of $\delta^4 X$ and that of $\delta^5 X$ (see table on pp. 188–89).

*Remark.* We can use with these formulas Cowell's application; i.e., we can write

$$x_i = h^2 \left[ \delta^2 X_i + \frac{X_i}{12} - \frac{\delta X_i}{240} + 31/60,480\ \delta^4 X_i + \cdots \right].$$

## V  FORMULAS WHICH APPEAL TO HIGHER ORDER DERIVATIVES[1]

### 22. Principle.

As for the single-step methods, one can imagine formulas for the system

$$x^{(p)} = X(x, \ldots, x^{(p-1)}),$$

making an appeal to $x^{(p+1)}$, $x^{(p+2)}$, . . . .

Some of these formulas can be related with an interpolation formula which appeals to the derivatives, for example, the well-known formula of Hermite. Others can be obtained by the method of undetermined coefficients.

One could, for example, take them from the form (for a system in canonical form):

$$x_{i+1} = \sum_{j=\mu}^{\nu} H_{i-j} x_{i-j} + h \sum_{j=\alpha}^{\beta} \bar{H}_{i-j} X_{i-j} + h^2 \sum_{j=\gamma}^{\delta} \bar{\bar{H}}_{i-j} x''_{i-j}.$$

Such formulas must naturally satisfy the stability conditions in order to be usable.

### 23. Example.

We will content ourselves with giving an example of a three point formula using the first and second derivatives and only the preceding value of the unknown function. For the system

$$x' = X(x, t)$$

we easily find

$$x_{i+1} = x_i + \frac{h}{240} [101 x'_{i+1} + 128 x'_i + 11 x'_{i-1}]$$

$$+ \frac{h^2}{240} [-13 x''_{i+1} + 40 x''_i + 3 x''_{i-1}].$$

The quadrature error is

[1] Muhin [2], Salzer [5, 6], Korganoff, Turton [2], Quade [2], Funk, Capra [1, 2].

$$\frac{8h^7 x^{(7)}}{7! \, 15} \, .$$

This formula is strongly stable and implicit.

# VI  FORMULAS OF THE OBRECHKOFF TYPE[1]

## 24. Principle.

The formulas which we are going to study in this paragraph are actually single-step formulas. However, they find their place in this chapter because their principle is of the same genus as that of the multistep formulas. Let the differential system be

$$x' = X(x, t), \qquad x(t_0) = x_0.$$

We propose to establish for this system formulas of as high an order as possible and in one of these forms:

$$x_{i+1} = x_i + \sum_{r=1}^{p} \frac{h^r}{r!} c_r x_i^{(r)} + \sum_{r=1}^{q} \frac{h^r}{r!} d_r x_{i+1}^{(r)} \qquad (G_{p,q} \text{ formulas}),$$

$$x_{i+1} = x_i + \sum_{r=1}^{p-q} \frac{h^r}{r!} x_i^{(r)} + \sum_{r=p-q+1}^{p} \frac{h^r}{r!} [e_r x_i^{(r)} + f_r x_{i+1}^{(r)}] \qquad (H_{p,q} \text{ formulas}).$$

For $q = 0$, the formulas $G$ and $H$ reduce to Taylor's formula. For $p = q$, both reduce to

$$x_{i+1} = x_i + \sum_{r=1}^{p} \frac{h^r}{r!} [a_r x_i^{(r)} + b_r x_{i+1}^{(r)}] \qquad (F_p \text{ formulas}).$$

## 25. Calculation of the coefficients.

For the various coefficients, one finds the following expressions:

$$a_r = \frac{C_{2p-r}^p}{C_{2p}^p}, \qquad b_r = (-1)^{r+1} \frac{C_{2p-r}^{p-r}}{C_{2p}^p},$$

$$c_r = \frac{C_{p+q-r}^q}{C_{p+q}^q}, \qquad d_r = (-1)^{r+1} \frac{C_{p+q-r}^{q-r}}{C_{p+q}^q},$$

$$f_{p-q+r} = (-1)^{r+1} \frac{C_{p-q+r-1}^{p-q} C_{2q-r}^q}{C_{p+q}^q},$$

$$e_{p-q+r} = 1 - \frac{Q_r f_{p-q+1}}{(r-1)!} - \frac{Q_r f_{p-q+2}}{(r-2)! \, Q_2} - \cdots - \frac{Q_r f_{p-q+r}}{Q_r},$$

with

$$Q_s = (p - q + 2) \ldots (p - q + s) \quad \text{and} \quad Q_1 = 1.$$

[1]Beck, Ceschino [6], Lotkin [2], Milne [2], Pflanz [2], Duffing.

## 26. Table of the first values.

| $a_r$ \ $p$ | 1 | 2 | 3 | 4 |
|---|---|---|---|---|
| 1 | 1/2 | 1/2 | 1/2 | 1/2 |
| 2 |  | 1/6 | 1/5 | 3/14 |
| 3 |  |  | 1/20 | 1/14 |
| 4 |  |  |  | 1/70 |

| $b_r$ \ $p$ | 1 | 2 | 3 | 4 |
|---|---|---|---|---|
| 1 | 1/2 | 1/2 | 1/2 | 1/2 |
| 2 |  | −1/6 | −1/5 | −3/14 |
| 3 |  |  | 1/20 | 1/14 |
| 4 |  |  |  | −1/70 |

$p = 2.$

| $c_r$ \ $q$ | 1 |
|---|---|
| 1 | 2/3 |
| 2 | 1/3 |

| $d_r$ \ $q$ | 1 |
|---|---|
| 1 | 1/3 |

$p = 3.$

| $c_r$ \ $q$ | 2 | 1 |
|---|---|---|
| 1 | 3/5 | 3/4 |
| 2 | 3/10 | 1/2 |
| 3 | 1/10 | 1/4 |

| $d_r$ \ $q$ | 2 | 1 |
|---|---|---|
| 1 | 2/5 | 1/4 |
| 2 | −1/10 |  |

$p = 4.$

| $c_r$ \ $q$ | 3 | 2 | 1 |
|---|---|---|---|
| 1 | 4/7 | 2/3 | 4/5 |
| 2 | 2/7 | 2/5 | 3/5 |
| 3 | 4/35 | 1/5 | 2/5 |
| 4 | 1/35 | 1/15 | 1/5 |

| $d_r$ \ $q$ | 3 | 2 | 1 |
|---|---|---|---|
| 1 | 3/7 | 1/3 | 1/5 |
| 2 | −1/7 | −1/15 |  |
| 3 | 1/35 |  |  |

$p = 2.$

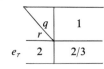

| $e_r$ \ $q$ | 1 |
|---|---|
| 2 | 2/3 |

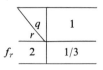

| $f_r$ \ $q$ | 1 |
|---|---|
| 2 | 1/3 |

$p = 3.$

| $e_r$ \ $q$ | 2 | 1 |
|---|---|---|
| 2 | 7/10 |  |
| 3 | 3/10 | 3/4 |

| $f_r$ \ $q$ | 2 | 1 |
|---|---|---|
| 2 | 3/10 |  |
| 3 | −1/5 | 1/4 |

$p = 4$.

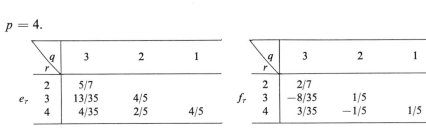

| $q$ $\backslash$ $r$ | 3 | 2 | 1 |
|---|---|---|---|
| $e_r$   2 | 5/7 | | |
| 3 | 13/35 | 4/5 | |
| 4 | 4/35 | 2/5 | 4/5 |

| $q$ $\backslash$ $r$ | 3 | 2 | 1 |
|---|---|---|---|
| $f_r$   2 | 2/7 | | |
| 3 | −8/35 | 1/5 | |
| 4 | 3/35 | −1/5 | 1/5 |

## 27. The application of these formulas.

We put these formulas to use in various ways. We are going to exhibit the case $p = 3$, $q = 3$. The formula is thus of order 6.

*Iteration*

$$x_{1a} = x_0 + hx_0' + \frac{h^2}{2} x_0'' + \frac{h^3}{6} x_0''',$$

$$x_{1b} = x_0 + \frac{h}{2} (x_0' + x_{1a}') + \frac{h^2}{10} (x_0'' - x_{1a}'') + \frac{h^3}{120} (x_0''' + x_{1a}'''),$$

$$x_{1c} = x_0 + \frac{h}{2} (x_0' + x_{1b}') + \frac{h^2}{10} (x_0'' - x_{1b}'') + \frac{h^3}{120} (x_0''' + x_{1b}'''),$$

$$x_1 = x_0 + \frac{h}{2} (x_0' + x_{1c}') + \frac{h^2}{10} (x_0'' - x_{1c}'') + \frac{h^3}{120} (x_0''' + x_{1c}''').$$

For the next step one can either recalculate $x_1'$, $x_1''$, $x_1'''$, or use the values

$$x_{1c}', \quad x_{1c}'', \quad x_{1c}'''.$$

In the first case, the step costs 12 horners. In the second it costs nine horners.

*Formulas $G_{pq}$*

$$x_{1a} = x_0 + hx_0' + \frac{h^2}{2} x_0'' + \frac{h^3}{6} x_0''',$$

$$x_{1b} = x_0 + \frac{h}{4} (3x_0' + x_{1a}') + \frac{h^2}{4} x_0'' + \frac{h^3}{24} x_0''',$$

$$x_{1c} = x_0 + \frac{h}{5} (3x_0' + 2x_{1b}') + \frac{h^2}{20} (3x_0'' - x_{1b}'') + \frac{h^3}{60} x_0''',$$

$$x_1 = x_0 + \frac{h}{2} (x_0' + x_{1c}') + \frac{h^2}{10} (x_0'' - x_{1c}'') + \frac{h^3}{120} (x_0''' + x_{1c}''').$$

The step costs nine horners if one recalculates the quantities at the beginning of the step, and only six horners if one does not recalculate them. We can gain one horner without changing the order at all by replacing $x_c''$ by $x_b''$ in the last formula.

*$H_{pq}$ Formulas*

$$x_{1a} = x_0 + hx_0' + \frac{h^2}{2} x_0 + \frac{h^3}{6} x_0''',$$

$$x_{1b} = x_0 + hx_0' + \frac{h^2}{2} x_0'' + \frac{h^3}{24} (3x_0''' + x_{1a}'''),$$

$$x_{1c} = x_0 + hx_0' + \frac{h^2}{20} (7x_0'' + 3x_{1b}'') + \frac{h^3}{60} (3x_0''' - 2x_{1b}'''),$$

$$x_1 = x_0 + \frac{h}{2} (x_0' + x_{1c}') + \frac{h^2}{10} (x_0'' - x_{1c}'') + \frac{h^3}{120} (x_0''' + x_{1c}''').$$

The method still costs nine horners if we recalculate the quantities at the beginning, and six horners if we do not recalculate them. We can gain several horners per step without having changed the order by writing

$$x_{1c} = x_0 + hx_0' + \frac{h^2}{20} (7x_0'' + 3x_{1b}'') + \frac{h^3}{60} (3x_0''' - 2x_{1a}'''),$$

$$x_1 = x_0 + \frac{h}{2} (x_0' + x_{1c}') + \frac{h^2}{10} (x_0'' - x_{1b}'') + \frac{h^3}{120} (x_0''' + x_{1a}''').$$

This formula costs three horners per step if one does not recalculate the quantities at the beginning of the step.

### 28. Example.

$$y' = y - 1.5e^{-0.5t}, \qquad y(0) = 1, \qquad h = 0.5.$$

| $t$ | Formulas $H$ | Formulas $G$ | Iteration | $y$ exact |
|---|---|---|---|---|
| 0 | 1 | 1 | 1 | 1 |
| 0.5 | 0.778,800,928,5 | 0.778,800,306,0 | 0.778,798,992,8 | 0.778,800,783,1 |
| 1.0 | 0.606,530,079,6 | 0.606,528,153,5 | 0.606,524,107,9 | 0.606,530,659,7 |
| 1.5 | 0.472,364,352,4 | 0.472,360,910,5 | 0.472,352,920,8 | 0.472,366,552,7 |
| 2 | 0.367,873,695,3 | 0.367,868,944,5 | 0.367,854,763,5 | 0.367,879,441,2 |
| 2.5 | 0.286,494,835,1 | 0.286,486,559,3 | 0.286,462,395,5 | 0.286,504,796,9 |

We have not recalculated the $Y$ at the beginning of the step.

## Problems

1. Consider the formula $y_{n+2} + 4y_{n+1} - 5y_n = h(4Y_{n+1} + 2Y_n)$ and investigate stability for the problem $y' = Y(x, y) = ay$ with $y(0) = 1$ and $h = 0.1$. Is stability affected by the sign of $a$?

2. Using a step size of 0.1, calculate by Störmer's formula the solution to problems 5 and 6 of Chapter 6 at the given values of $x$.

3. Do the same, using Stirling's interpolation formula (see section IV).

4. For problems 1 through 3 of Chapter 6 use formulas $H$ and $G$ to tabulate the solution, using a step size of 0.05 in the interval $0 \leqslant x \leqslant 0.5$.

# 8 APPLICATION OF THE RUNGE-KUTTA PRINCIPLE TO THE MULTISTEP METHODS

Here we give some applications of an idea which seems to be capable of an extensive development. Contrary to the Runge-Kutta method, which neglects at the beginning of each step all the previous values, the methods of Chapters 6 and 7 appear at first sight to be economical methods, utilizing at each step a certain number of previous values. Outside of these classical methods there exists in the literature a large number of formulas (see, for example, Clenshaw and Olver) which consist of starting from a known abscissa point $t_i$ and from a certain number of preceding values, determining the provisional points (in general, of abscissa $t_i + nh$) in order to deduce the following definite point of abscissa $t_{i+1}$. In general, these methods have a rather arbitrary basis, the only connecting link being the search for successive formulas to obtain a higher and higher order.

### 1.1 Principle.

The Runge-Kutta principle brings us in this domain a controlling idea. Let us consider the system

$$x^{(p)} = X(x, x', \ldots, x^{(p-1)}).$$

Starting from the assumed knowledge of the values

$$x_i, x_i', \ldots, x_i^{(p-1)}$$

and of certain preceding values, construct a certain number of intermediate provisional values and the corresponding $X$ and get a final value relative to the abscissa $t_{i+1}$ whose infinitesimal order $h$ is as high as possible. The difference with the preceding methods is that one does not look to attain successively higher and higher orders, but that one tries to obtain a final expression which is very good. This principle will permit us to judge the quality of a formula obtained by some other procedure by comparing the order attained with the maximum possible order, for an equal amount of work.

### 1.2 Liaison.

By this means, we obtain formulas which we will call the *multistep Runge-Kutta formulas*. For such a formula, we will define a new number, the *liaison number*. It is equal to the number of preceding values (except for the initial value of the step) to which one appeals. The Adams-type methods are, moreover, a particular case of the methods which we are going to define. Their order is equal to their liaison number.

### 2. Remark on the use of preceding values bearing errors.

Let us consider the system

$$x^{(p)} = X(x, \ldots, x^{(p-1)}).$$

Starting from the point $t_i, x_i, \ldots, x_i^{(p-1)}$, which one can take as a reference point, we obtain the next point by having recourse to a value such as $x_{i-1}$, which is not rigorously situated on the integral curve passing through $t_i, x_i, \ldots, x_i^{(p-1)}$. But the differences between these values and the corresponding values of the integral curve passing through $t_i, x_i, \ldots, x_i^{(p-1)}$ are really of infinitesimal order of the errors which we will permit ourselves at the new point $t_{i+1}, x_{i+1}, \ldots$. It will result in a general rule that one can, at least so far as establishing the formulas is concerned, assume the preceding values to be correct. This will not be the same when we proceed to the investigation of the error.

### 3. Stability.

The multistep Runge-Kutta formulas are subject to a stability requirement as all the multistep formulas.

### I GENERAL FORMULAS FOR A SYSTEM IN CANONICAL FORM

### 4. Notations.

Let the system be $x' = X(x)$. We will write

$$x_{i,\alpha} = \sum_{m=0}^{l} Q_{\alpha,m} x_{i-m} + h \sum_{\beta=0}^{\alpha-1} A_{\alpha,\beta} X_{i,\beta}$$

$$x_{i,q} = x_{i+1}.$$

We will avoid writing explicitly the terms relative to the $X_{i-j}$ by using the convention that the first substitutions are relative to the preceding points. Hence we set

$$\theta_1 = -1, \qquad Q_{1,1} = 1, \qquad Q_{1,m} = 0, \qquad m \neq 1,$$
$$\theta_2 = -2, \qquad Q_{2,2} = 1, \qquad Q_{2,m} = 0, \qquad m \neq 2,$$
$$\theta_l = -l, \qquad Q_{l,l} = 1, \qquad Q_{l,m} = 0, \qquad m \neq l,$$

if one uses $l$ preceding values. Moreover, $A_{\alpha,\beta} = 0$ for $\alpha = 1, 2, \ldots, l$.

### 5. Supplementary convention.

We will suppose that all the intermediate points are exact at the first order, i.e., that

$$\sum_m Q_{\alpha,m} = 1, \qquad \sum_\beta A_{\alpha,\beta} - \sum_m m Q_{\alpha,m} = \theta_\alpha.$$

### 6. Calculation of $X_{0,\alpha} - X_0$.

By means of the methods exactly calculated through those of Chapter 3, paragraph 10, we can write the development of $X_{0,\alpha} - X_0$. We find

$$
\begin{aligned}
X_{0,\alpha} - X_0 &= h\theta_\alpha C_1 + h^2 \{\theta_\alpha^2 C_2/2 + (\sum Q_{\alpha,m} m^2/2 + \sum A_{\alpha,\beta}\theta_\beta) J_1 C_1\} \\
&+ h^3 \{\theta_\alpha^3 C_3/6 + (\sum Q_{\alpha,m} m^2 \theta_\alpha/2 + \sum A_{\alpha,\beta}\theta_\alpha\theta_\beta) K_1 C_1 \\
&\quad + (-1/6 \sum Q_{\alpha,m} m^3/6 + \sum A_{\alpha,\beta} Q_{\beta,m} m^2/2 + \sum A_{\alpha,\beta} A_{\beta,\gamma}\theta_\gamma) J_1^2 C_1 \\
&\quad + (-\sum Q_{\alpha,m} m^3/6 + \sum A_{\alpha,\beta}\theta_\beta^2/2) J_1 C_2\} \\
&+ h^4 \{C_4 \theta_\alpha^4/4! + (\sum Q_{\alpha,m} \theta_\alpha^2 m^2/4 + \sum A_{\alpha,\beta}\theta_\alpha^2\theta_\beta/2) L_1 C_1 \\
&\quad + 1/2 (\sum Q_{\alpha,m} m^2/2 + \sum A_{\alpha,\beta}\theta_\beta)^2 R + (\sum A_{\alpha,\beta}\theta_\alpha\theta_\beta^2/2 \\
&\quad - \sum Q_{\alpha,m}\theta_\alpha m^3/6) K_1 C_2 + (\sum A_{\alpha,\beta}\theta_\alpha Q_{\beta,m} m^2/2 \\
&\quad - \sum Q_{\alpha,m}\theta_\alpha m^3/6 + \sum A_{\alpha,\beta} A_{\beta,\gamma}\theta_\alpha\theta_\gamma) K_1 J_1 C_1 \\
&\quad + (3 \sum Q_{\alpha,m} m^4/24 + \sum A_{\alpha,\beta} Q_{\beta,m}\theta_\beta m^2/2 + \sum A_{\alpha,\beta} A_{\beta,\gamma}\theta_\beta\theta_\gamma) J_1 K_1 C_1 \\
&\quad + (\sum Q_{\alpha,m} m^4/24 + \sum A_{\alpha,\beta}\theta_\beta^3/6) J_1 C_3 \\
&\quad + (\sum Q_{\alpha,m} m^4/24 - 1/6 \sum A_{\alpha,\beta} Q_{\beta,m} m^3 + \sum A_{\alpha,\beta} A_{\beta,\gamma} Q_{\gamma,m} m^2/2 \\
&\quad + \sum A_{\alpha,\beta} A_{\beta,\gamma} A_{\gamma,\delta}\theta_\delta) J_1^3 C_1 + (\sum Q_{\alpha,m} m^4/24 - 1/6 \sum A_{\alpha,\beta} Q_{\beta,m} m^3 \\
&\quad + \sum A_{\alpha,\beta} A_{\beta,\gamma}\theta_\gamma^2/2) J_1^2 C_2\}.
\end{aligned}
$$

### 7. Development of the exact and the approximate solution.

|  | Taylor | Multistep Runge-Kutta |
|---|---|---|
| $h^2 C_1$ | 1/2 | $\sum A_{q,\alpha}\theta_\alpha + 1/2 \sum m^2 Q_{q,m}$ |
| $h^3 C_2$ | 1/6 | $1/2 \sum A_{q,\alpha}\theta_\alpha^2 - \sum Q_{q,m} m^3/6$ |
| $J_1 C_1$ | 1/6 | $\sum A_{q,\alpha} A_{\alpha,\beta}\theta_\beta - \sum Q_{q,m} m^3/6 + \sum A_{q,\alpha} Q_{\alpha,m} m^2/2$ |
| $h^4 C_3$ | 1/24 | $1/6 \sum A_{q,\alpha}\theta_\alpha^3 + \sum Q_{q,m} m^4/24$ |
| $K_1 C_1$ | 3/24 | $\sum A_{q,\alpha} A_{\alpha,\beta}\theta_\alpha\theta_\beta + \sum A_{q,\alpha} Q_{\alpha,m}\theta_\alpha m^2/2 + 3/24 \sum Q_{q,m} m^4$ |
| $J_1^2 C_1$ | 1/24 | $\sum A_{q,\alpha} A_{\alpha,\beta} A_{\beta,\gamma}\theta_\gamma - 1/6 \sum A_{q,\alpha} Q_{\alpha,m} m^3$ $+ \sum A_{q,\alpha} A_{\alpha,\beta} Q_{\beta,m} m^2/2 + 1/24 \sum Q_{q,m} m^4$ |
| $J_1 C_2$ | 1/24 | $1/2 \sum A_{q,\alpha} A_{\alpha,\beta}\theta_\beta^2 - 1/6 \sum A_{q,\alpha} Q_{\alpha,m} m^3 + 1/24 \sum Q_{q,m} m^4$ |

| | Taylor | Multistep Runge-Kutta |
|---|---|---|
| $h^5 C_4$ | 1/120 | $1/24 \sum A_{q,\alpha} \theta_\alpha^4 - 1/120 \sum Q_{q,m} m^5$ |
| $L_1 C_1$ | 6/120 | $1/2 \sum A_{q,\alpha} A_{\alpha,\beta} \theta_\alpha^2 \theta_\beta + \sum A_{q,\alpha} Q_{\alpha,m} \theta_\alpha^2 m^2/4 - 6/120 \sum Q_{q,m} m^5$ |
| $R$ | 3/120 | $1/2 \sum A_{q,\alpha} (\sum A_{\alpha,\beta} \theta_\beta + \sum Q_{\alpha,m} m^2/2)^2 - 3/120 \sum Q_{q,m} m^5$ |
| $K_1 C_2$ | 4/120 | $1/2 \sum A_{q,\alpha} A_{\alpha,\beta} \theta_\alpha \theta_\beta^2 - 4/120 \sum Q_{q,m} m^5 - \sum A_{q,\alpha} Q_{\alpha,m} \theta_\alpha m^3/6$ |
| $K_1 J_1 C_1$ | 4/120 | $\sum A_{q,\alpha} A_{\alpha,\beta} A_{\beta,\gamma} \theta_\alpha \theta_\gamma + 1/2 \sum A_{q,\alpha} A_{\alpha,\beta} Q_{\beta,m} \theta_\alpha m^2$ |
| | | $- 4/120 \sum Q_{q,m} m^5 - \sum A_{q,\alpha} Q_{\alpha,m} \theta_\alpha m^3/6$ |
| $J_1 K_1 C_1$ | 3/120 | $\sum A_{q,\alpha} A_{\alpha,\beta} A_{\beta,\gamma} \theta_\beta \theta_\gamma + 3/24 \sum A_{q,\alpha} Q_{\alpha,m} m^4$ |
| | | $+ 1/2 \sum A_{q,\alpha} A_{\alpha,\beta} Q_{\beta,m} \theta_\beta m^2 - 3/120 \sum Q_{q,m} m^5$ |
| $J_1 C_3$ | 1/120 | $1/6 \sum A_{q,\alpha} A_{\alpha,\beta} \theta_\beta^3 + \sum A_{q,\alpha} Q_{\alpha,m} m^4/24 - 1/120 \sum Q_{q,m} m^5$ |
| $J_1^3 C_1$ | 1/120 | $\sum A_{q,\alpha} A_{\alpha,\beta} A_{\beta,\gamma} A_{\gamma,\delta} \theta_\delta + \sum A_{q,\alpha} Q_{\alpha,m} m^4/24$ |
| | | $- 1/6 \sum A_{q,\alpha} A_{\alpha,\beta} Q_{\beta,m} m^2$ |
| | | $+ 1/2 \sum A_{q,\alpha} A_{\alpha,\beta} A_{\beta,\gamma} Q_{\gamma,m} m^2 - 1/120 \sum Q_{q,m} m^5$ |
| $J_1^2 C_2$ | 1/120 | $1/2 \sum A_{q,\alpha} A_{\alpha,\beta} A_{\beta,\gamma} \theta_\gamma^2 + \sum A_{q,\alpha} Q_{\alpha,m} m^4/24$ |
| | | $- 1/6 \sum A_{q,\alpha} A_{\alpha,\beta} Q_{\beta,m} m^2 - 1/120 \sum Q_{q,m} m^5$ |

## 8. Example of a formula.

We take $l = 1$ and one intermediate point, and hence $\theta_1 = -1$. We will simplify the writing by setting

$$\theta_2 = \theta.$$

It can be shown that it is possible to satisfy all the relations up to the fourth order inclusive by letting $\theta$ be arbitrary. The coefficients to be taken are the following:

| 0 | 1 | |
|---|---|---|
| $1 - \theta^2 (3 + 2\theta)$ | $\theta^2 (3 + 2\theta)$ | $Q$ |
| $\dfrac{8 (1 - \theta)}{1 + 2\theta}$ | $\dfrac{10\theta - 7}{1 + 2\theta}$ | |

| 0 | 0 | |
|---|---|---|
| $\theta + \theta^2 (2 + \theta)$ | $\theta^2 (1 + \theta)$ | $A$ |
| $\dfrac{8\theta^2 - 2\theta - 2}{\theta (1 + 2\theta)}$ | $\dfrac{4\theta^2 - 2}{(1 + \theta)(1 + 2\theta)}$ | $\dfrac{2}{\theta (1 + \theta)(1 + 2\theta)}$ |

We will call this formula RKL 1, 3, 4. The first number is the liaison number, the second is the total number of values used in the step, and the last one is the order. For example, let us take $\theta = 0.7$. We find the following numerical values:

| 0 | 1 | $Q$ |
|---|---|---|
| $-1.156$ | 2.156 | |
| 1 | 0 | |

| 0 | 0 | $A$ |
|---|---|---|
| 2,023 | 0.833 | |
| 221/714 | $-1/102$ | 250/357 |

## 9. Stability.

Let us apply the preceding formula to $y' = 0$. We have

$$y_{i+1} = \frac{8(1 - \theta)}{1 + 2\theta} y_i + \frac{10\theta - 7}{1 + 2\theta} y_{i-1},$$

a linear recurrence relation with constant coefficients whose characteristic equation is

$$(1 + 2\theta)r^2 + 8(\theta - 1)r + 7 - 10\theta = 0.$$

It has the root $r = 1$; the other factor is written as

$$(1 + 2\theta)r + 10\theta - 7 = 0.$$

The value of $r$ which annuls this factor will be called parasitic root. To avoid the instability phenomenon pointed out in Chapter 7, paragraph 5, it is necessary that the modulus of this parasitic root be less than 1. This condition is realized for

$$0.5 < \theta < 1.$$

## 10. An example of the use of this formula.

Let us consider the equation

$$y' = y, \qquad y(0) = e^{-h}, \qquad y_1 = 1, \qquad \theta = 0.7.$$

We have

$$y_2 = 1 + 250h\,(2.156\,e^{-h} - 1.156 + 0.833\,he^{-h} + 2.023\,h)/357$$
$$- he^{-h}/102 + 221\,h/714 \approx 1 + h + h^2/2 + h^3/6 + h^4/24 - 4h^5/120.$$

## 11. Final remark.

The two limit values $\theta = 1/2$ and $\theta = 1$ correspond to the formulas

$$\begin{cases} y_{1/2} = y_{-1} + h\,(9\,Y_0 + 3\,Y_{-1})/8, \\ y_1 = 2y_0 - y_{-1} + h\,(4\,Y_{1/2} - Y_{-1} - 3\,Y_0)/3, \end{cases}$$

$$\begin{cases} y_1^* = -4y_0 + 5y_1 + h\,(4\,Y_0 + 2\,Y_{-1}), \\ y_1 = y_{-1} + h\,(Y_{-1} + 4\,Y_0 + Y_1^*)/3. \end{cases}$$

These two formulas are only weakly stable.

## II   SOLUTION OF $x'' = X(x, t)$ WITHOUT USING THE FIRST DERIVATIVE

In this paragraph, we attempt to apply the Runge-Kutta principle to the methods of the Störmer type.

### 12.1 Principle.[1]

Let the system be in vectorial form:

$$x'' = X(x).$$

We propose to give a solution corresponding to the conditions

$$x(t_0) = x_0, \qquad x(t_1) = x_1.$$

For this, we will make use of the formulas

$$x_{i,\alpha} = x_i + \theta_\alpha (x_i - x_{i-1}) + \frac{h^2}{2} \sum_{\beta=0}^{\alpha-1} B_{\alpha,\beta} X_{i,\beta},$$

$$x_{i+1} = x_{i,q}.$$

### 12.2 Fundamental formulas.

The method consists usually of developing the exact and approximate solution in a Taylor series about the point

$$t_i, \ x_i, \ x_i'.$$

In order to be able to utilize $X_{i-1}$, we take $\theta_1 = -1$ and $B_{1,0} = 0$. We will make the simplifying hypothesis that all the intermediate points are exact at order 2, which implies

$$\sum_{\beta=0}^{\alpha-1} B_{\alpha,\beta} = \theta_\alpha + \theta_\alpha^2.$$

In particular,

$$\sum_{\alpha=0}^{q-1} B_{q,\alpha} = 2.$$

### 13. Evaluation of $X_{0,\alpha} - X_0$.

A calculation for which we refer to the work of Nugeyre gives

$$
\begin{aligned}
X_{0,\alpha} - X_0 = {} & h\theta_\alpha C_1 + h^2 \theta_\alpha^2/2\, C_2 \\
& + h^3 \{\theta_\alpha^3 C_3/6 + (\theta_\alpha/6 + \textstyle\sum B_{\alpha,\beta}\theta_\beta/2) J_2 C_1\} \\
& + h^4 \{\theta_\alpha^4 C_4/24 + (\theta_\alpha^2/6 + \theta_\alpha/2 \textstyle\sum B_{\alpha,\beta}\theta_\beta) K_2 C_1 \\
& + (\textstyle\sum B_{\alpha,\beta}\theta_\beta^2/4 - \theta_\alpha/24) J_2 C_2\} \\
& + h^5 \{\theta_\alpha^5 C_5/120 + [\theta_\alpha^3/12 + \theta_\alpha^2/4 \textstyle\sum B_{\alpha,\beta}\theta_\beta] L_2 C_1 + [\theta_\alpha/4 \\
& \textstyle\sum B_{\alpha,\beta}\theta_\beta^2 - \theta_\alpha^2/24] K_2 C_2 + (\theta_\alpha/120 + \textstyle\sum B_{\alpha,\beta}\theta_\beta^3/12) J_2 C_3 + \\
& \textstyle\sum B_{\alpha,\beta}\theta_\beta/12 + 1/4 \textstyle\sum B_{\alpha,\beta}B_{\beta,\gamma}\theta_\gamma) J_2^2 C_1\}.
\end{aligned}
$$

[1]Nugeyre.

### 14. Development of the exact and the approximate solution.

We deduce the following table.

|  | Taylor | Runge-Kutta |
|---|---|---|
| $h^3/2\,C_1$ | 1/3 | $1/3 + \sum B_{q,\alpha}\theta_\alpha$ |
| $h^4/2\,C_2$ | 1/12 | $-1/12 + 1/2 \sum B_{q,\alpha}\theta_\alpha^2$ |
| $h^5/2\,C_3$ | 1/60 | $1/60 + 1/6 \sum B_{q,\alpha}\theta_\alpha^3$ |
| $J_2 C_1$ | 1/60 | $1/60 + 1/6 \sum B_{q,\alpha}\theta_\alpha + 1/2 \sum B_{q,\alpha}B_{\alpha,\beta}\theta_\beta$ |
| $h^6/2\,C_4$ | 1/360 | $-1/360 + 1/24 \sum B_{q,\alpha}\theta_\alpha^4$ |
| $K_2 C_1$ | 4/360 | $-4/360 + 1/6 \sum B_{q,\alpha}\theta_\alpha^2 + 1/2 \sum B_{q,\alpha}B_{\alpha,\beta}\theta_\alpha\theta_\beta$ |
| $J_2 C_2$ | 1/360 | $-1/360 + 1/4 \sum B_{q,\alpha}B_{\alpha,\beta}\theta_\beta^2 - 1/24 \sum B_{q,\alpha}\theta_\alpha$ |
| $h^7/2\,C_5$ | 1/2520 | $1/2520 + 1/120 \sum B_{q,\alpha}\theta_\alpha^5$ |
| $K_2 C_2$ | 5/2520 | $5/2520 + 1/4 \sum B_{q,\alpha}B_{\alpha,\beta}\theta_\alpha\theta_\beta^2 - 1/24 \sum B_{q,\alpha}\theta_\alpha^2$ |
| $J_2 C_3$ | 1/2520 | $1/2520 + 1/120 \sum B_{q,\alpha}\theta_\alpha + 1/12 \sum B_{q,\alpha}B_{\alpha,\beta}\theta_\beta^3$ |
| $J_2^2 C_1$ | 1/2520 | $1/2520 + 1/12 \sum B_{q,\alpha}B_{\alpha,\beta}\theta_\beta + 1/4 \sum B_{q,\alpha}B_{\alpha,\beta}B_{\beta,\gamma}\theta_\gamma$ |
| $L_2 C_1$ | 10/2520 | $10/2520 + 1/12 \sum B_{q,\alpha}\theta_\alpha^3 + 1/4 \sum B_{q,\alpha}B_{\alpha,\beta}\theta_\alpha^2\theta_\beta$ |

### 15. Investigation for $q = 1$.

The only possible formula for $q = 1$ is the classic formula

$$x_{i+1} = 2x_i - x_{i-1} + h^2 X_i,$$

which, in our notation, is written as

| 0 | |
|---|---|
| 2 | 0 |

and costs one horner per step. We can easily see that it is of order 3. We will call it RKLS 1, 1, 3. It is identical to a central difference formula (Chapter 7, paragraph 14 or 21.1).

### 16.1 Investigation for $q = 2$.

We have

$$B_{20} + B_{21} = \theta_2 + \theta_2^2,$$
$$B_{30} + B_{31} + B_{32} = 2,$$
$$h^3 \,\big|\, B_{31}\theta_1 + B_{32}\theta_2 = 0, \tag{1}$$
$$h^4 \,\big|\, B_{31}\theta_1^2 + B_{32}\theta_2^2 = 1/3. \tag{2}$$

As these formulas also permit indeterminacies, let us write the terms $h^5$:

$$h^5 \,\big|\, B_{31}\theta_1^3 + B_{32}\theta_2^3 = 0,$$
$$h^5 \,\big|\, B_{32}B_{21}\theta_1 = 0. \tag{3}$$

We cannot take $B_{32} = 0$ or $\theta_1 = 0$. Thus it is necessary to take $B_{21} = 0$.

The three equations (1), (2), and (3) are compatible if $\theta_1^2 = \theta_2^2$. The solution $\theta_1 = \theta_2$ leads to an incompatibility. Thus we have

$$\theta_2 = -\theta_1 = 1.$$

The coefficients of this formula are written in matrix form:

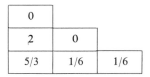

It costs two horners per step and is of order 5. We will call this formula RKLS 1, 2, 5.

### 16.2 Example.

Let the equation be

$$y'' = (1 + t^2)y, \qquad y(0) = 1, \qquad y(0.1) = 1.005,012,56, \qquad h = 0.1.$$

| $t$ | $y_i$ | Error |
|-----|-------|-------|
| 0.0 | 1.000,000,00 | |
| 0.1 | 1.005,012,56 | $-4 \cdot 10^{-8}$ |
| 0.2 | 1.020,201,46 | $-12$ |
| 0.3 | 1.046,028,10 | $-24$ |
| 0.4 | 1.083,287,48 | $-41$ |
| 0.5 | 1.133,149,10 | $-65$ |
| 1.0 | 1.648,725,02 | $-375$ |
| 1.5 | 3.080,233,89 | $-1704$ |
| 2.0 | 7,389,132,82 | $-7672$ |

### 17.1 Investigation for $q = 3$.

Let us write the equations which correspond to terms up to $h^6$ inclusive:

$$B_{10} = \theta_1 + \theta_1^2,$$
$$B_{20} + B_{21} = \theta_2 + \theta_2^2,$$
$$B_{30} + B_{31} + B_{32} = \theta_3 + \theta_3^2,$$
$$B_{40} + B_{41} + B_{42} + B_{43} = 2.$$

$h^3$   $B_{41}\theta_1 + B_{42}\theta_2 + B_{43}\theta_3 = 0,$        (1)

$h^4$   $B_{41}\theta_1^2 + B_{42}\theta_2^2 + B_{43}\theta_3^2 = 1/3.$        (2)

$h^5$   $B_{41}\theta_1^3 + B_{42}\theta_2^3 + B_{43}\theta_3^3 = 0,$        (3)

$h^5$   $B_{43}(B_{32}\theta_2 + B_{31}\theta_1) + B_{42}B_{21}\theta_1 = 0,$        (4)

$h^6$   $B_{41}\theta_1^4 + B_{42}\theta_2^4 + B_{43}\theta_3^4 = 2/15,$        (5)

$h^6$   $B_{43}\theta_3(B_{32}\theta_2 + B_{31}\theta_1) + B_{42}\theta_2 B_{21}\theta_1 = -1/15,$        (6)

$h^6$   $B_{43}(B_{32}\theta_2^2 + B_{31}\theta_1^2) + B_{42}B_{21}\theta_1^2 = 1/45.$        (7)

The compatibility of the system (1), (2), (3), and (5) requires that

$$(\theta_1 - \theta_2)(\theta_2 - \theta_3)(\theta_3 - \theta_1)\,[\theta_1\theta_2 + \theta_1\theta_3 + \theta_2\theta_3 + 2/5] = 0,$$

with $\theta_1 = -1$. The cases

$$\theta_1 = \theta_2, \qquad \theta_1 = \theta_3, \qquad \theta_2 = \theta_3,$$

as one can easily see, lead to incompatibility. Hence we have

$$\theta_1 = -1 \qquad \theta_2\theta_3 = \theta_2 + \theta_3 - 2/5,$$

$$B_{41} = -\frac{1}{3}\frac{\theta_2 + \theta_3}{\theta_1\,(\theta_3 - \theta_1)(\theta_2 - \theta_1)}, \qquad B_{42} = -\frac{1}{3}\frac{\theta_3 + \theta_1}{\theta_2\,(\theta_1 - \theta_2)(\theta_3 - \theta_2)},$$

$$B_{43} = -\frac{1}{3}\frac{\theta_1 + \theta_2}{\theta_3\,(\theta_2 - \theta_3)(\theta_1 - \theta_3)}, \qquad B_{21} = \frac{1}{5}\frac{\theta_2}{\theta_1}\frac{\theta_2 - \theta_1}{\theta_3 + \theta_1}.$$

$$B_{31} = -\frac{1}{15}\frac{\theta_3}{\theta_1}\frac{\theta_1 - \theta_3}{\theta_1^2 - \theta_2^2}\,(3\theta_1 - 2\theta_2 - \theta_3),$$

$$B_{32} = -\frac{1}{15}\frac{\theta_3}{\theta_2}\frac{(\theta_2 - \theta_3)(\theta_1 - \theta_3)}{\theta_1^2 - \theta_2^2}.$$

We can take, for example,

$$\theta_1 = -1, \qquad \theta_2 = 0.5, \qquad \theta_3 = -0.2,$$

which leads to the formula

| 0 | | | |
|---|---|---|---|
| | | *B* | |
| 0.625 | 0.125 | | |
| −5664/45,000 | −2432/45,000 | 896/45,000 | |
| −28/84 | 7/84 | 64/84 | 125/84 |

The formula costs three horners per step and is of order 6. We will call it RKLS 1, 3, 6.

### 17.2 Example.

$$y'' = -1/(te^y),$$
$$y(1) = 0, \qquad y(1.1) = 0.095,310,164,0.$$

| $t$ | $y$ exact | Exact values |
|---|---|---|
| 1.2 | 0.182,321,517 | 56 |
| 1.3 | 0.262,364,196 | 264 |
| 1.4 | 0.336,472,137 | 236 |
| 1.5 | 0.405,464,976 | 5108 |
| 2.0 | 0.693,146,873 | 7180 |
| 2.5 | 0.916,290,230 | 731 |
| 3.0 | 1.098,611,65 | 228 |
| 3.5 | 1.252,762,35 | 96 |
| 4.0 | 1.386,293,85 | 436 |
| 4.5 | 1.504,077,11 | 39 |
| 5.0 | 1.609,437,98 | 1 |

## Problems

1. Using a step size of 0.1 and the RKL 1, 3, 4, formula, repeat the computations for problems 1 through 3 of Chapter 6.

2. Using a step size of 0.1, compute the solution to problems 5 and 6 of Chapter 6 by means of (a) RKLS 1, 1, 3; (b) RKLS 1, 2, 5. Which method gives the least error?

# III

# THEORETICAL AND
# PRACTICAL CONSIDERATIONS

# 9 THEORETICAL CONSIDERATIONS

## I INVARIANCE PROPERTIES

### 1.1 A very general method.

Let us consider the system

$$x^{(p)} = X(x, x', \ldots, x^{(p-1)}).$$

We will apply to it the very general method

$$x_{i,\,\alpha}^{(p=k)} = \sum_{s=p-k}^{p-1} \sum_{j=\mu}^{v} K_{\alpha,\,j,\,s}^* \frac{h^s}{s!} x_{i-j}^{(s)} + \frac{h^k}{k!} \sum_{j=\mu}^{v} K_{\alpha,\,j,\,p}^* X_{i-j}$$

$$+ \frac{h^k}{k!} \sum_{\beta=0}^{\alpha-1} K_{\alpha,\,\beta} X_{i,\,\beta}, \qquad t_{i,\,\alpha} = t_i + h\theta_\alpha, \tag{I}$$

$$x_{i+1}^{(p-k)} = x_{i,\,q}^{(p-k)}.$$

This method contains as special cases those of Runge-Kutta ($\mu = v = 0$) and the multistep methods of Chapters 6, 7, and 8.

### 1.2 Order of such a method.

Let us suppose that all the $x_{i-j}$ entering into the second members are exact. From these formulas we deduce the values of $x_{i+1}^{(p-k)}$ exact up to the terms $h^{\omega_1}$, $^{\omega_2} h$, .... The order of the formula is

$$\omega = (\omega_1, \omega_2, \ldots).$$

We will suppose that all the intermediate values are exact of the order:

$$(1, 2, \ldots, k, \ldots, p).$$

This requires a certain number of easily written conditions on the coefficients.

## 2.1 Invariance by addition of a polynomial.

Let us set

$$x(t) = P_p(t) + z(t),$$

where $P_p(t)$ denotes a polynomial of degree $p$. The column $z(t)$ satisfies the differential system:

$$z^{(p)}(t) = X[P_p(t) + z(t), P'_p(t) + z'(t), \ldots, P_p^{(p-1)}(t) + z^{(p-1)}(t)] - P_p^{(p)}(t)$$
$$= Z(z, z', \ldots, z^{(p-1)}).$$

If we apply the above-mentioned method at the same time to the system which gives $x$ and to the system which gives $z$, the intermediate values would correspond through the formulas

$$x_{i,\alpha}^{(p-k)} = z_{i,\alpha}^{(p-k)} + P_p^{(p-k)}(t_i + \theta_\alpha h),$$

provided that such is the case at the start of the calculation. Let us remark that $P_p^{(p)}(t)$ is a constant which we will denote by $P$. The demonstration is done by the repetition over $i$ and over $\alpha$. If the property is exact for all the values of the subscripts $i$ and $\alpha$, we can write

$$x_{i,\alpha}^{(p-k)} - z_{i,\alpha}^{(p-k)} = \sum_{s,j} \frac{h^2}{s!} [x_{i-j}^{(s)} - z_{i-j}^{(s)}] K^*_{\alpha,j,s}$$

$$+ \frac{h^k}{k!} \sum_j K^*_{\alpha,j,p} [X_{i-j} - Z_{i-j}] + \frac{h^k}{k!} \sum_\beta K_{\alpha,\beta} (X_{i,\beta} - Z_{i,\beta})$$

$$= \sum_{s,j} \frac{h^s}{s!} K^*_{\alpha,j,s} P_p^{(s)}(t_{i-j}) + \frac{h^k}{k!} \sum_j K^*_{\alpha,j,p} P + \frac{h^k}{k!} \sum_\beta K_{\alpha,\beta} P$$

$$= P_p^{(p-k)}(t_i + h\theta_\alpha).$$

The condition of exactness of the intermediary values of the order

$$(1, 2, \ldots, p)$$

immediately brings about the equality of the third and fourth members, which demonstrates the property.

We can use the property to restore the initial conditions to

$$x_0 = x'_0 = \cdots = x_0^{(p-1)} = 0.$$

## 2.2 Invariance by a linear transformation with constant coefficients.

Let us return to the preceding system, and submit it to the transformation

$$x = Cz,$$

where $C$ is a constant nonsingular matrix. We have

$$x' = Cz', \qquad x^{(p-1)} = Cz^{(p-1)}, \qquad X(Cz, Cz', \ldots) = CZ.$$

We immediately deduce that the intermediary values

$$x_{i,\alpha}^{(p-k)} \quad \text{and} \quad z_{i,\alpha}^{(p-k)}$$

correspond through the transformation $C$, provided that it also holds for the starting values.

## II  PROPERTIES OF THE CHARACTERISTIC ROOTS

### 3. Investigation of a linear and homogeneous system with constant coefficients.

Consider the linear homogeneous system with constant coefficients:

$$x^{(p)} = L(x, x', \ldots, x^{(p-1)}). \qquad (E)$$

Its solution is normally expressed by means of exponentials:

$$e^{at}, e^{bt}, \ldots.$$

The numbers $a, b, \ldots$ are the characteristic values of system $(E)$. They are given by an easily written algebraic equation; it is the characteristic equation of system $(E)$.

The relations $(I)$ of paragraph 1.1 applied to $(E)$ give a system $(I')$ which is also linear and homogeneous with constant coefficients. We can associate with it a characteristic equation which we find by looking for $(I')$ particular solutions of the form

$$x_{i, \alpha}^{(p-k)} = a_{\alpha,\, p-k,\, \rho} r_{\rho}^{i}.$$

We will call $r_{\rho}$ the characteristic roots of the solution of the system $(E)$ obtained by means of the approximate formulas $(I)$.

### 4.1  Properties of these roots for a system in canonical form.

Let the linear and homogeneous system be in the canonical form

$$x' = Mx, \qquad (E')$$

and its approximate solution given by means of formulas $(I)$. If the eigenvalues of $C$ are all distinct, we can find a linear transformation with constant coefficients

$$x = Cx^*$$

which reduce the system $(E')$ to the form

$$y' = ay, \qquad z' = bz, \qquad u' = cu, \ldots, \qquad (E'')$$

i.e., to $n$ linear and homogeneous first order equations. The numbers $a$, $b$, $c$, $\ldots$ are the characteristic roots of the differential system $(E')$.

The same transformation $C$ applied to the approximate solution formula decomposes it to $n$ partial formulas, each one relative to one of the constituent equations of $(E'')$. It results that the characteristic roots of the solution of $(E')$ by the approximate formulas $(I)$ depend each only on one of the characteristic roots $a$, $b$, $c$, ... of $(E')$. We will express this property by saying that the formulas $(I)$ do not establish a coupling between the characteristic roots or a system in the canonical form.

### 4.2 Example.

Let us consider the system in canonical form:

$$y' = z, \qquad z' = (a + b)z - aby,$$

whose characteristic roots are $a$ and $b$. Let us apply to it Nyström's approximate solution formula (Chapter 6, paragraph 9.1):

$$x_{i+1} = x_{i-1} + 2hX_i.$$

We have

$$y_{i+1} = y_{i-1} + 2hz_i, \qquad z_{i+1} = z_{1-1} + 2h[(a + b) z_i - aby_i],$$

whose characteristic roots are given by

$$\begin{vmatrix} r^2 - 1 & -2hr \\ 2habr & r^2 - 1 - 2hr(a + b) \end{vmatrix} = 0,$$

which reduces to

$$(r^2 - 1 - 2rha)(r^2 - 1 - 2rhb) = 0.$$

The two roots of the first factor depend only on $a$; the two roots of the second factor depend only on $b$.

### 4.3 Example of a system not in canonical form.

Let us consider the equation

$$y'' - (a + b)y' + ab\, y = 0,$$

whose characteristic roots are $a$ and $b$, and let us apply to it the Runge-Kutta method of order 1, defined by

$$y'_{i+1} = y'_i + h[(a + b)y'_i - aby_i],$$

$$y_{i+1} = y_i + hy'_i + \left(\frac{h^2}{2}\right)[(a + b)y'_i - aby_i].$$

The characteristic roots of this linear system are given by

$$\begin{vmatrix} r - 1 - h(a + b) & hab \\ -h - \left(\frac{h^2}{2}\right)(a + b) & r - 1 + \left(\frac{h^2}{2}\right)ab \end{vmatrix} = 0,$$

i.e., in expanded form:

$$(r - 1)^2 - (r - 1)\left[h(a + b) - \left(\frac{h^2}{2}\right)ab\right] + h^2ab = 0.$$

The expansions of these roots in powers of $h$ are written as

$$r_1 = 1 + ah + \frac{a^2 b}{2(b-a)} h^2 + \cdots,$$

$$r_2 = 1 + bh + \frac{ab^2 h^2}{2(b-a)} + \cdots.$$

We see that the two roots depend on $a$ and $b$ at the same time.

### 5. Investigation of the principal roots.

In Chapter 7, paragraph 6.4, we distinguished between the principal and the parasitic roots among the characteristic roots of a linear homogeneous system with constant coefficients. Essentially, we will suppose that the number of the characteristic roots tending to 1 as $h$ tends to zero, is equal to the order of the system. These are the roots which we will call the principal roots.

If the proposed system is in the canonical form, we will suppose that its characteristic roots are distinct, and by virtue of 4.1, we will content ourselves with the study of the first order equation

$$y' = ay.$$

### 6.1 Properties of the principal roots in the case of a system in canonical form.

Let $\omega$ be the order of the formulas ($I$). According to paragraph 4.1, we can content ourselves by studying one single equation. In applying ($I$) to

$$y' = ay,$$

we find a linear and homogeneous system. If in this system we eliminate the

$$y_{i,\alpha},$$

we arrive at a linear and homogeneous system which we can write

$$y_{i+1} = \sum_{j=\mu}^{v} M_j(h) y_{i-j}.$$

According to the definition of the order, if we substitute in this system

$$y_{i=j} = e^{-jha}$$

we find that the equality is verified up to $O(h^{\omega+1})$. The characteristic equation of the approximate solution can be written as

$$r^{v+1} = \sum_{j=\mu}^{v} M_j(h) r^{v-j}.$$

According to the preceding, the substitution $r = e^{ah}$ verifies this equation up to $O(h^{\omega+1})$. By hypothesis one root of this equation tends to 1 as $h$ tends to zero, and thus $e^{ah}$ is an approximation of this root up to $O(h^{\omega+1})$.

### 6.2 Case of the Runge-Kutta formulas.

Let us apply to $y' = ay$ a Runge-Kutta formula whose order $q$ is equal to the rank. The approximate solution after one step is

$$1 + \frac{ah}{1} + \cdots + \frac{a^q h^q}{q!} = \alpha.$$

Actually, this value has to be an approximation of $e^{ah}$ exact up to order $q$. Moreover, it is easy to see that it is a polynomial in $h$ of degree $q$, which achieves the determination of the approximation.

It is quite clear that $\alpha$ is the characteristic root of the approximate solution, because the approximate relation is written as

$$y_{i+1} = \varphi(a, h) \, y_i,$$

whence

$$\varphi(a, h) = \alpha.$$

### 7.1 Case of a system not in canonical form.

We will content ourselves with explaining what happens in the case of the equation

$$y'' = (a + b) \, y' - aby.$$

The order of the formulas $(I)$ is then

$$\omega = (\omega_1, \omega_2).$$

$\omega_1$ corresponds to $y'$, $\omega_2$ corresponds to $y$. We set

$$\sigma = \min(\omega_1, \omega_2).$$

It is quite evident that $\sigma \geqslant 1$.

In applying $(I)$ to the equation mentioned above and clearing off the $y_{i,\alpha}$ and $y'_{i,\alpha}$, we arrive at two relations:

$$y'_{i+1} = \sum_j M_j(h) y'_{i-j} + h \sum_j N_j(h) y_{i-j},$$

$$y_{i+1} = h \sum_j M_j^*(h) y'_{i-j} + \sum_j N_j^*(h) y_{i-j}.$$

According to the definition of the order, the substitution of

$$y_i = e^{aih}, \qquad y'_i = a e^{aih}$$

in these relations gives between the two members differences, which are

$$O(h^{\sigma+1}), \qquad O(h^{\sigma+1}).$$

As $\sigma \geqslant 1$, we can affirm that there is a root of the form

$$e^{ah} + O(h^k)$$

and another of the form

$$e^{bh} + O(h^{k'}).$$

$k$ and $k' \geqslant 2$.

In order to study the infinitesimal order of the root in the neighborhood of $e^{ah}$, let us write the characteristic equation of the approximate relation:

$$\begin{vmatrix} r^{v+1} - \sum_j M_j(h)r^{v-j} & h \sum_j N_j(h)r^{v-j} \\ -h \sum_j M_j^*(h)r^{v-j} & r^{v+1} - \sum_j N_j^*(h)r^{v-j} \end{vmatrix} = 0,$$

where $r = e^{ah}$. If we multiply the second column by $-1/a$ and then add it to the first one, we arrive at the results:

$$O(h^{\omega_1+1}), \qquad O(h^{\omega_2+1}).$$

For $r = e^{ah}$, the two terms of the second column are clearly $O(h)$, and hence the determinant is

$$O(h^{\sigma+2}).$$

As the difference $e^{ah} - e^{bh}$ is $O(h)$, the root near $e^{ah}$ is

$$e^{ah} + O(h^{\sigma+1}).$$

Thus $e^{ah}$ and $e^{bh}$ are the approximations of the characteristic roots of the approximate system at least up to the order $\sigma$.

### 7.2 Examples.

1. In paragraph 4.3 we studied the preceding equation by Euler's method. We found roots exact up to order 1:

$$\omega_1 = 1, \qquad \omega_2 = 2, \qquad \sigma = 1.$$

2. $y'' = y$ by the formula:

$$y'_{i+1} = y'_i + \frac{h(Y_i + Y_{i+1})}{2},$$

$$y_{i+1} = y_i + hy'_i + \frac{h^2(Y_i + 2Y_{i+1})}{6}.$$

In this case we have

$$\omega_1 = 2, \qquad \omega_2 = 3, \qquad \sigma = 2.$$

The characteristic equation is

$$\begin{vmatrix} r - 1 & -\dfrac{h(r+1)}{2} \\ -h & r - 1 - \dfrac{h^2(1+2r)}{6} \end{vmatrix} = 0.$$

For the root close to $eh$, we find

$$1 + h + \frac{h^2}{2} + \frac{7h^3}{24}.$$

The approximation is of order 2.

**8.1 Case of the equation $y'' = Y(y, t)$ by a method which does not use the first derivatives.**

The preceding method is not applicable to this case; the formula relative to the first derivative does not exist. Let us return to the theory. Let $\omega$ be the order of the method and $a$ a characteristic root of the equation. The substitution of $e^{ah}$ in the approximate solution formulas gives a result:

$$O(h^{\omega+1}).$$

But there are two principal roots and, therefore, the considered principal root is approximated by $e^{ah}$ with only an error of

$$O(h^{\omega}).$$

We see that in comparison with methods using the first derivative, we lose one unit of the order of the approximation of $e^{ah}$.

**8.2 Example.**

Let $y'' = y$ by the formula

$$y_{i+1} = 2y_i - y_{i-1} + h_2 Y_i,$$

$$\omega = 3.$$

For the principal root close to $e^h$ we find

$$1 + h + \frac{h^2}{2} + \frac{h^3}{8},$$

which is only an approximation of order 2.

*Remark.* We would lose, likewise, $p - 1$ units of the order of approximation of $e^{ah}$ in a formula of the type shown in Chapter 7, paragraph 13 and the following.

### III  PROPAGATION MATRICES

In this paragraph, we propose to study the behavior of the infinitely small variations of a given integral. It will suffice for us to consider systems in the canonical form, since the passage to the canonical form transforms the finite variations of an integral into finite variations of an integral.

**9. Variational system of a system in canonical form.**

Consider the system

$$\begin{cases} y' = Y(y, z, t), \\ z' = Z(y, z, t), \end{cases}$$

and an integral $y + y^*$, $z + z^*$ close to the integral $y(t)$, $z(t)$. We can write

$$y' + (y^*)' = Y(y + y^*, z + z^*, t), \qquad z' + (z^*)' = Z(y + y^*, z + z^*, t),$$

or also

$$(y^*)' = Y(y + y^*, z + z^*, t) - Y(y, z, t),$$
$$(z^*)' = Z(y + y^*, z + z^*, t) - Z(y, z, t).$$

If we consider $y^*$ and $z^*$ to be infinitesimally small, we can write

$$\begin{cases} (y^*)' = Y'_y(y, z, t)y^* + Y'_z(y, z, t)z^*, \\ (z^*)' = Z'_y(y, z, t)y^* + Z'_z(y, z, t)z^*. \end{cases}$$

This system is called the *variational system* of the given system. This is a linear and homogeneous system.

## 10. Propagation matrix.

We will set

$$J(t) = \begin{Vmatrix} Y'_y(y, z, t) & Y'_z(y, z, t) \\ Z'_y(y, z, t) & Z'_z(y, z, t) \end{Vmatrix}.$$

We will call the following matrix a *propagation matrix* and denote it by $M(t, t_0)$:

$$\begin{Vmatrix} y_1^*(t) & y_2^*(t) \\ z_1^*(t) & z_2^*(t) \end{Vmatrix}$$

whose columns are the solutions of the variational system

$$M'_t = J \cdot M$$

satisfying the initial conditions:

$$y_1^*(t_0) = 1, \qquad y_2^*(t_0) = 0,$$
$$z_1^*(t_0) = 0, \qquad z_2^*(t_0) = 1,$$

or $M(t_0, t_0) = I$. It is clear that, if one sets

$$\Lambda = \begin{Vmatrix} \lambda \\ \mu \end{Vmatrix},$$

$M(t, t_0)\Lambda$ represents the solution of the variational system satisfying the initial conditions:

$$y^*(t_0) = \lambda, \qquad z^*(t_0) = \mu.$$

## 11. Property of invariance of the propagation matrix.

a. The propagation matrix is invariant under a change of variable. Indeed, such a change transforms finite variations into finite variations and therefore, before and after,

$$\Lambda(t) = M(t, t_0)\Lambda(t_0),$$

which requires the invariance of $M(t, t_0)$.

b. A linear transformation with constant coefficients applied to the unknown functions

$$\left\| \begin{matrix} u \\ v \end{matrix} \right\| = C \left\| \begin{matrix} y \\ z \end{matrix} \right\|$$

replaces $M$ by $CMC^{-1}$ for the same reason.

### 12.1 Algebraic properties of the propagation matrix.

We are going to show that

$$M(u, v) \cdot M(v, w) = M(u, w).$$

Indeed, consider

$$M(u, v) \, M(v, w) = P(u).$$

This matrix satisfies

$$P'(u) = JP(u), \qquad P(v) = M(v, w).$$

These two conditions constitute an initial value problem whose solution we already know. It is $M(u, w)$; hence

$$P(u) = M(u, w).$$

### 12.2 Differential properties of the propagation matrix.

The matrix $M(u, v)$ is differentiable, not only with respect to $u$, but also with respect to $v$. In order to obtain an identity on this subject, consider the relation

$$M(t, u) \, M(u, v) = M(t, v),$$

and differentiate the two members with respect to $u$. We have

$$M'_u(t, u) \, M(u, v) + M(t, u) \, M'_u(u, v) = 0.$$

Let us take $u = v$, and we arrive at

$$M'_u(t, u) = -M(t, u) \, J(u).$$

### 12.3 Integration of a nonhomogeneous equation.

Consider the equation

$$z' = Jz + \theta(t)$$

and let us look for its solution, which is zero, for $t = t_0$ by the method of the variation of constants.

Set

$$z(t) = M(t, t_0) \, A(t).$$

Then

$$M'_t(t, t_0) \, A(t) + M(t, t_0) \, A'(t) = JM(t, t_0) \, A(t) + \theta(t),$$

whence

$$A'(t) = M^{-1}(t, t_0)\theta(t),$$

$$A(t) = \int_{t_0}^{t} M^{-1}(u, t_0)\theta(u)\, du,$$

$$z(t) = M(t, t_0) \int_{t_0}^{t} M^{-1}(u, t_0)\theta(u)\, du$$

$$= \int_{t_0}^{t} M(t, u)\theta(u)\, du.$$

### 13  Use of the propagation matrix as a characteristic of a problem.

Frequently, questions are posed on the subject of the difficulty of a problem of approximate integration. It is quite obvious that this difficulty depends to a more or less large extent on the interval of integration. But the length of the interval itself is without significance. For example, the two problems

$$y' = 100y, \qquad 0 \leqslant x \leqslant 0.1,$$
$$y' = y, \qquad 0 \leqslant t \leqslant 10$$

are one and the same problem, since one can pass from one to the other by setting

$$x = 0.01\ t.$$

It is better to characterize a problem by its propagation matrix.

At first, we will examine the case of only one first order equation.

### 14.  Propagation function.

Let the problem be

$$y' = Y(y, t), \qquad y(t_0) = y_0$$

and $y(t)$ its solution. The propagation matrix reduces to

$$\lambda(t) = \exp\left( \int_{t_0}^{t} Y'_y[y(u), u]\, du \right), \qquad \lambda(t_0) = 1.$$

We will call this quantity the *propagation function*. The value of this function $\lambda(t)$ at the point $t$ gives the ratio of the variations for the abscissas $t$ and $t_0$ of $y(t)$ and an infinitely small variation. It will serve to indicate the degree of the difficulties which result from the propagation of errors.

### 15.1  Propagation parameter.

Very often the propagation function has a regular behavior. Therefore,

$$\lambda(t_0) = 1.$$

It is hence sufficiently defined by its value at the end of the interval of integration:

$$\lambda = \exp\left(\int_{t_0}^{t_n} Y_y'[y(u), u]\, du\right).$$

We will call this number the *propagation parameter*.

### 15.2 Dimension of this quantity.

Let us suppose that the equation

$$y' = Y(y, t)$$

is homogeneous in the sense of the measure of the magnitudes. Whatever the dimensions attributed to $y$ and to $t$, the propagation parameter is a dimensionless number. Indeed, $t$ is of dimension $\tau$; $y$ is of dimension $\eta$; $Y = y'$ is of dimension $\eta^{\tau-1}$; $Y_y' = \partial Y / \partial y$ is of dimension $\tau^{-1}$; $\int Y_y' \, dt$ is of dimension 1.

### 15.3 Examples of propagation parameters.

Let us return to the major examples presented previously.

1.                    $$y' = -y, \qquad 0 \leqslant t \leqslant 3.$$

The propagation function is $\lambda(t) = e^{-t}$. The propagation of errors is well portrayed by $\lambda(3) \approx 0.05$.

2.                    $$y' = y - 1.5e^{-0.5t}, \qquad 0 \leqslant t \leqslant 3,$$
$$\lambda(t) = e^t.$$

The propagation of errors is portrayed by $\lambda(3) \approx 20$.

*Remark.* For linear problems, the propagation function is independent of the considered integral.

3.              $$y' = y - \frac{2t}{y}, \qquad y(0) = 1, \qquad 0 \leqslant t \leqslant 2.$$

We find

$$y = \sqrt{2t + 1}, \qquad \lambda(t) = \frac{e^{2t}}{\sqrt{2t + 1}},$$

which gives

| $t$ | 0 | 1 | 2 |
|---|---|---|---|
| $\lambda$ | 1 | 4.25 | 24.5 |

The propagation of errors is given well by $\lambda(2) \approx 24.5$.

4.                    $$y' = 0.1\, y^2 - ty, \qquad y(0) = 1.$$

We find

| $t$ | 0 | 0.1 | 0.2 | 0.4 | 0.8 | 1.2 |
|---|---|---|---|---|---|---|
| $\lambda$ | 1 | 1 | 1.02 | 0.82 | 0.53 | 0.33 |

The propagation of errors is fairly well given by $\lambda(1.2) \approx 0.33$.

5. $$y' = -2ty^2, \qquad y(0) = 1, \qquad 0 \leqslant t \leqslant 2.$$

We find

$$\lambda(t) = \frac{1}{(1 + t^2)^2}.$$

$\lambda(2) = 0.04$ characterizes the propagation of error.

### 16. Case of several unknown functions.

A simple example will show that, in this case, the situation is much more complicated. Let the system be

$$y' = y, \qquad z' = -z.$$

It is its proper variational system. So far as $z$ is concerned, the integrals approach; they diverge so far as $y$ is concerned. In other words, a small circle in plane $t = 0$ transforms itself into an ellipse in the plane $t = a \, (a > 0)$. The axis of this ellipse situated in the $y$ plane grows indefinitely with $a$, whereas the axis in the $z$ plane tends toward zero (Fig. 9-1).

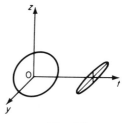

Fig. 9-1

### 17.1 Explanation of the phenomenon stated in Chapter 2, paragraph 10.

We have stated numerically that it would be more advantageous to integrate $y'' = y$, $y(0) = -y'(0)$ by passing to the canonical form rather than to keep the second derivative. In order to explain, let us write the canonical form: $y' = z$, $z' = y$ or by setting

$$y + z = u, \qquad y - z = v, \qquad \begin{cases} u' = u, \\ v' = -v. \end{cases}$$

We see that for the chosen initial conditions, the integration in the canonical form reduces to the integration of

$$v' = -v,$$

whose propagation function is $e^{-t}$. On the other hand, if we keep the second derivative, the errors carry over at the same time to $y$ and $z$, and hence to $u$ and $v$. But the propagation function of $u$ is $e^{t}$.

*Remark.* This circumstance presents itself only for particularly chosen initial conditions.

### 17.2 Return to the rule of conservation of orders.[1]

In a more precise manner, let us examine what occurs at the time of integration of the preceding equation by a method which gives a different

[1]Ceschino-Kuntzmann [2], Rutishauser [2, 3].

infinitesimal order for $y$ and $y'$. In Chapter 2, paragraph 3 we posed the rule of conservation of orders. This rule is valid for a finite number of steps. We will see that it is not so for a finite interval, where the number of steps increases indefinitely as $h$ tends to zero. Actually, in order to study the propagation of the error, it is necessary to pass to the canonical form

$$y' = z, \qquad z' = y.$$

In the $y$, $z$ plane, the error vector at one step has its component in the $Oy$ direction of a higher order than that of its component in the $Oz$ direction. But in order to study the propagation, it is necessary to project on the $Ou$ and $Ov$ axes the eigenvectors of the propagation matrix. These components have the same infinitesimal order as the component on the $Oz$ axis. The component in the direction of $Ou$ is amplified; the component in the direction of $Ov$ is diminished by the propagation. If, at the end of a finite interval, we return to the $Oy$ and $Oz$ axes, we will find two vectors having the same infinitesimal order.

### 18. Remark on the previous derivation method.

This method was presented in Chapter 5. Let us study its effect on the propagation of errors. Let the example be

$$y' = -y.$$

The propagation function of the equation is $e^{-t}$; i.e., the propagation diminishes the errors.

By the previous derivation we obtain

$$y'' = y.$$

But the situation is not the same as in paragraph 16. As a matter of fact, at the beginning of each step, we use again $y' = -y$. If we study the propagation, along the exact integrals, of the error committed at a certain abscissa we perceive that this error does not involve any component which propagates like

$$z' = z.$$

The previous derivation hence does not modify the propagation of errors.

### 19.1 Statistical consideration.

Let us return to the finite variations for a system which, in the canonical form, would contain, for example, four unknown functions $x(t)$, $y(t)$, $z(t)$, $u(t)$. Suppose that, at the abscissa $t_0$, we give the initial conditions $x_0$, $y_0$, $z_0$, $u_0$ and very small variations $\delta x_0$, $\delta y_0$, $\delta z_0$, $\delta t_0$, with

$$\delta x_0^2 + \delta y_0^2 + \delta z_0^2 + \delta t_0^2 = K.$$

Further, let us assume that this distribution is bearing a uniform probability density on the hypersphere:

$$\delta x_0^2 + \delta y_0^2 + \delta z_0^2 + \delta t_0^2 = K.$$

We propose to investigate the mean value of

$$\delta^2 x(t) + \delta^2 y(t) + \delta^2 z(t) + \delta^2 u(t).$$

We have

$$X = M(t, t_0) X_0,$$

where $X_0$ and $X$ denote the vectors with components

$$\delta x_0, \delta y_0, \delta z_0, \delta u_0 \quad \text{and} \quad \delta x, \delta y, \delta z, \delta t,$$

respectively. Or, expressing the quantities in terms of the appropriate matrix, we have

$$X^* X = X_0^* M^* M X_0.$$

The matrix $M^* M$ is symmetric, and positive definite. In putting it back into the diagonal form by a change of rectangular cartesian co-ordinates and denoting its eigenvalues by

$$a^2, b^2, c^2, d^2,$$

we are led to investigate:

$$\frac{\iiint (a^2 \delta x_0^2 + b^2 \delta y_0^2 + c^2 \delta z_0^2 + d^2 \delta u_0^2)\, d\sigma}{\iiint (\delta x_0^2 + \delta y_0^2 + \delta z_0^2 + \delta u_0^2)\, d\sigma}$$

where $\sigma$ is the element of area of the hypersphere. This relation gives

$$\frac{a^2 + b^2 + c^2 + d^2}{4}.$$

This quantity is easily calculated by starting from the matrix $M$; it is in the general case of $n$ unknown functions that

$$\left(\frac{1}{n}\right) \times \text{sum of the squares of the elements of } M.$$

It is the square root of this quantity in which we are interested as the function of propagation. Note that the large eigenvalues are more important than the small ones.

### 19.2 Example.

For $y' = y$, $z'' = -z$, we find for the above-mentioned quantity

$$(\cosh 2t)^{1/2}$$

For $t$ large, this quantity is of the order $e^t / \sqrt{2}$.

## IV  THEORETICAL INVESTIGATION OF ERRORS DUE TO THE SINGLE-STEP METHODS[1]

In all of this section, we shall limit ourselves for simplicity's sake to systems in canonical form. The general case would certainly be treated in the same way. We neglect completely the round-off error, for we are interested only in the truncation error.

Many publications on this question are "out of date" because they introduce prematurely the absolute values and furnish, in certain cases, error bounds without any relation to reality.

### 20. Notion of a tube.

Let $x(t)$ be a column of functions, continuous, differentiable, and defined in the interval

$$a \leqslant t \leqslant b.$$

We can represent it in the space of $n + 1$ dimensions of $(x, t)$ by a curve $C$. Let $R$ be a region bounded by that space containing $C$ in its interior. We will call the tube attached to $C$ the portion of this region satisfying

$$a \leqslant t \leqslant b.$$

### 21. Notion of a coaxial.

We will call thus a pair of two tubes $T$ and $T_1$ springing from two regions $R$ and $R_1$ attached to the same curve $C$, with $R_1$ being strictly interior to $R$.

### 22. Theorem on the error per step in a coaxial.

Let there be given a coaxial and a differential system:

$$x' = X(x, t).$$

We will assume that $X(x, t)$ is continuous and differentiable as many times as necessary in the tube $T$. Being given an approximate single-step integration method, we can easily show that there exists a number $k > 0$ such that each integration step of length smaller than $k$, whose origin $t_i$, $x_i$ is in the tube $T_1$ and whose end point satisfies

$$a \leqslant t_{i+1} \leqslant b,$$

has all its intermediate points in $T$.

**Theorem.**  The error at one step in a Runge-Kutta method of order $q$ can be written as

$$h^{q+1} \varphi(x_0, t_0, h),$$

where $x_0$, $t_0$ are the starting values of the step. The function

---

[1]Huskey, Lozinskii [1, 2, 3, 4], Bukovics [2, 3], Carr, Elterman, Henrici [4].

$$\varphi(x, t, h)$$

is continuous with respect to its three variables for

$$-k \leqslant h \leqslant k,$$

where $x_0$, $t_0$ are in $T_1$.

We will give a general proof of the theorem only for the case of the improved tangent method ($q = 2$, $\theta_1 = 1/2$):

$$x_{1/2} = x_0 + \frac{hX_0}{2}, \qquad x_1 = x_0 + hX_{1/2}.$$

It is evident at first that $X_0$, $x_{1/2}$, $X_{1/2}$, $x_1$ are continuous functions of the considered variables. In order to continue, we will use Taylor's formula with the remainder in integral form:

$$f(t) = f(t_0) + \frac{t - t_0}{1!} f'(t_0) + \cdots + \frac{(t - t_0)^n}{n!} f^{(n)}(t_0)$$
$$+ \int_{t_0}^t \frac{(t - u)^n}{n!} f^{(n+1)}(u) \, du.$$

We will write the error in the form

$$x(h) - x_1 = \int_{t_0}^{t_0+h} X(t) \, dt - hX_{1/2}$$
$$= \int_{t_0}^{t_0+h} X(t) \, dt - hX\left(t_0 + \frac{h}{2}\right) + h\left[X\left(t_0 + \frac{h}{2}\right) - X_{1/2}\right] \quad (1)$$

We will transform the first two terms of (1) by setting

$$t = t_0 + \frac{h}{2} + hv,$$

$$h\left[\int_{-1/2}^{1/2} X\left(t_0 + \frac{h}{2} + hv\right) dv - X\left(t_0 + \frac{h}{2}\right)\right].$$

Expanding

$$\int_0^u X\left(t_0 + \frac{h}{2} + hv\right) dv$$

between 0 and 1/2, then between $-1/2$ and 0, we find for the above-mentioned quantity:

$$h^3\left[\int_0^{1/2} \left(\frac{1}{2} - u\right)^2 X''\left(t_0 + \frac{h}{2} + hu\right) du\right.$$
$$\left. + \int_{-1/2}^0 \left(-\frac{1}{2} - u\right)^2 X''\left(t_0 + \frac{h}{2} + hu\right) du\right],$$

which is in the desired form. Now it remains only to study

$$h\left[X\left(t_0 + \frac{h}{2}\right) - X_{1/2}\right].$$

In order to continue, we set

$$X^*(\lambda) = X\left[\lambda\left(x + \frac{hX_0}{2}\right) + (1 - \lambda)x\left(t_0 + \frac{h}{2}\right), t_0 + \frac{h}{2}\right].$$

The quantity to be studied is written as

$$-h[X^*(1) - X^*(0)] = -h\int_0^1 X_\lambda'^*(\lambda)\,d\lambda.$$

But

$$X_\lambda'^*(\lambda) = J(\lambda)\left[x_0 + \frac{hX_0}{2} - x\left(t_0 + \frac{h}{2}\right)\right].$$

Hence, it only remains to be shown that

$$x_0 + \frac{hX_0}{2} - x\left(t_0 + \frac{h}{2}\right) = h^2\psi(x_0, t_0, h).$$

But this is the property analogous to that which we just demonstrated for Euler's method. It would be demonstrated as above.

### 23. Fundamental recurrence relative to the global error.

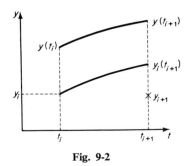

**Fig. 9-2**

With the usual notations (see Fig. 9-2 for the case of one unknown function) we shall write

$$x_{i+1} - x(t_{i+1}) = (x_{i+1} - x_i(t_{i+1})) + (x_i(t_{i+1}) - x(t_{i+1})) \qquad (1)$$

The first parenthesis of the second member represents the error at the $(i + 1)^{st}$ step. Therefore, we will write it as

$$h^{q+1}\varphi(x_{i+1}, t_{i+1}, h).$$

The second parenthesis representing the global error at $t_i$ is

$$x_i - x(t_i),$$

propagated up to $t_{i+1}$. We are going to study this quantity in more detail.

### 24. Lemma on the finite variations of integrals.

Let $x_1(t)$ and $x_2(t)$ be two integrals of the system in canonical form:

$$x' = X(x, t)$$

contained in the same tube. We can write

$$x_2'(t) - x_1'(t) = (x_2(t) - x_1(t))\int_0^1 J(\lambda x_2(t) + (1 - \lambda)x_1(t))\,d\lambda.$$

Indeed, the quantity under the integral sign is the exact derivative of

$$X(\lambda x_2(t) + (1 - \lambda)x_1(t)).$$

**25. Upper bound of the truncation error for $h$ sufficiently small.**

In the following we will denote by

$$\{x\}$$

the component of the vector $x$ with the largest absolute value. According to the integral relation of 24 and the hypotheses made on the differential system, there exists a number $\mu$ such that

$$\{x_2' - x_1'\} \leqslant \mu\{x_2 - x_1\}, \qquad a \leqslant t \leqslant b.$$

By integrating over one step of length $h \leqslant h_0$, we deduce

$$\{x_2 - x_1\}_{t_{i+1}} \leqslant e^{\mu h}\{x_2 - x_1\}_{t_i}.$$

On the other hand, we suppose that

$$\varphi(x, t, h) \leqslant L, \quad \text{for} \quad |h| \leqslant h_0.$$

Thus, for the error of the global method, we can write

$$x_i - x(t_i) = \epsilon_i,$$

$$\{\epsilon_{i+1}\} \leqslant e^{\mu h}\{\epsilon_i\} + h^{q+1}L.$$

Since $\{\epsilon_0\} = 0$, we deduce that

$$\{\epsilon_i\} \leqslant h^{q+1}L(1 + e^{\mu h} + \cdots + e^{(i-1)\mu h}) \leqslant \frac{h^{q+1}L e^{i\mu h}}{e^{\mu h} - 1},$$

which we will write, by noting that $ih$ is the attained abscissa, and that

$$e^{\mu h} - 1 > \mu h,$$

$$\{\epsilon\}_x \leqslant h^q L e^{\mu x}.$$

Immediately, one deduces that $h$ can be taken very small so that the approximate solution is in the interior tube of the coaxial for

$$a \leqslant t \leqslant b.$$

Equally, it results that the approximate solution tends toward the exact solution as $h$ tends to zero.

Now we are going to obtain a closer approximation. Furthermore, we will see that the infinitesimal order obtained above is correct.

**26. Investigation of the propagation of the error.**

We now put ourselves in the interior tube of a coaxial whose generating curve is the exact solution. We will use a single-step method, the steps being equal among each other. We propose to compare the equation

$$z' = z \int_0^1 J[\lambda x_2 + (1 - \lambda)x_1, t]\, d\lambda$$

of paragraph 24 relative to two finite integrals and the equation

$$u' = J(x_2, t)u$$

relative to an infinitely small variation of $x_2$. We will assume that

$$\{x_2(t) - x_1(t)\} \leqslant v h^q,$$

where $v$ denotes a convenient constant.

For $u$ and $z$ we will take, not columns, but square matrices which reduce to the unit matrix at the beginning of the step

$$t_i, t_{i+1}.$$

We can write

$$J(\lambda x_2 + (1 - \lambda)x_1, t) = J(x_2, t) + O(h^q)$$

and, consequently,

$$z' = J(x_2, t)z + O(h^q).$$

Setting $z = uv$, $v(t_i) = I$, we have

$$v' = u^{-1} O(h^q) \, uv = O(h^q)v,$$

whence

$$v(t_{i+1}) = I + O(h^{q+1})$$

and

$$z(t_{i+1}) = u(t_{i+1}) \, [I + O(h^{q+1})].$$

In other words, the substitution of the finite variations by the infinitely small variations perturbs the propagation factor at one step by

$$I + O(h^{q+1}).$$

### 27. Principal part of the error.

We are now able to investigate the principal part of the error. Returning to equation (1) of paragraph 23, let us set

$$\epsilon_i = x_{i+1} - x(t_{i+1}) = h^q \eta_i.$$

Dividing through by $h^q$, we arrive at

$$\eta_{i+1} = M(t_{i+1}, t_i)[1 + O(h^{q+1})]\eta_i + h\varphi(x_{i+1}, t_{i+1}, h), \qquad (1)$$

where $M(t, u)$ is the matrix defined in paragraph 10. This can also be written as

$$\eta_{i+1} = M(t_{i+1}, t_i)\eta_i + h\varphi(x_{i+1}, t_{i+1}, h) + O(h^{q+1})$$

or, by multiplying the left-hand side by $M(t_0, t_{i+1})$,

$$M(t_0, t_{i+1})\eta_{i+1} = M(t_0, t_i)\eta_i + hM(t_0, t_{i+1})\varphi(x_{i+1}, t_{i+1}, h) + O(h^{q+1}),$$

whence

$$M(t_0, t_i)\eta_i = h \sum_{j=0}^{i} M(t_0, t_j)\varphi(x_j, t_j, h) + (t_i - t_0)O(h^q),$$

since $\eta_0 = 0$. The sum of the second member tends toward

$$\int_{t_0}^{t_i} M(t_0, u)\varphi(x(u), u, 0) \, du$$

as $h$ tends toward zero. We deduce that the principal part of $\eta$ at $t$ is

$$\int_{t_0}^{t} M(t, u)\varphi(x(u), u, 0)\, du.$$

But this is the null solution of the system for $t = t_0$.

$$z' = J(x(t), t)z + \varphi(x(t), t, 0). \tag{E}$$

We will call this system the error system of the proposed system. The principal part of the error at $t$ is

$$h^q z(t).$$

*Remark.* In order to obtain the next terms of the error expansion in powers of $h$, it would be necessary to improve the limit from the sum to the integral.

## 28. Linearized theory of errors.

We will call thus the preceding theory in which $h$ and the error are treated as infinitely small quantities and where we suppose that all the quantities which we need (error at a step, propagation factor, ...) are evaluated for the exact integral.

## 29. Change of the integration direction.[1]

The linearized error for the case where one integrates from $a$ to $b$ can be written as

$$\epsilon_1 = h^q \int_{a}^{b} M(b, u)\varphi(x(u), u, 0)\, du.$$

If one integrates from $b$ to $a$, it is written as

$$\epsilon_2 = (-h)^q \int_{b}^{a} M(a, u)\varphi(x(u), u, 0)\, du.$$

Thus, by noting that

$$M(a, u) = M(a, b)M(b, u),$$

one has

$$\epsilon_2 = (-1)^{q-1} M(a, b)\epsilon_1.$$

## 30. Investigation of the principal problem.

We recall that the principal problem consists of determining the error by which an approximate integral is affected, this approximate solution being known. We can give the following *theoretical* solution to this problem. Take a coaxial which is such that the approximating points are interior to the interior tube and that one has the following property: Each step whose initial point is in the center tube, and whose length is smaller than a fixed

[1]Ceschino-Kuntzmann [3].

number $h_0$ is entirely contained (intermediary values and exact solution) in the exterior tube. We can make an error evaluation by assuming that all the elements are in the exterior tube. We examine if this evaluation permits us to affirm that the exact solution is contained in the interior tube. If this condition is not fulfilled, it is necessary to take up the problem anew and start from another tube.

## V    THEORETICAL INVESTIGATION OF THE ERRORS DUE TO THE USE OF A MULTISTEP METHOD[1]

As in the preceding section, we will confine ourselves to systems in canonical form. Without doubt, the generalization would not be difficult. In a precise manner, we will consider only the two formulas

$$x_{i+1} = x_i + \frac{h(23X_i - 16X_{i-1} + 5X_{i-2})}{12} \qquad \text{(Adams of order 3),}$$

$$x_{i+1} = x_{i+1} + \frac{h(X_{i+1} + 4X_i + X_{i+1})}{3} \qquad \text{(central differences).}$$

### 31.  Use of a coaxial.

We will consider anew a coaxial and assume that all the values utilized in the formula, having a subscript smaller than, or equal to, $i$ are in the interior tube. It is almost obvious that there exists a value $h_0$ which is such that for $h \leqslant h_0$, $x_{i+1}$ is in the exterior tube of the coaxial. We will make all the further evaluations by assuming that this is the case. We permit that in the exterior tube $x$ and $X$ are differentiable as many times as will be necessary and that their derivatives are bounded by fixed numbers.

### 32.  Quadrature error.

We will consider a coaxial having as a median curve an exact integral. As it was indicated in the preceding paragraph, we assume that $x_i, x_{i-1}, \dots$ are situated in the interior tube (the numbering stops at the values actually used in the formula). We call the quadrature error the vector

$$x_{i+1} - x_i(t_{i+1}).$$

In the case of Adams' formula of order 3, we can write

$$x_{i+1} - x_i(t_{i+1}) = \frac{h}{12}(23X_i - 16X_{i-1} + 5X_{i-2}) - \int_{t_i}^{t_{i+1}} X(x_i(t), t)\, dt,$$

[1]The literature on this subject is voluminous. Bahvalov [1, 2], Brodskii, Cernysenko, Dahlquist [1], Gray, Hull, and Newberry, Henrici [5, 6], Chadaja [1], Lotkin [4], Matthieu [2, 3, 4], Mohr, Servais, Tollmien [2], Tornig, Sura Bura, Vietoris [1, 2], Weissinger [1, 3], Steffensen. The fundamental work is Henrici's [9].

which we will transform to

$$\left\{ \frac{h}{12} [23X(x_i(t_i), t_i) - 16X(x_i(t_{i-1}), t_{i-1}) + 5X(x_i(t_{i-2}), t_{i-2})] \right.$$

$$\left. - \int_{t_i}^{t_{i+1}} X(x_i(t), t) \, dt \right\} + \frac{h}{12} [23(X_i - X(x_i(t_i), t_i))$$

$$- 16[X_{i-1} - X(x_i(t_{i-1}), t_{i-1})] + 5(X_{i-2} - X[(x_i(t_{i-2}), t_{i-2})].$$

Set

$$x_{i-1} = x_i(t_{i-1}) + \epsilon_i h^3,$$

$$x_{i-2} = x_i(t_{i-2}) + \epsilon_i^* h^3,$$

$$x_{i+1} - x_i(t_{i+1}) = h^4 \varphi(x_i, t_i, \epsilon_i, \epsilon_i^*, h).$$

We are going to prove the following theorem.

**Theorem.**   Under the preceding conditions, the function $\varphi$ is a continuous function of its five variables.

Indeed, the first part of the above-mentioned formula is the remainder of an approximate quadrature formula which can be written by means of transformations such as those in paragraph 22:

$$h^4 \varphi_1(x_i, t_i, h),$$

the function $\varphi_1$ being continuous. On the other hand, the terms such as

$$\frac{-16h}{12} [X_{i-1} - X(x_i(t_{i-1}), t_{i-1})]$$

can be written as

$$\frac{-16h}{12} h^4 \epsilon_i \int_0^1 J[x_i(t_{i-1}) + \lambda \epsilon_i h^3, t_{i-1}] \, d\lambda,$$

which is clearly of the form

$$h^4 \varphi_2(x_i, t_i, \epsilon_i, h),$$

which finishes the proof.

*Remark*. This function is more precisely of the form

$$h^4 \varphi_1(x_i, t_i, h) + h^4 \varphi_1'(x_i, t_i, \epsilon_i, h)\epsilon_i + h^4 \varphi_1''(x_i, t_i, \epsilon_i^*, h)\epsilon_i^* .$$

For the central difference formula, we would call the *quadrature error* the vector

$$x_{i+1} - x_{i-1}(t_{i+1}) = h^5 \varphi(x_{i-1}, t_{i-1}, \epsilon_i, \epsilon_i^*, h),$$

by setting

$$h^4 \epsilon_i = x_{i+1} - x_{i-1}(t_{i+1}),$$

$$h^4 \epsilon_i^* = x_i - x_{i-1}(t_i).$$

Again, we could prove that $\varphi$ is a continuous function of its variables.

*Remark.* The relation thus found is implicit, since the first member is $h^4 \epsilon_i$.

### 33. A theorem on the error of Adams' method.

Let us return to Adams' formula of order 3. Let us assume that

$$\{x_2(t_1) - x_1\} = B_2 h^4 ,$$
$$\{x_2(t_0) - x_0\} = A_2 h^4 .$$

We will set

$$\{x_{i+1}(t_i) - x_i\} = B_{i+1} h^4 ,$$
$$\{x_{i+1}(t_{i-1}) - x_{i-1}\} = A_{i+1} h^4 .$$

We are going to show that $B_{i+1}$ and $A_{i+1}$ are bounded by numbers independent of $i$, provided that $h$ is small and $B_2$ and $A_2$ are equally small. Indeed, according to paragraph 32, there exist two numbers $M$ and $K$ such that

$$\{x_i(t_{i+1}) - x_{i+1}\} \leqslant [M + K(B_i + A_i)h]h^4$$

from which we derive, by going back along the integral curves to the abscissas $t_i$ and $t_{i-1}$,

$$B_{i+1} \leqslant [M' + K'(B_i + A_i)h],$$
$$A_{i+1} \leqslant [M' + K'(B_i + A_i)h] + B_i .$$

Suppose $h$ to be such that $3K'h < 1$ and

$$A_2 < \frac{2M'}{1 - 3K'h}, \qquad B_2 < \frac{M'}{1 - 3K'h}.$$

We deduce the preceding inequalities:

$$B_{i+1} < \frac{M'}{1 - 3K'h}, \qquad A_{i+1} < \frac{2M'}{1 - 3K'h}.$$

### 34. Global error in Adams' method.

For this method, we can use the same fundamental recurrence relation as for the single-step methods (23). If we use Adams' formula of order 3 with starting values satisfying

$$\{x_2(t_1) - x_1\} \leqslant \frac{M'h^4}{1 - 3K'h}, \qquad \{x_2(t_0) - x_0\} \leqslant \frac{2M'h^4}{1 - 3K'h},$$

then, according to the preceding result, we can write

$$\{\epsilon_{i+1}\} \leqslant e^{Mh}\{\epsilon_i\} + Hh^4 ,$$

whence we deduce exactly, as in paragraph 25, that the global error is of order $h^4$. Operating as in paragraph 27 and setting

$$\epsilon_i = h^3 z_i,$$

we can assert that $z_i$ possesses a limit as $h$ tends to zero. This limit is the solution of the equation

$$z' = Jz + \varphi(x(t), t, 0, 0, 0).$$

This system is also called the *differential system of the error*.

### 35. Investigation of errors in the central difference method by means of an example.

We will take the very simple equation

$$y' = ay.$$

The characteristic equation of the approximate formula is:

$$r^2 - 1 = \frac{ah(r^2 + 4r + 1)}{3},$$

whose roots are

$$r_1 = e^{ah} + Kh^5, \qquad r_2 = -1 + Lh.$$

As an approximate solution we find

$$y_i = Ar_1^i + Br_2^i.$$

As initial conditions we will take

$$y(0) = 1, \qquad y(h) = e^{ah} + \epsilon_1.$$

We obtain

$$A = \frac{e^{ah} + 1 + \epsilon_1 - Lh}{e^{ah} + 1 - Lh}, \qquad B = \frac{-\epsilon_1 + Kh^5}{e^{ah} + 1 - Lh},$$

or, in developing in powers of $h$ and setting $ih = t$:

$$y_i = Ae^{at}(1 + Kxh^4 e^{-ah}) + (-1)^i Be^{-Lt},$$

and for the principal part of the error

$$\frac{(-Kh^5 + \epsilon_1)}{2} e^{at} + Kxh^4 e^{at} + (-1)^i \frac{(\epsilon_1 - Kh^5)}{2} e^{-Lt}.$$

We take

$$\epsilon_1 = Mh^5.$$

The first term of the error is, therefore, negligible compared to the second one. The third can dominate (even if not of the lowest infinitesimal order) if $a < 0$, since then $L$ is also negative.

### 36. Comparison of the Runge-Kutta method with various multistep methods.

In order to compare a multistep method and a single-step method, it suffices, according to the foregoing, to compare the quadrature error and the error per step. This is what we will do below. We will compare, at equal cost, the following methods:

—Runge-Kutta method of order 4 classic.
—Runge-Kutta method of order 4 optimal.
—explicit Adams method of order 4.
—implicit Adams method of order 4.
—central difference method.

We assume that the implicit methods are used by a procedure which requires one iteration cycle. In order to have to calculate four horners over a length of $4h$, we will take:

—one step of length $4h$ for the two Runge-Kutta methods.
—one step of length $2h$ for the two implicit methods.
—one step of length $h$ for the explicit Adams method.

It should be clearly understood that in all cases the system is in canonical form.

We obtain the following table of the error terms (without sign):

|  | R. K. Clas. | R. K. Opt. | Adams impl. | Adams expl. | Central differences |
|---|---|---|---|---|---|
| $C_4$ | 16/45 | 1024/3600 | 76/45 | 251/180 | 32/45 |
| $L_1 C_1$ | 32/15 | 0 | 152/15 | 251/30 | 64/15 |
| $R$ | 32/5 | 3072/880 | 76/15 | 251/60 | 32/15 |
| $K_1 C_2$ | 32/15 | 0 | 304/45 | 251/45 | 128/45 |
| $K_1 J_1 C_1$ | 128/15 | 1024/120 | 304/45 | 251/45 | 128/45 |
| $J_1 C_3$ | 64/45 | 4096/3600 | 76/45 | 251/180 | 32/45 |
| $J_1 K_1 C_1$ | 64/15 | 0 | 76/15 | 251/60 | 32/15 |
| $J_1^3 C_1$ | 128/15 | 1024/120 | 76/45 | 251/180 | 32/45 |
| $J_1^2 C_2$ | 32/15 | 0 | 76/45 | 251/180 | 32/45 |

Taking as a criterion the sum of the absolute values of the errors, we find, in order of decreasing quality: central differences (768/45), Runge-Kutta optimal (990/45), Adams method (explicit) (1506/45), Runge-Kutta classic (1616/45), and Adams (implicit) (1824/45).

Any preference between the single-step and multistep methods is mostly an academic question, or one of expediency, depending on the peculiarities of the problem. These methods are sufficiently related to one another that it is possible to prove or to disprove almost any of the assertions on the subject of their comparative precision by a conveniently chosen example.

*Remark.* The preceding conclusions are completely different for a linear system. For such a system, especially if it is of not too high an order, the best methods are, without doubt, the implicit methods (probably the wholly implicit Runge-Kutta methods).

### VI  THE COMPLETELY IMPLICIT RUNGE-KUTTA METHODS

In Chapter 4 we presented such methods. We are going to return to their principle.

### 37. Return to the quadrature formulas.

Let the quantities

$$\theta_0, \ldots, \theta_{q-1}$$

be fixed. It is possible to find coefficients $A_{q,j}, j = 0, \ldots, q - 1$, such that

$$\sum_j A_{q,j}\theta_j^r = \frac{1}{(r+1)}, \qquad r = 0, \ldots, q - 1.$$

Indeed, these equations form a system of $q$ linear equations with $q$ unknown and with a nonzero determinant. The $A_{q,j}$ are then such that

$$\int_{0'}^h f(t)\, dt - h \sum_j A_{q,j}f(\theta_j) = O(h^{q+1})$$

for every function $f(t)$ differentiable up to order $q$ inclusive.

### 38. Definition of $A_{i,j}$.

We will define, the coefficients $A_{i,j}$ for $i = 0, 1, \ldots, q - 1$ by

$$\sum_{j=0}^{q-1} A_{i,j}\theta_j^\alpha = \frac{\theta_i^{\alpha+1}}{(\alpha + 1)}, \qquad \alpha = 0, \ldots, q - 1.$$

As previously, this completely determines the coefficients $A_{i,j}$.

### 39. Entirely implicit Runge-Kutta formula.

For the system in canonical form we will set

$$x' = X(x, t),$$

$$x_{i,\alpha} = x_i + h \sum_\beta A_{\alpha,\beta} X_{i,\beta}, \qquad \alpha = 0, \ldots, q - 1,$$

$$x_{i+1} = x_i + h \sum_\alpha A_{q,\alpha} X_{i,\alpha},$$

the coefficients $A_{\alpha,\beta}$ and $A_{q,\alpha}$ having been defined above. We are going to show that

$$x_{i,\alpha} - x_i(t_{i,\alpha}) = O(h^{q+1}).$$

Indeed,

$$x_i(t_{i,\alpha}) = x_i + h \sum_\beta A_{\alpha,\beta} X(t_{i,\beta}) + O(h^{q+1}),$$

or, subtracting, we have

$$x_{i,\alpha} - x_i(t_{i,\alpha}) = h \sum_\beta A_{\alpha,\beta}(X_{i,\beta} - X(t_{i,\beta})) + O(h^{q+1}).$$

Let us suppose that

$$x_{i,\beta} - x(t_{i,\beta}) = O(h^r), \qquad r < q+1 \quad \text{for all } \beta.$$

Then we have

$$X_{i,\beta} - X(t_{i,\beta}) = O(h^r)$$

and

$$x_{i,\alpha} - x(t_{i,\alpha}) = O(h^{r+1}).$$

This shows that there is a contradiction if $r < q + 1$. To recapitulate, in the implicit Runge-Kutta formulas, the intermediary values are affected by the errors of order $h^{q+1}$. It is the same for the final value.

### 40.  Particular case of Gauss' formulas.

These abscissas are such that

$$\sum_i A_{q,i} \theta_i^\alpha = \frac{1}{(\alpha + 1)} \quad \text{for} \quad \alpha = 0, \ldots, 2q - 1.$$

We will consider the same quantities $A_{i,j}$ as above. Furthermore, we set

$$\sum_{j=0}^{q-1} A_{i,j} \theta_j^r = \frac{\theta_i^{r+1}}{r + 1} + S_{i,r} \quad \text{for} \quad r = q, \ldots, 2q - 1.$$

We are going to show that

$$\sum_\alpha A_{q,\alpha} \theta_\alpha^r S_{\alpha,\beta} = 0 \quad \text{for} \quad \beta = q, \ldots, 2q - r - 2.$$

For this, consider the table:

$$
\begin{Vmatrix}
1 & \cdots & 1 & \theta_i \\
\theta_0 & \cdots & \theta_{q-1} & \dfrac{\theta_i^2}{2} \\
\multicolumn{4}{c}{\cdots\cdots\cdots\cdots\cdots\cdots\cdots} \\
\theta_0^{q-1} & \cdots & \theta_{q-1}^{q-1} & \dfrac{\theta_i^q}{q} \\
\theta_0^\beta & \cdots & \theta_{q-1}^\beta & \dfrac{\theta_i^{\beta+1}}{r+1} + S_{i,\beta}
\end{Vmatrix}
\qquad
\begin{aligned}
& i = 0, \ldots, q - 1, \\
& \beta = q, \ldots, 2q - r - 2.
\end{aligned}
$$

This table is formed by $2q$ columns with $q + 1$ rows. It does not have more than $q$ independent columns, because every column is a linear combination of the first $q$ column. It will be the same for every table resulting from the preceding by a linear combination of columns. Combining these columns with the factors

$$A_{q,0}(1 - \theta_0^{r+1}),\ A_{q,1}(1 - \theta_1^{r+1}) \ldots ,\ -(r+1)A_{q,0}\theta_0^r,$$

we obtain the column

$$0$$

$$0$$

$$\vdots$$

$$\sum_\alpha A_{q,\,\alpha} \theta_\alpha^r S_{\alpha,\,\beta}.$$

It is necessary that this quantity be zero in order to furnish a column which depends on the first $q$ columns. This conclusion is correct so long as

$$\beta + r + 1 \leqslant 2q - 1,$$

or

$$\beta \leqslant 2q - r - 2,$$

which is the previously given assertion.

Moreover, we are going to show that

$$\sum_\alpha A_{q,\,\alpha} \theta_\alpha^r A_{\alpha,\,\beta} = A_{q,\,\beta} \frac{(1 - \theta_\beta^{r+1})}{r + 1}, \qquad r = 0, \ldots, q - 1.$$

Multiplying the two members of these relations by

$$\theta_\beta^s, \qquad s = 0, \ldots, q - 1,$$

and adding, we get for the first member

$$\sum_\alpha A_{q,\,\alpha} \theta_\alpha^r \frac{\theta_\alpha^{s+1}}{s + 1} = \frac{1}{(s + 1)(r + s + 2)}$$

and for the second member

$$\frac{1}{r + 1} \left( \frac{1}{s + 1} - \frac{1}{r + s + 2} \right).$$

The two quantities are equal. But the determinant of the matrix of the $\theta_\beta^s$ is a Vandermonde determinant and hence nonzero.

### 41.  Runge-Kutta-Gauss formula.

Let us consider the quantities

$$Y_r = h^{r+1} \sum_\alpha A_{q,\,\alpha} \theta_\alpha^r (X(t_{i,\,\alpha}) - X_{i,\,\alpha}), \qquad r = 0, \ldots, q - 1.$$

We will study these quantities by neglecting everything which is $O(h^{2q+1})$. Expanding, we can write it

$$Y_r = h^{r+1} \sum_\alpha A_{q,\,\alpha} \theta_\alpha^r J(t_{i,\,\alpha})(x(t_{i,\,\alpha}) - x_{i,\,\alpha}).$$

Actually, $[x(t_{i,\alpha}) - x_{i,\alpha}]^2$ is $O(h^{2q+2})$, and hence negligible. By formally expressing $J(t_{i,\alpha})$ on the integral curve, we obtain

$$Y_r = \sum_{\alpha,\,s} A_{q,\,\alpha} \theta_\alpha^{r+s} K_s h^{r+s+1}(x(t_{i,\,\alpha}) - x_{i,\,\alpha}),$$

$$s = 0, \ldots, q - r - 1.$$

But

$$x(t_{i,\alpha}) - x_{i,\alpha} = x(t_{i,\alpha}) - x_i - h \sum_\beta A_{\alpha,\beta} X(t_{i,\beta}) + h \sum_\beta A_{\alpha,\beta}[X(t_{i,\beta}) - X_{i,\beta}],$$

$$x(t_{i,\alpha}) - x_i - h \sum_\beta A_{\alpha,\beta} X(t_{i,\beta}) = \sum_{p=0}^{2q-r-s-2} h^{p+1} L_p \left[ \frac{\theta_\alpha^{p+1}}{p+1} - \sum A_{\alpha,\beta} \theta_\beta^p \right]$$

$$= - \sum_{p=q}^{2q-r-s-2} h^{p+1} L_p S_{\alpha, p}.$$

However,

$$\sum_\alpha A_{q,\alpha} \theta_\alpha^{r+s} S_{\alpha, p} = 0.$$

We have thus only

$$Y_r = \sum_{\alpha, s, \beta} A_{q,\alpha} \theta_\alpha^{r+s} K_s h^{r+s+2} A_{\alpha,\beta}[X(t_{i,\beta}) - X_{i,\beta}],$$

whence we deduce that

$$Y_r = \sum_{s, \beta} \frac{A_{q,\beta}}{r+s+1} (1 - \theta_\beta^{r+s+1}) h^{r+s+2} K_s[X(t_{i,\beta}) - X_{i,\beta}],$$

i.e.,

$$Y_r = \sum_s K_s \frac{h^{r+s+2}}{r+s+1} Y_0 - \sum \frac{K_s}{r+s+1} Y_{r+s+1}, \qquad s = 0, \ldots, q-r-2.$$

If we attempt to deduce from this table infinitesimal orders, we find that:

$$\text{order of } Y_{q-1} = \text{order of } Y_0 + q + 1;$$
$$\text{order of } Y_{q-2} = \text{order of } Y_0 + q;$$
$$\text{order of } \quad Y_0 \ = \text{order of } Y_0 + 2.$$

The result is that all these quantities are zero, or, more exactly, $O(h^{2q+1})$. In particular,

$$Y_0 = O(h^{2q+1}).$$

But this quantity is none other than

$$x(t_{i+1}) - x_{i+1} + O(h^{2q+1});$$

thus

$$x_{i+1} = x(t_{i+1}) + O(h^{2q+1}),$$

which completes the proof.

## VII  APPLICATION OF THE STEP METHODS TO INTEGRAL EQUATIONS OF THE VOLTERRA TYPE[1]

### 42. Calculation of an integral in the Runge-Kutta method.

Let

$$x^{(p)} = X(x, \ldots, x^{(p-1)}, t)$$

be the system to be integrated by a Runge-Kutta method, which gives an

[1]Aparo, Oules, Pouzet [1, 2, 3, 4], Kuntzmann [5].

error of order $h^{q+1}$ at one step. Let us find an approximate value of the integral

$$\int_{t_i}^{t_{i+1}} f(x, \ldots, x^{(p)}, t)\, dt,$$

the function $f$ being differentiable as many times as is necessary. Let us show that

$$\int_{t_i}^{t_{i+1}} f(x, \ldots, x^{(p)}, t)\, dt = h \sum_{\alpha} A_{q, \alpha} f_{i, \alpha}$$

gives an error of order $h^{q+1}$. Set

$$z' = f(x, x', \ldots, x^{(p)}, t)$$

and consider the system

$$x^{(p)} = X(x, \ldots, x^{(p-1)}, t),$$
$$z' = f(x, \ldots, x^{(p)}, t).$$

The integration of this system by the Runge-Kutta method consists of integrating first the primitive system, then applying to the last equation the Runge-Kutta formula:

$$z(t_{i+1}) = z(t_i) + h \sum_{\alpha} A_{q, \alpha} f_{i, \alpha},$$

which gives an error at one step which is of order $h^{q+1}$.

### 43.1  Application to an integro-differential equation.

Let us consider the very general integro-differential equation

$$f^{(p)}(t) = F\Big[t, f(t), \ldots, f^{(p-1)}(t),$$

$$\int_{t_0}^{t} G(t, f(t), \ldots, f^{(p-1)}(t), s, f(s), \ldots, f^{(p)}(s))\, ds\Big].$$

We assume that the functions $F$ and $G$ are continuous and differentiable as many times as will be necessary. Furthermore, we suppose

$$f(t_0), \ldots, f^{(p-1)}(t_0)$$

to be known. Finally, we assume that the problem has a unique solution.

### 43.2  Hypothesis on the function $G$.

We will assume that one can write it for arbitrary $t$, and $0 \leqslant s \leqslant h_0$, $h_0$ is the upper bound of the step.

$$G(t, \ldots, f^{(p-1)}(t), s, \ldots, f^{(p)}(s)) = \sum_{u, v, \ldots, w} M_{u, v, \ldots, w}(t, \ldots, f^{(p-1)}(t))$$

$$(s - t_0)^u (f(s) - f(t_0))^v \ldots (f^{(p)}(s) - f^{(p)}(t_0))^w + A(t, s)h^Q.$$

$Q$ is higher than the order of the method and $A(t, s)$ is bounded.

### 43.3 Investigation of the first step.

Let us set

$$z'_{u, v, \ldots, w}(t) = (t - t_0)^u [f(t) - f(t_0)]^v \ldots [f^{(p)}(t) - f^{(p)}(t_0)]^w$$

and consider the system

$$f^{(p)}(t) = F[t, \ldots, f^{(p-1)}(t), \sum_{u, v, \ldots w} M(t, \ldots, f^{(p-1)}(t))z_{u, v, \ldots, w}]$$

$$z'_{u, v, \ldots, w} = (t - t_0)^u [f(t) - f(t_0)]^v \ldots [f^{(p)}(t) - f^{(p)}(t_0)]^w$$

with the initial conditions

$$z(u, v, \ldots, w) = 0, \quad \text{for} \quad t = t_0,$$

$$f(t_0), \ldots, f^{(p-1)}(t_0) \quad \text{given}.$$

In the second member of $f^{(p)}(t)$ we have neglected a term of order $h^{\varrho+1}$. The Runge-Kutta method, applied to this system, gives

$$f^{(p-k)}(t_\alpha) = f^{(p-k)}(t_i) + \cdots + \frac{h^k}{k!} \sum_\beta K_{\alpha, \beta} F(t_\beta, \ldots, f^{(p-1)}(t_\beta),$$

$$\sum_{u, v, \ldots, w} M_{u, v, \ldots, w}(t_\beta, \ldots, f^{(p-1)}(t_\beta))z_{u, v, \ldots, w, \beta})$$

$$z_{u, v, \ldots, w, \beta} = h \sum_\gamma A_{\beta, \gamma}(t_\gamma - t_0)^u \ldots [f^{(p)}(t_\gamma) - f^{(p)}(t_0)]^w.$$

But

$$\sum_{u\, v \ldots\, w} M_{u, v, \ldots, w}(t_\beta, \ldots,)z_{u, v \ldots\, w, \beta} = h \sum_\gamma A_{\beta, \gamma} G(t_\beta, \ldots, f_\gamma^{(p)}) + Kh^{\varrho+1}.$$

Without changing the order of the method, we can write

$$f^{(p-k)}(t_\alpha) = f^{(p-k)}(t_i) + \cdots + \frac{h^k}{k!} \sum_\beta K_{\alpha, \beta} F[t_\beta, \ldots, f^{(p-1)}(t_\beta),$$

$$h \sum A_{\beta, \gamma} G(x_\beta, \ldots, f_\beta^{(p-1)}, x_\gamma, \ldots, f_\gamma^{(p)})].$$

### 43.4 Investigation of the succeeding steps.

The succeeding steps are different from the first in the sense that it is necessary to write

$$\int_{t_0}^t G \, ds = \int_{t_0}^{t_i} + \int_{t_i}^t.$$

After the evaluation of

$$\int_{t_0}^{t_i} G(\ldots) \, ds = H_i(t),$$

we return to the first step. We can write

$$H_{i+1}(t) - H_i(t) = \int_{t_i}^{t_{i+1}} G(t, \ldots, f^{(p-1)}(t), s, f^{(p)}(s)) \, ds$$

$$= h \sum A_{q, \alpha} G(t, \ldots, f^{(p-1)}(t), s_\alpha, \ldots, f^{(p)}(s_\alpha)) + Mh_{q+1}.$$

### 44. Use of Adams' type formulas.

For integral equations we can likewise use formulas of Adams' type. For example, for the integral equation

$$y(t) = f(t) + \int_{t_0}^{t} F(t, u, y(u))\, du,$$

we can write, after having determined $y_1$, an approximate value of $y(h)$ by another method:

$$y_{i+1} = f(t_{i+1}) + \int_{t_0}^{t_i} F(t_{i+1}, u, y(u))\, du + \frac{h}{2}\left(3F(t_i, t_i, y_i) - F(t_i, t_{i-1}, y_{i-1})\right).$$

We evaluate:

$$\int_{t_0}^{t_i}$$

by an approximate quadrature formula.

## Problems

Find the propagation function for the following equations:
1. $y' = x + y,$      $y(0) = 1,$    $0 \leqslant x \leqslant 1.$
2. $y' = y/x - y^2,$   $y(1) = 1,$   $1 \leqslant x \leqslant 2.$
3. $y' = -3y - z,$   $y(0) = 2,$   $0 \leqslant x \leqslant 0.5,$
    $z' = y - z,$      $z(0) = -1.$
4. By applying Nyström's approximation formula (Chapter 6, paragraph 9.1) to the problem

$$y' = -3y + az,$$
$$z' = by - z,$$

find the characteristic roots and determine the values of the parameters $a$ and $b$ for which stability occurs.

# 10 PRACTICAL CONSIDERATIONS

In this chapter, we shall occupy ourselves with various questions, in particular with the evaluation of the errors.[1]

### 1. Brief summary of the results of the preceding chapter.

Let us consider a method of integration by steps. In the execution of one step, two types of errors are committed:

—replacement of the exact integration by an approximate procedure. The corresponding error is called, according to the cases, the error of the step method or the quadrature error.

—the round-off or truncation error in the different operation. The totality of these two errors is called the *error per step*. This error is reflected in the continuation of the calculation by a propagation mechanism which we will summarize as follows: Let us suppose that in the approximate integration of the equation

$$y' = Y(y, t), \qquad y(t_0) = y_0$$

by a single-step method, we commit an error $\delta$ (for whatever cause it may be) at a certain abscissa $\tau$. This error amounts to replacing $y(\tau)$ by $y(\tau) + \delta$. (See Fig. 10-1.) It is quite obvious that, if this error were the only one committed in the course of the calculation, its effect would consist instead of continuing along the integral curve $y(t)$, continuing along the integral curve defined by:

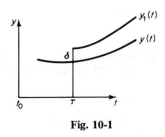

Fig. 10-1

[1]On this subject see: Bahavalov [1, 2], Bareiss, Papoulis, Sterne, Schröder [2 and 3].

$$y_1'(t) = Y(y_1, t), \qquad y_1(\tau) = y(\tau) + \delta$$

The order of magnitude of the consequences of this sole error will depend upon the behavior of the cluster of the finite variations of $y(t)_0$. In the case of Fig. 10-2, where the integrals are going to approach each other, the error will be diminished. On the other hand, in the case of Fig. 10-3, the error will be amplified.

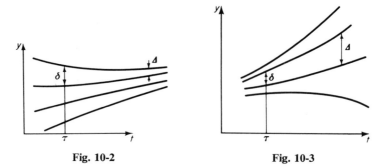

| Fig. 10-2 | Fig. 10-3 |

It is essential to note that the manner in which this error propagates itself is independent of the approximate integration method. It is likewise independent of the transformation to which one can subject the system, provided these transformations preserve the solutions.

For a system the principle is the same, but the situation can be much more complicated. For a multistep method, the theory is more complicated, but at least for an Adams method the behavior is almost the same as for a single-step method. The total error arises from the propagation of the various errors at a step. In the preceding chapter, we have seen that we can represent the behavior of the error of the whole method by means of the error system

$$z' = Jz + \frac{\tau}{h},$$

where $\tau$ is the truncation error at one step or the quadrature error. In the following, we assume that $\tau$ is distinctly larger than the round-off error at one step.

### I   EVALUATION OF THE TRUNCATION ERROR AT ONE STEP FOR THE SINGLE-STEP METHODS

#### 2.1 Method of variation of step.[1]

The method of variation of step consists of integrating at first the system with the step $h$, next or at the same time with another step (in general twice the size). If the error at one step is

[1] Anderson, Collatz [5], Richardson and Gaunt [2].

$$Ah^{q+1},$$

we find, by neglecting the addition or subtraction of the error due to propagation:

$$Akh^{q+1}$$

for $k$ steps if $h' = kh$. Integrating directly with the step $kh$, the error is

$$A(kh)^{q+1}.$$

The ratio of the two errors is

$$k^q = \left(\frac{h'}{h}\right)^q.$$

Let $\eta$ be the difference between the results of the two calculations; the error of each of them has for the principal part

$$\frac{\eta(h'/h)^q}{(h'/h)^q - 1}, \qquad \frac{\eta}{(h'/h)^q - 1},$$

    Calculation with the step $h'$    Calculation with the step $h$

and, consequently, the error at one step during the calculation with the step $h$ is

$$\frac{\eta}{(h'/h)^{q+1} - h'/h}$$

For example, if $h' = 2h$, the error of the calculation with the step $h$ is

$$\frac{\eta}{2^{q+1} - 2}.$$

Hence, for the various Runge-Kutta methods, we find

| $RK1$ | $RK2$ | $RK3$ | $RK4$ |
|:-----:|:-----:|:-----:|:-----:|
| $\dfrac{\eta}{2}$ | $\dfrac{\eta}{6}$ | $\dfrac{\eta}{14}$ | $\dfrac{\eta}{30}$ |

One will note that the cost of this method is exactly 50 per cent of the cost of the principal calculation, if one doubles the step and if one evaluates the error for both steps, which may not be necessary.

### 2.2 Examples.

1.      $y' = y - e^t \sin t$    (Euler's method),    $h = 0.2$.

At various points of the solution

$$y = e^t \cos t$$

we find the errors per step, actual and calculated:

| $t$ | $y$ | $\tau$ calculated | $\tau$ actual |
|---|---|---|---|
|  | 1.0000 |  |  |
| 0.2 | 1.1989 | 0.001,03 | 0.001,91 |
| 0.4 | 1.3818 | 0.006,08 | 0.007,79 |
| 0.6 | 1.5196 | 0.013,0 | 0.015,8 |
| 0.8 | 1.5767 | 0.022,0 | 0.026,2 |
| 1.0 | 1.5078 | 0.033,4 | 0.039,1 |
| 2.0 | $-2.9438$ | 0.116 | 0.131 |

In order to know the degree of precision, we will form the ratio

$$\frac{\Sigma |\text{differences}|}{\Sigma |\text{errors}|} = \frac{1253}{11412} \approx 11\%.$$

### 3.1 Case where all the errors do not have the same infinitesimal order.

This case presents itself with certain single-step methods for systems containing higher order derivatives. We will treat only a particular case. Let

$$y'' = Y(y, y', t)$$

or also

$$y' = z, \qquad z' = Y(y, z, t).$$

We use a single-step method, which gives an error of order $h^{q+1}$ for $y'$ and one of $h^{q+2}$ for $y$. After one step, we can write

$$z(h) - z_1 = Ph^{q+1} = \delta z_1,$$
$$y(h) - y_1 = Qh^{q+2} = \delta y_1.$$

Incidentally, the propagation of this error is given by

$$(\delta y)' = \delta z, \qquad (\delta z)' = Y'_y \, \delta y + Y_z \delta z'.$$

At the start of the second step, we have, therefore,

$$\delta y_2 = 2\delta y_1 + h \, \delta z_1 = 2Qh^{q+2} + Ph^{q+2},$$
$$\delta z_2 = 2\delta z_1 + h[Y'_y \, \delta y_1 + Y'_z \, \delta z_1] = 2Ph^{q+1} + \text{higher order terms.}$$

Without specifying the subscript, we write

$$\delta y = Ph^{q+2} + 2Qh^{q+2},$$
$$\delta z = 2Ph^{q+1}.$$

With the step doubled, we have immediately

$$\overline{\delta y} = 2^{q+2} h^{q+2} Q,$$
$$\overline{\delta z} = 2^{q+1} h^{q+1} P.$$

The difference between the two is

$$\overline{\delta y} - \delta y = 2(2^{q+1} - 1)h^{q+2} Q - Ph^{q+2},$$
$$\overline{\delta z} - \delta z = (2^{q+1} - 2)h^{q+1} P.$$

We infer then

$$h^{q+1}P = \frac{\overline{\delta z} - \delta z}{2^{q+1} - 2},$$

$$h^{q+2}Q = \frac{\overline{\delta y} - \delta y + h\frac{(\overline{\delta z} - \delta z)}{2^{q+1} - 2}}{2(2^{q+1} - 1)}.$$

In particular, for Euler's method ($q = 1$):

$$h^2 P = \frac{\overline{\delta z} - \delta z}{2},$$

$$h^3 Q = \frac{\overline{\delta y} - \delta y + (1/2)h(\overline{\delta z} - \delta z)}{6}.$$

For the improved tangent method ($q = 2$):

$$h^3 P = \frac{\overline{\delta z} - \delta z}{6}, \qquad h^4 Q = \frac{\overline{\delta y} - \delta y + (1/6)h(\overline{\delta z} - \delta z)}{14}.$$

### 3.2 Example.

$$y'' = y' - y - e^t \sin t, \qquad y(0) = 1, \qquad y'(0) = 1, \qquad h = 0.2.$$

(Improved tangent method)

| $t$ | $y$ | | $y'$ | |
|---|---|---|---|---|
| | Actual error | Calculated error | Actual error | Calculated error |
| 0.2 | −0.000,35 | −0.000,35 | −0.0106 | −0.0105 |
| 0.4 | −0.000,50 | −0.000,49 | −0.0152 | −0.0149 |
| 0.6 | −0.000,67 | −0.000,66 | −0.0204 | −0.0199 |
| 0.8 | −0.000,86 | −0.000,85 | −0.0263 | −0.0255 |
| 1.0 | −0.001,07 | −0.001,05 | −0.0325 | −0.0314 |
| ... | ... | ... | ... | ... |
| 2.0 | −0.001,48 | −0.001,38 | −0.0441 | −0.0414 |

### 4.1 Method of reverse integration.[1]

The method of reverse integration is based on the result of Chapter 9, paragraph 29. If the truncation error at one step, for a system in canonical form, is

$$Ah^q,$$

and if $q$ is even, by integrating from $t_i$ to $t_{i+1}$, and then with the calculated values from $t_{i+1}$ to $t_i$, we find

$$x_i^* - x_i = 2Ah^q.$$

The cost of this evaluation, if we want to use it at each step (which is perhaps not necessary), is $q - 1$ horners for a method of rank $q$.

[1]Call-Reeves, Ceschino-Kutzmann [3].

### 4.2 Various other methods.

One can well imagine other procedures which allow the evaluation of the error at one step. Here is an example: It is proposed to use two methods giving approximations of different order and having as many horners as possible in common. The difference of these two results gives the principal part of the error for the formula of the least order. Unfortunately, in comparison to the ordinary Runge-Kutta formulas, these formulas, in general, cost additional horners.

### 4.3 Examples.

1. *Euler's method for*

$$x' = X(x, t).$$

$$x_{i+1} = x_i + hX_i,$$

$$x^*_{i+1} = x_i + \frac{h}{2}(X_i + X_{i+1}).$$

The method does not cost additional horners, since it is by all means necessary to calculate $X_{i+1}$ in order to execute the following step.

2. *Method of order 2 costing three horners per step*

$$\theta_1 = \frac{1}{4}, \qquad \theta_2 = \frac{1}{2}, \qquad \theta_3 = 1.$$

| $\frac{1}{4}$ | | | |
|---|---|---|---|
| 0 | $\frac{1}{2}$ | | |
| 1 | $-2$ | 2 | |
| $\frac{1}{6}$ | 0 | $\frac{4}{6}$ | $\frac{1}{6}$ |

$x_{i+1} = x_{i,3}$ is an approximate value of order 2; $x_{i,4}$ is an approximate value of order 4. The method costs three horners per step (whereas the Runge-Kutta method of the same order costs two).

Applying this method to the equation

$$y' = y - 1.5e^{-0.5t}, \qquad y(0) = 1, \qquad h = 0.4,$$

we find

| $t$ | $y_{i,\alpha}$ | Calculated error per step | Exact error per step |
|---|---|---|---|
| 0.4 | 0.819,375 | −0.000,656 | −0.000,645 |
| 0.8 | 0.671,811 | −0.000,540 | −0.000,530 |
| 1.2 | 0.551,476 | −0.000,438 | −0.000,438 |
| 1.6 | 0.453,668 | −0.000,372 | −0,000,365 |
| 2.0 | 0.374,661 | −0.000,314 | −0.000,308 |

### 5.1  Evaluation of the error at one step by approximate quadrature.[1]

This method is applicable only in its actual form to systems in canonical form.

### 5.2  Derivation of identities.

There exists a relation between $n + 2$ values of a polynomial of degree $n$ and its derivatives at the abscissa points $0, 1, \ldots, n + 1$. Here is a list of these relations up to the sixth degree.

*Second degree*

$$f_1' = -2f_0 - f_0' + 2f_1. \qquad \text{II}$$

*Third degree*

$$f_2 = 5f_0 + 2f_0' - 4f_1 + 4f_1', \qquad \text{III}$$

$$f_0 = 5f_2 - 2f_2' - 4f_1 - 4f_1', \qquad \text{III (a)}$$

$$f_2' = 12f_0 + 5f_0' + 8f_1' - 12f_1, \qquad \text{III*}$$

$$f_0' = -12f_2 + 5f_2' + 8f_1' + 12f_1. \qquad \text{III* (a)}$$

*Fourth degree*

$$f_2' = -3f_0 - f_0' - 4f_1' + 3f_2. \qquad \text{IV}$$

*Fifth degree*

$$f_3 = 10f_0 + 3f_0' + 9f_1 + 18f_1' - 18f_2 + 9f_2' \qquad \text{V}$$

$$f_0 = 10f_3 - 3f_3' + 9f_2 - 18f_2' - 18f_1 - 9f_1' \qquad \text{V(a)}$$

$$f_3' = 33f_0 + 10f_0' + 24f_1 + 57f_1' + 57f_2 + 24f_2',$$
$$\text{V*}$$

$$f_0' = -33f_3 + 10f_3' - 24f_2 + 57f_2' + 57f_1 + 24f_1'.$$
$$\text{V*(a)}$$

*Sixth degree*

$$f_3' = -\left(\frac{11}{3}\right)f_0 - f_0' - 9f_1 - 9f_1' + 9f_2$$

$$- 9f_2' + \left(\frac{11}{3}\right)f_3. \qquad \text{VI}$$

From these relations, one can easily deduce relations valid for any function and a step $h$.

*Second degree*

$$hf_1' = -2f_0 - hf_0' + 2f_1 + O(h_3).$$

*Third degree*

$$\left.\begin{array}{l} f_2 = 5f_0 + 2hf_0' - 4f_1 + 4hf_1' \\ f_0 = 5f_2 - 2hf_2' - 4f_1 - 4hf_1' \\ hf_2' = 12f_0 + 5hf_0' + 8hf_1' - 12f_1 \\ hf_0' = -12f_2 + 5hf_2' + 8hf_1' - 12f_1 \end{array}\right\} + O(h^4).$$

[1]Kuntzmann [3], Morel.

*Fourth degree*

$$hf_2' = -3f_0 - hf_0' - 4hf_1' + 3f_2 + O(h^5).$$

*Fifth degree*

$$\left.\begin{array}{l} f_3 = 10f_0 + 3hf_0' + 9f_1 + 18hf_1' - 18f_2 + 9hf_2' \\ f_0 = 10f_3 - 3hf_3' + 9f_2 - 18hf_2' - 18f_1 - 9hf_1' \\ hf_3' = 33f_0 + 10hf_0' + 24f_1 + 57hf_1' - 57f_2 + 24hf_2' \\ hf_0' = -33f_3 + 10hf_3' - 24f_2 + 57hf_2' + 57f_1 + 24hf_1' \end{array}\right\} + O(h^6).$$

*Sixth degree*

$$hf_3' = -\left(\frac{11}{3}\right)f_0 - hf_0' - 9f_1 - 9hf_1' + 9f_2 - 9hf_2' + \left(\frac{11}{3}\right)f_3 + O(h^7).$$

### 5.3 Transition of the $x(t_i)$ to the $x_i$ and to the errors per step.

As a reference we take

$$x_n(t).$$

We can write

$$x_n(t_n + ih) = x_{n+i} + \eta_{n+i}$$

and, neglecting higher order terms,

$$hX(t_n + ih) = hX_{n+i} + hJ\,\eta_{n+i}.$$

We can express the $\eta_{n+i}$ in terms of the errors at one step $\tau_{n+j}$ by the formulas:

$$\eta_n = 0,$$
$$\eta_{n+1} = \tau_n,$$
$$\eta_{n+2} = (1 + hJ)\tau_n + \tau_{n+1},$$
$$\eta_{n-1} = -(1 - hJ)\tau_{n-1},$$
$$\eta_{n-2} = -(1 - hJ)\tau_{n-2} - (1 - 2hJ)\tau_{n-1},$$

and finally from there the $x_n(t_n + ih)$ by means of $x_{n+i}$ and of $\tau_{j+n}$

$$x_n(t_n) = x_n,$$
$$x_n(t_{n+1}) = x_{n+1} + \tau_n,$$
$$x_n(t_{n+2}) = x_{n+2} + (1 + hJ)\tau_n + \tau_{n+1},$$
$$x_n(t_{n-1}) = x_{n-1} - (1 - hJ)\tau_{n-1},$$
$$x_n(t_{n-2}) = x_{n-2} - (1 - hJ)\tau_{n-2} - (1 - 2hJ)\tau_{n-1}.$$

### 5.4 Derivation of the error formulas.

The error formulas are obtained by writing the above-cited identities for $x_n(t)$ and by replacing the $x_n(t)$ and $X_n(t)$ by their expressions. Let us take, for example, the formula of degree 6. It gives

$$hX_{n+1} + hJ\tau_n = -\frac{11}{3}[x_{n-2} - (1 - hJ)\tau_{n-2} - (1 - 2hJ)\tau_{n-1}]$$
$$- h[X_{n-2} - J(1 - hJ)\tau_{n-2} - J(1 - 2hJ)\tau_{n-1}]$$
$$- 9[x_{n-1} - (1 - hJ)\tau_{n-1}] - 9h[X_{n-1} - J(1 - hJ)\tau_{n-1}]$$
$$+ 9x_n - 9hX_n + \frac{11}{3}(x_{n+1} + \tau_n).$$

We will neglect the terms of order $h^2 \tau_j$, and regroup in the first member the known terms. We have

$$h[X_{n+1} + 9X_n + 9X_{n-1} + X_{n-2}] - \frac{11}{3}x_{n+1} - 9x_n + 9x_{n-1} + \frac{11}{3}x_{n-2}$$

$$= \frac{11}{3}\tau_n + 9\tau_{n-1} + \frac{11}{3}\tau_{n-2} + \frac{11}{3}\tau_n$$

$$+ hJ\left[-\tau_n - \frac{11}{3}\tau_{n-2} - \frac{22}{3}\tau_{n-1} + \tau_{n-2} + \tau_{n-1} - 9\tau_{n-1} + 9\tau_{n-1}\right].$$

In order to continue, we combine $h\tau_n$, $h\tau_{n-1}$, and $h\tau_{n-2}$ in one term. Moreover, we allow a linear variation in $\tau$ for three steps. We have then

$$20\tau_{n-1}\frac{1 - hJ}{2} = hX_{n+1} + 9X_n + 9Y_{n-1} + X_{n-2}$$

$$- \frac{11}{3}x_{n+1} - 9x_n + 9x_{n-1} + \frac{11}{3}x_{n-2}.$$

### 5.5 Actual formulas of evaluation.

We obtain then the following formulas:

$$2\tau_{n+1}\left(1 - \frac{1}{2}hJ\right) = h(X_{n+1} + X_n) - 2x_{n+1} + 2x_n$$
$$+ \text{ terms of order } h^3, \quad \text{II}$$

$$6\tau_{n+1/6}\left(1 - \frac{h}{2}J\right) = h(4X_n + 2X_{n-1}) - x_{n+1} - 4x_n + 5x_{n-1}$$
$$+ \text{ terms of order } h^4, \quad \text{III}$$

$$6\tau_{n-1/6}\left(1 - \frac{h}{2}J\right) = h(2X_n + 4X_{n-1}) + x_{n-2} + 4x_{n-1} - 5x_n$$
$$+ \text{ terms of order } h^4, \quad \text{III(a)}$$

$$\tau_n\left(1 - \frac{h}{2}J\right) = \frac{h}{12}(5X_{n-1} + 8X_n - X_{n+1}) + x_{n-1} - x_n$$
$$+ \text{ terms of order } h^4, \quad \text{III*}$$

$$\tau_n\left(1 - \frac{h}{2}J\right) = \frac{h}{12}(8X_{n-1} + 5X_n - X_{n-2}) + x_{n-1} - x_n$$
$$+ \text{ terms of order } h^4, \quad \text{III*(a)}$$

$$6\tau_{n+1/2}\left(1 - \frac{h}{2}J\right) = h(X_{n+1} + 6X_n + X_{n-1}) - 3x_{n+1} + 3x_{n-1}$$
$$+ \text{ terms of order } h^5, \quad \text{IV}$$

$$30\tau_{n-3/10}\left(1 - \frac{h}{2}J\right) = h(9X_n + 18X_{n-1} + 3X_{n-2}) - x_{n+1}$$
$$- 18x_n + 9x_{n-1} + 10x_{n-2}$$
$$+ \text{ terms of order } h^6, \quad \text{V}$$

$$30\tau_{n+3/10}\left(1 - \frac{h}{2}J\right) = h(3X_{n+1} + 18X_n + 9X_{n-1}) + x_{n-2}$$
$$+ 18x_{n-1} - 9x_n - 10x_{n+1}$$
$$+ \text{ terms of order } h^6, \quad \text{V(a)}$$

$$90\tau_{n-11/30}\left(1 - \frac{h}{2}J\right) = h(10X_{n-2} + 57X_{n-1} + 24X_n - X_{n+1})$$
$$+ 33x_{n-2} + 24x_{n-1} - 57x_n$$
$$+ \text{ terms of order } h^6, \quad \text{V*}$$

$$90\tau_{n+11/30}\left(1 - \frac{h}{2}J\right) = h(10X_{n+1} + 57X_n + 24X_{n-1} - X_{n-2})$$
$$- 33x_{n+1} - 24x_n + 57x_{n-1}$$
$$+ \text{ terms of order } h^6, \quad \text{V*(a)}$$

$$20\tau_{n-1}\left(1 - \frac{h}{2}J\right) = h(X_{n+1} + 9X_n + 9X_{n-1} + X_{n-2}) - \frac{11}{3}x_{n+1}$$
$$- 9x_n + 9x_{n-1} + \frac{11}{3}x_{n-2}$$
$$+ \text{ terms of order } h^7. \quad \text{VI}$$

### 6.1 Application of these formulas.

We will note that these formulas can be used as soon as their order exceeds that of the error at one step. But if the error is of order $h^p$ and we use a formula of order $p + 1$, we cannot localize the error exactly, i.e., state precisely if the calculated quantity is $\tau_n$, or $\tau_{n-1}$, or $\tau_{n+1}$, or an intermediary quantity. This becomes possible if we use formulas of at least $p + 2$ order. We use, then, with the various methods, the following formulas:

|  | Without localization | With localization |
|---|---|---|
| RK 1 | II | III, III (a), III*. III* (a) |
| RK 2 | III, III (a), III*, | IV |
| (Euler Cauchy, improved tangent) | III* (a) | |
| RK 3 | IV | V, V (a), V*, V* (a) |
| RK 4 | V, V (a), V*, V* (a) | VI |

The result obtained by these methods are, in general, very good.

**6.2 Examples.**

1.                          $y' = -y, \qquad y(0) = 1$

(classic Runge-Kutta method).

| $t$ | Actual error | Calculated error |
|-----|--------------|------------------|
| 0 | | |
| 0.1 | $-92 \cdot 10^{-9}$ | |
| 0.2 | $-75 \cdot 10^{-9}$ | $-76 \cdot 10^{-9}$ |
| 0.3 | $-67 \cdot 10^{-9}$ | $-68 \cdot 10^{-9}$ |
| 0.4 | $-62 \cdot 10^{-9}$ | $-61 \cdot 10^{-9}$ |
| 0.5 | $-55 \cdot 10^{-9}$ | $-55 \cdot 10^{-9}$ |
| 1.0 | $-34 \cdot 10^{-9}$ | $-33 \cdot 10^{-9}$ |
| 1.5 | $-21 \cdot 10^{-9}$ | $-21 \cdot 10^{-9}$ |

2.                          $y' = -ty, \qquad y(0) = 1$

(classic Runge-Kutta method).

| $t$ | Actual error | Calculated error |
|-----|--------------|------------------|
| 0 | | |
| 0.1 | $-2 \cdot 10^{-9}$ | |
| 0.2 | 0 | $0.17 \cdot 10^{-9}$ |
| 0.3 | $-1.$ | $0.63 \cdot 10^{-9}$ |
| 0.4 | 0 | $1.3 \ \cdot 10^{-9}$ |
| 0.5 | 0 | $1.2 \ \cdot 10^{-9}$ |
| 1.0 | $-37 \cdot 10^{-9}$ | $-37. \ \cdot 10^{-9}$ |
| 1.5 | $-190 \cdot 10^{-9}$ | $-190. \ \cdot 10^{-9}$ |

3.                  $y' = y - 1.5e^{-0.5t}, \qquad y(0) = 1$

(classic Runge-Kutta method).

| $t$ | Actual error | Calculated error |
|-----|--------------|------------------|
| 0 | | |
| 0.1 | $24 \cdot 10^{-9}$ | |
| 0.2 | $28 \cdot 10^{-9}$ | $28 \cdot 10^{-9}$ |
| 0.3 | $27 \cdot 10^{-9}$ | $27 \cdot 10^{-9}$ |
| 0.4 | $26 \cdot 10^{-9}$ | $26 \cdot 10^{-9}$ |
| 0.5 | $25 \cdot 10^{-9}$ | $25 \cdot 10^{-9}$ |
| 1.0 | $19 \cdot 10^{-9}$ | $20 \cdot 10^{-9}$ |
| 1.5 | $15 \cdot 10^{-9}$ | $15 \cdot 10^{-9}$ |

## II  EVALUATION OF THE QUADRATURE ERROR AT ONE STEP IN THE MULTISTEP METHODS[1]

Most ways of application of the multistep methods (differences, Milne) allow one evaluation of the error. This is, again, one of the big arguments invoked in their favor. In passing, let us remark that the error thus evaluated is the quadrature error at one step which removes a little of its value in the argument. In order to render these evaluations rigorous, it is necessary to make investigations, which we present below.

### 7.1  Evaluation of the quadrature error at one step by differences.

Actually, it is possible to express the principal part of the quadrature error in terms of differences (Chapter 6, paragraph 12), but the quantities with which one forms these differences are the quantities taken from a certain integral of the differential system. It is necessary to show that one can replace these quantities by the approximate quantities. The question is not trivial, since it is to start with the final value of evaluating the principal part of an infinitesimal quantity, and it must be certain that the changes (also infinitesimally small) produced on the values are of a sufficient order so as not to disturb the result.

Consider, for example, the Adams formula of order 3:

$$x_{i+1} = x_i + \frac{h(23X_i - 16X_{i-1} + 5X_{i-2})}{12}$$

whose quadrature error is

$$\frac{3h}{8} \nabla^3 X_i$$

(i.e., of order $h^4$). It would be necessary to form

$$\frac{3h}{8}[X_i - 3X(x_i(t_{i-1}), t_{i-1}) + 3X(x_i(t_{i-2}), t_{i-2}) - X(x_i(t_{i-3}), t_{i-3})].$$

Actually, we form

$$\frac{3h}{8}(X_i - 3X_{i-1} + 3X_{i-2} - X_{i-3}).$$

The difference between these quantities is

$$\frac{3h}{8}\{-3[X_{i-1} - X(x_i(t_{i-1}), t_{i-1})] + 3[X_{i-2} - X(x_i(t_{i-2}), t_{i-2})]$$
$$- [X_{i-3} - X(x_i(t_{i-3}), t_{i-3})]\}.$$

From the results of Chapter 9, paragraph 33, it follows easily that each of the partial differences is of order $h^4$; i.e., that the difference considered is at least of order $h^5$.

---

[1]The examples of this section have been calculated by J. Bertrand (Grenoble).

### 7.2  Further investigation of the infinitesimal order of the above quantity.

We are going to show that the above quantity is $o(h^5)$. We discard the factor $h$. Suppressing all the negligible terms in favor of $h^4$, we can write

$$X_{i-1} - X(x_i(t_{i-1}), t_{i-1})) = J(t_i)(x_{i-1} - x_i(t_{i-1})).$$

Therefore, it is necessary to show that

$$- 3(x_{i-1} - x_i(t_{i-1})) + 3(x_{i-2} - x_i(t_{i-2})) - (x_{i-3} - x_i(t_{i-3})) \quad (A)$$

is negligible compared to $h^4$. We write

$$x_{i-3} - x_i(t_{i-3}) = \{x_{i-3} - x_{i-2}(t_{i-3})\} + \{x_{i-2}(t_{i-3}) - x_i(t_{i-3})\}.$$

Each of the partial differences is of order $h^4$. Thus we can neglect the terms $h^5$ only by displacing them by one or two steps along the integral curves. We obtain then

$$x_{i-3}(t_{i-2}) - x_{i-2} + x_{i-2} - x_i(t_{i-2}).$$

Likewise, we replace

$$x_{i-2} - x_i(t_{i-2}) \quad \text{by} \quad x_{i-2}(t_{i-1}) - x_{i-1} + x_{i-1} - x_i(t_{i-1}).$$

The quantity $(A)$ is then written with exception of the terms of order $h^5$:

$$- [x_{i-3}(t_{i-2}) - x_{i-2}] + 2[x_{i-2}(t_{i-1}) - x_{i-2}] - [x_{i-1}(t_i) - x_i],$$

which we will write according to Chapter 9, paragraph 32, as

$$h^4\{\varphi_1(x_{i-2}, t_{i-2}, h) - 2\varphi_1(x_{i-1}, t_{i-1}, h) + \varphi_1(x_i, t_i, h)\},$$

a quantity negligible compared to $h^4$, since $\varphi$ is continuous.

### 7.3  Example.

Let us return to example 3 of Chapter 6, paragraph 8.3. For $y$ we find

| $t$ | Evaluated error per step: $- (3/8)\, \nabla^3 y_i$ | Actual error per step |
|---|---|---|
| 0.3 | $- 4 \cdot 10^{-9}$ | $- 4$ |
| 0.4 | $-11$ | $-12$ |
| 0.5 | $-13$ | $-14$ |
| 0.6 | $-16$ | $-17$ |
| 0.7 | $-20$ | $-21$ |
| 0.8 | $-23$ | $-24$ |
| 1.0 | $-29$ | $-28$ |
| 1.5 | $-37$ | $-37$ |
| 2.0 | $-35$ | $-36$ |
| 2.5 | $-26$ | $-27$ |
| 3.0 | $-10$ | $-11$ |

### 8.1  Evaluation of the quadrature error in Milne's method.[1]

Reasoning analogous to the preceding permits us to show that the procedure indicated in Chapter 6, paragraph 22, is correct, although the utilized values are the approximate values and not the values corresponding to the same integral curve.

### 8.2  Example.

Let the equation be

$$y' = -y + \cos t, \qquad y(0) = \frac{1}{2}, \qquad h = 0.1,$$

which we will integrate by means of the formulas

$$y_{i+1}^* = y_i + \frac{h}{12}(23\,Y_i - 16\,Y_{i-1} + 5\,Y_{i-2}), \qquad \text{predictor}$$

$$y_{i+1} = y_i + \frac{h}{12}(5\,Y_{i+1}^* + 8\,Y_i - Y_{i-1}), \qquad \text{corrector}$$

the error per step being evaluated by

$$\frac{y_i - y_i^*}{10}.$$

These curves are given by Fig. 10-4.

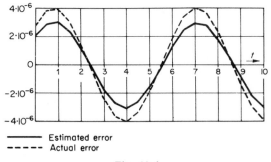

——— Estimated error
- - - - - Actual error

**Fig. 10-4**

### 9.1  Evaluation of the quadrature error at one step by the formulas of paragraph 5.5.

The formulas of paragraph 5.5 are capable of furnishing the principal part of the quadrature error at one step. In order to justify the fact that we use approximate values and not values relative to the same integral curve, we can use reasoning analogous to that of paragraph 7.1.

Of course, it is necessary that the adopted formula be relative to a

[1] It is possible to evaluate the quadrature error in the explicit multistep formulas without adding to the amount of calculation (Ceschino [7]).

polynomial whose degree is at least equal to the order of the infinitesimal
quantity which we propose to evaluate.

### 9.2 Example.

$$y' = -2ty^2, \qquad y(0) = 1, \qquad h = 0.1$$

Adams' method of order 2) by formula VI.

| $t$ | $\tau$ calculated | $\tau$ actual |
|-----|-----------------|--------------|
| 0.3 | $-4.42 \cdot 10^{-4}$ | $-6.34 \cdot 10^{-4}$ |
| 0.4 | $-2.54 \cdot 10^{-4}$ | $-2.30 \cdot 10^{-4}$ |
| 0.5 | $3.17 \cdot 10^{-5}$ | $4.86 \cdot 10^{-5}$ |
| 0.6 | $2.24 \cdot 10^{-4}$ | $2.47 \cdot 10^{-4}$ |
| 1.0 | $2.00 \cdot 10^{-4}$ | $1.98 \cdot 10^{-4}$ |
| 1.5 | $6.48 \cdot 10^{-6}$ | $5.03 \cdot 10^{-6}$ |

$$y' = \tan t, \qquad y(0) = 1, \qquad h = 0.05$$

(Adams' method of order 2) by formula VI.

| $t$ | $\tau$ calculated | $\tau$ actual |
|-----|-----------------|--------------|
| 0.15 | $1.001 \cdot 10^{-5}$ | $1.212 \cdot 10^{-5}$ |
| 0.20 | $1.299 \cdot 10^{-5}$ | $1.292 \cdot 10^{-5}$ |
| 0.25 | $1.417 \cdot 10^{-5}$ | $1.407 \cdot 10^{-5}$ |
| 0.30 | $1.586 \cdot 10^{-5}$ | $1.574 \cdot 10^{-5}$ |
| 0.35 | $1.816 \cdot 10^{-5}$ | $1.801 \cdot 10^{-5}$ |
| 0.50 | $3.066 \cdot 10^{-5}$ | $3.032 \cdot 10^{-5}$ |
| 0.80 | $1.351 \cdot 10^{-4}$ | $1.322 \cdot 10^{-4}$ |
| 1.20 | $3.602 \cdot 10^{-3}$ | $3.320 \cdot 10^{-3}$ |

### 9.3 Peculiarities due to the use of starting values.

The preceding method assumes a certain regularity of the errors per step.
This condition runs the risk of not being satisfied in a multistep method in
the neighborhood of the starting values, since these values are determined by
a special procedure. We are going to examine only the case of an Adams
formula of order 3 for a system in canonical form

$$x' = X(x, t).$$

We will assume that, to evaluate the error, we use the formula VI of 5 and
that the values $x_0$, $x_1$, and $x_2$ are exact. It is necessary to return to the calculation of paragraph 5.4 by setting

$$x(t_0) = x_0, \qquad x(t_1) = x_1, \qquad x(t_2) = x_2.$$

For the error $\tau_2$ we have

$$\tau_2\left(\frac{11}{3} - hJ\right) = h[X_0 + 9X_1 + 9X_2 + X_3]$$

$$+ \frac{11}{3}x_0 + 9x_1 - \frac{11}{3}x_2 + 9x_3.$$

### 9.4 Examples.

For the following equations integrated by the third order Adams method, the above formula gives

| | | | Error $\tau_2$ evaluated | Error $\tau_2$ actual |
|---|---|---|---|---|
| $y' = -2y$ | $y(0) = 1$ | $h = 0.1$ | $3.2 \cdot 10^{-6}$ | $3.2 \cdot 10^{-6}$ |
| $y' = xy$ | $y(0) = 1$ | $h = 0.1$ | $2.45 \cdot 10^{-5}$ | $2.5 \cdot 10^{-5}$ |
| $y' = 2y$ | $y(0) = 1$ | $h = 0.1$ | $8 \cdot 10^{-4}$ | $8 \cdot 10^{-4}$ |
| $y' = y \tan x$ | $y(0) = 1$ | $h = 0.05$ | $1.2 \cdot 10^{-5}$ | $1.2 \cdot 10^{-5}$ |

## III  EVALUATION OF THE GLOBAL TRUNCATION ERROR

From the beginning of the theoretical investigation of Chapter 9, we can imagine different procedures for evaluating the global truncation error. Actually, only one is practical: the method of variation of the step. Before investigating it, we will give some other possibilities.

### 10.1 Application of the error equation.

This method would consist of integrating

$$z' = Jz + \frac{\tau}{h}, \qquad (E)$$

where $\tau$ denotes the local error. This method amounts to integrating a differential system of the same order as the proposed system, after the local error has been evaluated. We can effect this integration by a more abridged method (for example, Euler's method), but it is necessary to calculate the functions in the square matrix $J$.

### 10.2 Remark on the evaluation of $J$ in the case of a single equation of the first order.

In this particular case, we can often evaluate $J = Y'_y$ by the differential quotient:

$$\frac{Y(y^*) - Y(y)}{y^* - y},$$

where $y^*$ and $y$ in general have been calculated previously. Likewise in the Euler-Cauchy method

$$y^*_{i+1} = y_i + hY_i,$$

$$y_{i+1} = y_i + \frac{h}{2}(Y_i + Y^*_{i+1}),$$

we take

$$y^*_{i+1} \quad \text{and} \quad y_{i+1}.$$

Likewise in the classic Runge-Kutta method, for a single equation we take

$$y^*_{i+1} = y_{i,3}.$$

Finally, in the multistep method applied by means of the predictor and corrector, we take

$$y^*_{i+1} \quad \text{and} \quad y_{i+1}.$$

### 10.3 Example.

$$y' = -2ty^2$$

(classic Runge-Kutta method $h = 0.1$).

| $t$ | $Y'_y$ calculated | $Y'_y$ actual |
|-----|-------------------|---------------|
| 0.1 | $-0.3956$ | $-0.3960$ |
| 0.2 | $-0.7698$ | $-0.7692$ |
| 0.3 | $-1.1008$ | $-1.1009$ |
| 0.4 | $-1.3793$ | $-1.3793$ |
| 1.0 | $-1.9997$ | $-2.0000$ |
| 1.1 | $-1.9906$ | $-1.9909$ |
| 1.9 | $-1.6484$ | $-1.6486$ |
| 2.0 | $-1.5998$ | $-1.6000$ |

The same equation—Euler-Cauchy method $h = 0.1$.

| $t$ | $Y'_y$ calculated | $Y'_y$ actual |
|-----|-------------------|---------------|
| 0.1 | $-0.398$ | $-0.396$ |
| 0.2 | $-0.773$ | $-0.769$ |
| 0.3 | $-1.104$ | $-1.100$ |
| 0.4 | $-1.382$ | $-1.379$ |
| 1.0 | $-1.998$ | $-2.004$ |
| 1.1 | $-1.989$ | $-1.995$ |
| 1.9 | $-1.650$ | $-1.654$ |
| 2.0 | $-1.601$ | $-1.606$ |

### 10.4 Application of the adjoint-system.[1]

In the preceding method, we determined the error at large of the interval of integration. It happens frequently that we are interested only in the error

[1]Sterne.

at the end point. Let us return to Chapter 9, paragraph 27. We see there that, in order to integrate $(E)$, we have at our disposal the explicit formula

$$z(t) = \int_{t_0}^{t} M(t, u)\varphi(u)\mathrm{d}u.$$

If we take $t = b$,

$$z(b) = \int_{t_0}^{b} M(b, u)\varphi(u)\mathrm{d}u.$$

According to Chapter 9, paragraph 12.2, the function $M(b, u)$ is the solution of the differential system

$$M_u'(b, u) = -M(b, u) J(u),$$

with the initial condition

$$M(b, b) = \mathrm{I}.$$

In this form, the method is prohibitive, since it is necessary to integrate at a differential system of order $n^2$ in order to find $M(b, u)$.

An important simplification presents itself if one is interested only in the error of a linear combination with constant coefficients of unknown functions (and that for the final value). Let $Cx$ be that combination:

$$Cz(b) = \int_{t_0}^{b} CM(b, u)\varphi(u)\mathrm{d}u.$$

$CM(b, u)$ is the solution of the system

$$(CM(b, u))_u' = -(CM(b, u)) J(u)$$

with the initial conditions

$$(CM(b, b)) = C.$$

Therefore, one has to integrate only a differential system of order $n$, after having determined the local error, i.e., the same procedure as in 9 for determining only the error of a linear combination of the unknown functions and for the final value of the variable. Another objection to this method is that the interpretation of an isolated value of the error is very delicate. Fig. 10-4a presents the development for a differential equation, the calculated error (curve $\alpha$) and for the actual error (curve $\beta$). We see that they are the exact image of each other if we consider them as a pair of two curves, but if we

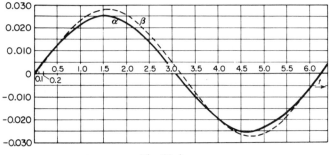

Fig. 10-4a

consider the abscissa 3.2, we find: calculated error 0, actual error −0.005. If we know only the calculated error for this value, we can believe that the error is smaller than $10^{-3}$, whereas it is 5 times larger. We risk likewise rough errors by taking as the order of magnitude of the error, at every point of the calculation, the established error for the final value. Indeed, for $t = 3$, the error is of order 0.002, and for $t = 4$, it is 0.025.

### 11.1 Method of doubling of the step.

If one places oneself in the framework of the linearized theory of errors, it is clear that by integrating a system by a method of order $q$ with the steps $h$ and $2h$, one commits at the abscissa $t$ two global errors of the method whose ratio is

$$2^q.$$

One deduces immediately that the error which a quantity $y$ is bearing has for its principal part

$$\frac{y_{2h}(t) - y_h(t)}{2^q - 1}.$$

### 11.2 Example.

$$y' = y + \cos t, \qquad y(0) = \frac{1}{2}$$

(Euler's method).

| $t$ | $h = 0.1$ | $h = 0.2$ | Calculated error | Actual error | $y$ exact |
|---|---|---|---|---|---|
| 0 | 0.5000 | 0.5000 | | | |
| 0.2 | 0.5945 | 0.6000 | 55 | 51 | 0.5894 |
| 0.4 | 0.6653 | 0.6760 | 107 | 101 | 0.6552 |
| 0.6 | 0.7095 | 0.7250 | 155 | 145 | 0.6950 |
| 0.8 | 0.7255 | 0.7451 | 196 | 185 | 0.7070 |
| 1.0 | 0.7125 | 0.7354 | 229 | 216 | 0.6909 |
| 1.2 | 0.6711 | 0.6964 | 253 | 239 | 0.6472 |
| 1.4 | 0.6030 | 0.6296 | 266 | 253 | 0.5777 |
| 1.6 | 0.5108 | 0.5377 | 269 | 256 | 0.4852 |
| 1.8 | 0.3982 | 0.4243 | 261 | 248 | 0.3733 |
| 2.0 | 0.2698 | 0.2940 | 242 | 233 | 0.2465 |
| 2.2 | 0.1306 | 0.1520 | 214 | 206 | 0.1100 |
| 2.4 | −0.0138 | 0.0039 | 177 | 162 | −0.0310 |
| 2.6 | −0.1577 | −0.1444 | 133 | 130 | −0.1707 |
| 2.8 | −0.2952 | −0.2869 | 83 | 84 | −0.3036 |
| 3.0 | −0.4210 | −0.4180 | 30 | 139 | −0.4241 |
| 3.2 | −0.5301 | −0.5324 | − 23 | − 18 | −0.5283 |
| 3.4 | −0.6179 | −0.6255 | − 76 | − 68 | −0.6111 |
| 3.6 | −0.6812 | −0.6938 | −126 | −116 | −0.6696 |
| 3.8 | −0.7173 | −0.7344 | −171 | −159 | −0.7014 |
| 4.0 | −0.7248 | −0.7457 | −209 | −196 | −0.7052 |
| 5.0 | −0.3622 | −0.3879 | −257 | −244 | −0.3376 |
| 6.0 | 0.3334 | 0.3265 | − 69 | − 70 | 0.3404 |

### 11.3 Improvement of results by doubling of the step.

When a method does not give an upper bound of the error, but its principal part, one can use it eventually to improve a result. It suffices to subtract the principal part of the error from the best of the results.

### 11.4 Examples.

1.                                    $y' = y - 1.5\,e^{-0.5t}$.

By integrating by Euler's method with $h = 0.1$ and $0.2$, we find

| $t$ | $h = 0.1$ | $h = 0.2$ | Improved | Exact |
|---|---|---|---|---|
| 1 | 0.590,109 | 0.575,690 | 0.604,528 | 0.606,531 |
| 2 | 0.315,324 | 0.272,432 | 0.358,212 | 0.367,879 |
| 3 | 0.080,774 | —0.025,719 | 0.187,267 | 0.223,130 |

The first two results are good, the third much less so. That depends on the length of the integration.

2. For the same example, the improved tangent method gives

| $t$ | $h = 0.2$ | $h = 0.4$ | improved | Exact |
|---|---|---|---|---|
| 1.2 | 0.547,013 | 0.542,161 | 0.548,630 | 0.548,812 |
| 2.4 | 0.294,277 | 0.275,982 | 0.300,375 | 0.301,194 |
| 3.6 | 0.141,948 | 0.063,200 | 0.168,197 | 0.165,299 |
| 4.8 | 0.013,425 | —0.241,364 | 0.098,355 | 0.090,718 |

The results remain good over a greater length.

### 12. Remark on the method of variation of step.

1. The simultaneous integration with the step $h$ and the step $2h$, but by the same method, yields conclusions which it would not be possible to obtain if we integrated by two different methods.

2. An error of calculation in one of the two integrations is, in general, transmitted by a big variation of the difference between the two approximate integrations. Hence, we have at our disposal a partial means of verification.

3. On the other hand, this way of proceeding does not permit the disclosure of a fault of the method (for example, a wrong coefficient).

## IV   CHOICE OF THE STEP[1]

### 13. Unit error.

Frequently, it is useful to introduce, instead of the error at one step, the error referred to a unit length, i.e.,

[1]Anderson, Capra [1], Garnier.

$$\frac{\tau}{h} = \eta,$$

if $\tau$ is the error at one step and $h$ the length of the step.

### 14.1 Rapid determination of the elements necessary for the choice of the step.

Suppose that one has decided to perform an integration in an interval $(a, b)$ with a well-defined method, and with a global error smaller than a quantity given in advance. For this, one would have to choose the step. This necessitates a rapid evaluation of the error per step or of the unit error and of the elements of the propagation matrix. We are going to show an example of how one can proceed.

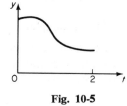

Fig. 10-5

Let it be required to integrate

$$y' = -2ty^2, \qquad 0 \leqslant t \leqslant 2, \qquad y(0) = 1$$

by Euler's method. A quick investigation shows that the function decreases steadily from 1 toward 0.2. (See Fig. 10-5) We will study the neighborhoods of the three points:

$$t = 0, \quad y = 1; \quad t = 1, \quad y = 0.5; \quad t = 2, \quad y = 0.2.$$

$Y_y' = -4ty$ evaluated at these points is

$$0, \qquad -2, \qquad -1.6.$$

The propagation factor

$$\exp\left(\int_t^2 Y_y'(u)\, du\right)$$

is evaluated by an approximate integration. We find

| $t$ | 0 | 1 | 2 |
|---|---|---|---|
| $\exp\left(\int_t^2 Y_y'(u)\, du\right)$ | $\frac{1}{12}$ | $\frac{1}{6}$ | 1 |

In order to know the error per step, we can either evaluate $y''$

$$y'' = -4tyy' - 2y^2 = 8t^2y^3 - 2y^2,$$

or make some steps in the neighborhood of the above values and use the methods of section I.

In the neighborhood of the above values we find the errors per step,

$$-h^2, \qquad 0.25h^2, \qquad 0.12h^2.$$

This extremely coarse information is sufficient.

### 14.2 Approximate evaluation of the global error.

Suppose we have an interval of integration of length $l$ which we partition into partial intervals of lengths

$$l_1, \quad l_2, \quad l_3.$$

For each of these intervals let

$$M_1, \quad M_2, \quad M_3$$

be the mean value of the matrix controlling the propagation between a point of this interval and the end point. The total error can be majorized by

$$l_1 |M_1 \eta_1| + l_2 |M_2 \eta_2| + l_3 |M_3 \eta_3|.$$

$|M_1 \eta_1|$ is the length of the vector $M_1 \eta_1$.

*Remark.* One could be interested in working with the components of $M_i \eta_i$ and not with its length;
—specifically to take into account the sign changes of certain components.

### 14.3 Example.

Let us return to the example of 14.1. We propose to integrate with constant step and with a global error smaller than $10^{-3}$. We will consider three intervals

$$0 \text{ to } 0.5, \quad 0.5 \text{ to } 1.5, \quad 1.5 \text{ to } 2$$

with the propagation matrices

$$\frac{1}{10} \quad \frac{1}{6} \quad \frac{1}{1.6}$$

and the unit errors

$$- 0.69h \quad 0.25h \quad 0.15h.$$

For the global error, we have

$$-0.07h + 0.04h + 0.10h = 0.07h.$$

For $h \approx 1/70$ the global error will be smaller than $10^{-3}$. The computation made with $h = 1/50$ gives a global error of $1.3 \times 10^{-3}$, which checks quite well with our evaluation.

### 15. Another method for the determination of the elements necessary for the choice of the step.

In the interval under consideration, one integrates with the step $h$, then starts from the abscissas $0, l/3, 2l/3$ with a double step. One determines thus four approximate values for the final result, from which it is easy to deduce various pieces of information.

Let $p$ be the final value corresponding to the integration with the step $h$; let $a, b, c$ be the final values of the integrations obtained with the step $2h$ starting from the beginning, from one third, from two thirds. Let $\alpha, \beta, \gamma$ be the exact final values relative to the integral, starting from 0, from $l/3$, and from $2l/3$. (See Fig. 10-6.) One assumes that the error at one step is of order $h^{q+1}$. The four points $p, a, b, c$ and $p, \alpha, \beta, \gamma$ form two similar figures in the ratio

$$\frac{1}{2^q - 1}$$

Then one has

$$\alpha\beta = \frac{ab}{2^q - 1}, \qquad \beta\gamma = \frac{bc}{2^q - 1},$$

$$\gamma p = \frac{cp}{2^q - 1}.$$

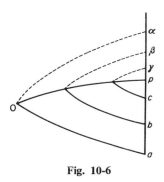

Fig. 10-6

But $\alpha\beta$, $\beta\gamma$, and $\gamma p$ are the contributions of the first, second, and third thirds of the global error.

### 16. Example of a precise problem.

Let us consider the equation

$$y' = -2ty^2$$

with initial condition $y(0) = 1$. We propose to integrate this system by Euler's method, by taking eventually different steps in the partial intervals

$$0\text{--}1, \qquad 1\text{--}2, \qquad 2\text{--}3,$$

but in a way that the global error never exceeds $10^{-3}$. We integrate the system with a step 0.02 between 0 and 3; then we repeat from 0, 1, and 2 (with the found values) with the step 0.04. Figure 10-7 shows the difference between these various calculations. Let us recall that for Euler's method, the error has for the principal part the difference between the two calculations, and that this error is proportional to $h$. We see that, for the first third, it is necessary

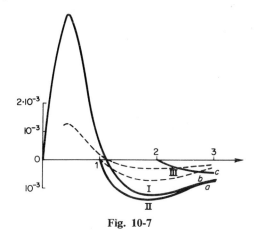

Fig. 10-7

to divide the step by 5:

$$h = 0.004 \quad \text{between 0 and 1.}$$

We find that we can neglect the propagation of this error in the other two-thirds of the calculation (it gives a contribution equal to one-fourth the difference between the curves I and II). For the second third, it is necessary to divide the error by 1.5; we take $h = 0.01$. The consequences of this error on the third third are given by one-half of the difference between the curves II and III. For the third third one can add the step. We will choose to double it.

$$h = 0.04.$$

Thus the calculation gives the following errors:

| | | | |
|---|---|---|---|
| 0.1 | $5 \cdot 10^{-4}$ | 1.5 | $7 \cdot 10^{-4}$ |
| 0.2 | 6 | 1.6 | 7 |
| 0.3 | 9 | 1.7 | 7 |
| 0.4 | 10 | 1.8 | 7 |
| 0.5 | 9 | 1.9 | 7 |
| 0.6 | 7 | 2.0 | 7 |
| 0.7 | 6 | 2.2 | 10 |
| 0.8 | 5 | 2.4 | 11 |
| 0.9 | 3 | 2.6 | 12 |
| 1.0 | 1 | 2.8 | 12 |
| 1.4 | 5 | 3.0 | 15 |

### 17. Recollection of a theorem.[1]

In order to minimize the error with a given number of steps, it is necessary to choose the lengths of these in a manner so that all the steps give the same contribution to the final error. Below we are going to examine a particular case where it is possible to choose the length of the step during the course of the calculation, without an analogous preliminary study, as was necessary in the preceding section.

### 18.1 Use of a variable step for systems having a very small propagation factor.[2]

For systems having a very small propagation factor where the number of integrals is convergent, it is at the same time convenient and prudent to pose the condition that the unit error is prescribed in advance.

### 18.2 Determination of the step giving a fixed unit error.

When the order $q$ of the method is known, it is easy to determine a step such that the unit error has a preassigned value. One accomplishes this by an integration with the step $h$. By doubling (or otherwise) one determines the corresponding unit error; let it be $\eta$, which is proportional to $h^q$. Hence it suffices to restore the unit error to a fixed value $\eta_1$ by choosing $h$ conveniently.

[1]Ceschino-Kuntzmann [3].
[2]Garnier.

### 18.3 Practical way of operation.

The transition from one point to another consists of the following phases:
—integration with a step $h_{i,0}$.
—determination by means of the unit error of the step, which one would theoretically have to use instead of $h_{i,0}$. For this, one has to solve an equation of the form

$$h_{i,1}^q = k_1,$$

$k_i$ being known.
One will avoid the extraction of a root by making use of a small table of the $h^q$. This has, moreover, the advantage of leading to values of the length of the step having only one or two decimals.

*Choice of an effective step.* Three cases present themselves:
(a) If the value found for $h_{i,1}$ is greater or even slightly smaller than $h_{i,0}$, for example, $h_{i,1} \geqslant 0.9\, h_{i,0}$, one accepts the result of the integration and takes $h_{i,1}$ (or $h_{i,1}.q$ with $q < 1$ in the case where $h_{i,1} < h_{i,0}$) for the length of the following step.
(b) If $h_{i,1}$ is considerably smaller than $h_{i,0}$, it is necessary to start over with the length of the step $h_{i,1}$.
(c) If $h_{i,1}$ is very large, one finds oneself very likely in the case of instability of the length of the step (see paragraph 19).

### 18.4 Other considerations which can enter into the determination of the length of the step.

Let us cite for this subject:
—the presence of functions admitting a certain periodicity, the step having to be smaller than this period.
—the existence among the quantities, which enter into play, of discontinuities at points whose abscissa is or is not evident in advance.
—the use of tables which define certain functions for the determined abscissas (at times, these functions can be the result of a first integration).

### 19.1 Instability of the length of the step.

The unit error for a length of the given step is, in general, a function having a regular behavior (Fig. 10-8). The length of the step furnishing a given unit error is a negative power of the absolute value of this quantity. Therefore, it will be infinite for values for which the unit error vanishes. Practically, one can state that the length of the determined step, as was said in paragraph 18.3, has abrupt increases followed by likewise abrupt decreases. To avoid this phenomenon, which harms the accuracy, one imposes in the ratio of lengths of two successive steps that it not exceed a certain value, for example, 1.5 or 2.

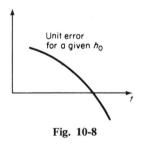

Unit error
for a given $h_0$

Fig. 10-8

**19.2 Example.**

$$y' = -ty \quad \text{with} \quad y(0) = 1.$$

Improved tangent method.

One works with a unit error of $10^{-3}$. The error at one step is determined by the doubling of the step. Figure 10-9 shows the curve giving the lengths of steps.

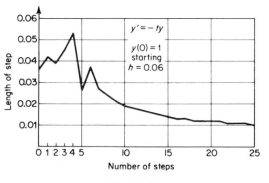

Fig. 10-9

**19.3 Other procedures to stabilize the length of the step.**

$$y' = -2ty^2, \qquad y(0) = 1 \quad \text{(Euler-Cauchy method).}$$

The unit error is taken to be constant. The error per step is evaluated by

$$\frac{h}{12}[5Y_{i+1} - 6Y^*_{i+1} + 2Y_i - Y_{i-1}].$$

The error per step changes sign near the origin. This is expressed by irregular points. One can eliminate these points by the following artifice. The error is written as

$$h^3\left[\frac{y'''}{12} - \frac{Y'_y y''}{4}\right] = \tau.$$

One evaluates not only the error, but the term

$$h^3\frac{Y'_y y''}{4} = \tau_1,$$

and one substitutes into the error the quantity

$$\text{Max}\,(\tau, \tau_1/5).$$

**20. Example of the gain realized by the use of a variable step.**

This gain can be very large if the phenomenon to be studied admits passive and active phases.

*Example.* Let the equation be

$$y'' + (59t + 45)y' + 59(t + 1)y = 0,$$
$$y(0) = 1, \qquad y'(0) = 0, \qquad 0 \leqslant t \leqslant 2.$$

At the start, $y'$ varies very rapidly. The errors decay very rapidly, and one can proceed by imposing a unit error smaller than 0.01. Here are the results:

*Minimum step*                     0.001
*Actual number of steps*    158

If one had taken a constant step of 0.001, one would have performed 2000 steps.

## V  CHANGING OF STEP IN THE MULTISTEP METHODS

### 21. Ordinary procedure of dividing or doubling.

This method consists of multiplying or dividing the length of the step by 2. We will not give details on it, because it presents the following inconveniences:

—if $r$ is the order of the method, it multiplies or divides roughly the local quadrature error by

$$2^{r+1}.$$

—the multiplication of the step by 2 requires the reutilization of the previous values which are, without a doubt, no longer accessible if one works with a computer. For example, if one takes a formula which makes use of

$$X_i, \quad X_{i-1}, \quad X_{i-2},$$

it will be necessary to double the step to recover

$$X_{i-4}.$$

—the division of the step by 2 is complicated, because it requires one to interpolate in order to obtain the necessary points.

### 22.1 Principle of another method.[1]

For example, let the formula be

$$x_{i+1} = x_i + h \sum_{j=0}^{r} A_j X_{i-j}. \tag{1}$$

Suppose that, starting at a point with subscript $s$, we want to pass from a step $h$ to a step

$$h\omega, \qquad \omega \leqslant 1.$$

We will use formulas of the type:

$$x_{s+(k+1)\omega} = x_{s+k\omega} + h \sum_{j=0}^{k-1} B_{j,k} x_{s+(k-j)\omega} + h \sum_{j=0}^{r-k} C_{j,k} X_{s-j} \tag{2}$$

[1]Ceschino [5].

with successively $k = 0, 1, \ldots, r - 1$. Disposing of the quantities

$$X_{s+r\omega}, \quad X_{s+(r-1)\omega}, \ldots, X_s,$$

we could use again the starting formula (1) with the step $\omega h$.

### 22.2 Derivation of the transition formulas.

In the formulas (2), we have separated the terms relative to the $X$ with subscript $s - j$, and the terms relative to the $X$ with subscript $s + (k - j)\omega$. We can easily establish the formulas:

$$B_{j,k} = \frac{(-1)^j C_k^j \omega}{k! \, [(k-j)\omega + 1][(k-j)\omega + 2]\ldots[(k-j)\omega + r - k]} \int_0^1 \frac{P_k(u)du}{u + j},$$

$$C_{j,k} = \frac{(-1)^{j+k} C_{r-k}^j \omega^{k+2}}{(r-k)!(\omega + j)(2\omega + j)\ldots(k\omega + j)} \int_0^1 \frac{P_k(u)\,du}{(u+k)\omega + j},$$

where

$$P_k(u) = u(u+1)\ldots(u+k)[(u+k)\omega + 1]\ldots[(u+k)\omega + r - k].$$

### 22.3 Actual formulas for the explicit Adams method.

$r = 1$. There is one intermediary point to calculate:

$$X_{s+\omega} = x_s + \frac{h\omega}{2}[(2 + \omega)X_s - \omega X_{s-1}].$$

The principal part of the error at this step is

$$-\frac{\omega^2}{12}(2\omega + 3)h^3 x'''.$$

$r = 2$. There are two intermediary points to calculate:

$$X_{s+\omega} = x_s + \frac{\omega h}{12}[(12 + 9\omega + 2\omega^2)X_s - 4\omega(3 + \omega)X_{s-1} + \omega(3 + 2\omega)X_{s-2}].$$

The error at this step is

$$-\frac{\omega^2}{24}(\omega + 2)^2 h^4 x^{IV}.$$

$$X_{s+2\omega} = X_{s+\omega} + \frac{\omega h}{6(\omega + 1)}[(14\omega + 9)X_{s+\omega} - (3 + 5\omega)(1 + \omega)X_s + 5\omega^2 X_{s-1}].$$

The error at this step is

$$-\frac{\omega^3}{72}(17\omega + 10)h^4 x^{IV}.$$

$r = 3$. Three intermediary values to calculate:

$$X_{s+\omega} = x_s + \frac{\omega h}{24}[(\omega^3 + 8\omega^2 + 22\omega + 24)X_s - \omega(3\omega^2 + 20\omega + 36)X_{s-1}$$
$$+ \omega(3\omega^2 + 16\omega + 18)X_{s-2} - \omega(\omega + 2)^2 X_{s-3}].$$

The error at this step is

$$-\frac{\omega^2}{720}(6\omega^3 + 45\omega^2 + 110\omega + 290)h^5 x^{\mathrm{V}}.$$

$$x_{s+2\omega} = x_{s+\omega} + \frac{\omega h}{4}\left[\frac{15\omega^2 + 28\omega + 12}{(\omega + 1)(\omega + 2)}X_{s+\omega} - \frac{17\omega^2 + 30\omega + 12}{6}X_s\right.$$
$$\left. + \frac{\omega^2(17\omega + 20)}{3(\omega + 1)}X_{s-1} - \frac{\omega^2(17\omega + 10)}{6(\omega + 2)}X_{s-2}\right].$$

The error at this step is

$$-\frac{\omega^3}{2880}(293\omega^2 + 510\omega + 200)h^5 x^{\mathrm{V}}.$$

$$x_{s+3\omega} = x_{s+2\omega} + \frac{\omega h}{24}\left[\frac{119\omega + 46}{2\omega + 1}\cdot X_{s+2\omega} - \frac{2(43\omega + 16)}{\omega + 1}X_{s+\omega}\right.$$
$$\left. + (27\omega + 10)X_s - \frac{54\omega^3}{(2\omega + 1)(\omega + 1)}X_{s-1}\right].$$

The error at this step is

$$-\frac{\omega^4}{1440}(367\omega + 135)h^5 x^{\mathrm{V}}.$$

## 22.4 Remark on the quadrature error.

This method has the advantage of adjusting a progressive variation of the local quadrature error. For $\omega = 1/2$, here are the principal parts of the errors at the successive steps:

|         | $s$ | $s + \omega$ | $s + 2\omega$ | $s + 3\omega$ | $s + 4\omega$ | |
|---------|-----|--------------|---------------|---------------|---------------|---|
| $r = 1$ | $\frac{-5}{12}$ | $\frac{-1}{12}$ | $\frac{-5}{96}$ | | | $h^3 x'''$ |
| $r = 2$ | $\frac{-3}{8}$ | $\frac{-75}{1152}$ | $\frac{-111}{3456}$ | $\frac{-3}{128}$ | | $h^4 x^{\mathrm{IV}}$ |
| $r = 3$ | $\frac{-251}{720}$ | $\frac{-357 \times 251}{1004 \times 720}$ | $\frac{-2113 \times 251}{32128 \times 720}$ | $\frac{-1907 \times 251}{48192 \times 720}$ | $\frac{-251}{32 \times 720}$ | $h^5 x^{\mathrm{V}}$ |

## 22.5 Advantage of this method relative to the integration scheme.

The application of this method does not modify the integration scheme itself. Only the coefficients to be used vary during the change of step.

## 22.6 Example.

Let

$$y' = -y + \frac{t}{(1 + t)^2}, \qquad y(0) = 1$$

by the formula

$$x_{i+1} = x_i + \frac{h(55X_i - 59X_{i-1} + 37X_{i-2} - 9X_{i-3})}{24}.$$

We propose to double the step starting from $t = 0.9$:

—$y_1$ and $\epsilon_1(\epsilon_1 = y_1 - y_{\text{exact}})$ are relative to the rough doubling of the step.

—$y_2$ and $\epsilon_2(\epsilon_2 = y_2 - y_{\text{exact}})$ are relative to the application of the procedure described on page 265.

We will not develop further the use of the variable step in the multistep methods. The reader desirous of using them can practically refer to section IV, most remarks of which remain valid for this part. Indeed, one could make up a small table of values of the coefficients of the integration formulas corresponding to some values of $h$.

*Remark.* There is no theoretical difficulty in introducing multistep formulas of arbitrary lengths. But the coefficients of these formulas are complicated. As an example, here is one formula:

$$x_{i+1} = x_i + h_i \left[ \frac{(6h_{i-2}h_{i-1} + 3h_i h_{i-2} + 6h_{i-1}^2\, 6h_{i-1}h_i + 2h_i^2)}{6h_{i-1}(h_{i-2} + h_{i-1})} X_i \right.$$
$$\left. - \frac{h_i^2(3h_{i-2} + 3h_{i-1} + 2h_i)}{6h_{i-2}h_{i-1}} X_{i-1} + \frac{h_i^2(3h_{i-1} + 2h_i)}{6h_{i-2}(h_{i-2} + h_{i-1})} X_{i-2} \right].$$

Likewise, one can use the divided difference notation (see Shue).

| $t$ | $y$ exact | $y_1$ | $y_2$ | $\epsilon_1 \cdot 10^{-8}$ | $\epsilon_2 \cdot 10^{-8}$ |
|---|---|---|---|---|---|
| . | . | . | . | | |
| . | . | . | . | | |
| . | . | . | . | | |
| 0.8 | 0.555,555,555 | 0.555,597,14 | 0.555,597,14 | 41 5 9 | 41 5 9 |
| 0.85 | 0.540,540,540 | 0.540,580,54 | 0.540,580,54 | 40 0 0 | 40 0 0 |
| 0.9 | 0.526,315,789 | 0.526,354,22 | 0.526,354,22 | 38 4 3 | 38 4 3 |
| 1 | 0.5 | 0.500,047,51 | 0.500,037,51 | 47 5 1 | 37 5 1 |
| 1.1 | 0.476,190,476 | 0.476,241,02 | 0.476,228,98 | 50 5 4 | 38 5 0 |
| 1.2 | 0.454,545,454 | 0.454,598,48 | 0.454,585,68 | 50 0 3 | 40 2 3 |
| 1.3 | 0.434,782,608 | 0.434,835,05 | 0.434,823,76 | 52 4 4 | 41 1 5 |
| 1.4 | 0.416,666,666 | 0.416,717,91 | 0.416,707,54 | 51 1 4 | 40 8 7 |
| 1.5 | 0.4 | 0.400,049,01 | 0.400,039,76 | 49 0 2 | 39 7 6 |

## 22.7 Actual formulas for the implicit Adams method.

$r = 1$. No intermediary point is to be calculated.

$r = 2$. One intermediary point is to be calculated:

$$x_{s+\omega} = x_s + h \left[ \frac{\omega(3 + 2\omega)}{6(1 + \omega)} X_{s+\omega} + \frac{\omega(3 + \omega)}{6} X_s - \frac{\omega^3}{6(1 + \omega)} X_{s-1} \right].$$

The error at one step is

$$\frac{\omega^3(\omega + 2)}{72} h^4 x^{\text{IV}}.$$

$r = 3$. Two intermediary points are to be calculated:

$$x_{s+\omega} = x_s + h\left[\frac{\omega(\omega + 2)}{4(\omega + 1)} X_{s+\omega} + \frac{\omega(\omega^2 + 6\omega + 12)}{24} X_s\right.$$
$$\left. - \frac{\omega^3(\omega + 4)}{12(\omega + 1)} X_{s-1} + \frac{\omega^3}{24} X_{s-2}\right].$$

The error at one step is

$$\frac{\omega^3 h^5}{1440}(3\omega^2 + 15\omega + 20)x^{\mathrm{V}}.$$

$$x_{s+2\omega} = x_s + h\left[\frac{\omega(17\omega + 10)}{24(2\omega + 1)} X_{s+2\omega} + \frac{\omega(11\omega + 8)}{12(\omega + 1)} X_{s+\omega}\right.$$
$$\left. - \frac{\omega(3\omega + 2)}{24} X_s + \frac{\omega^4 X_{s-1}}{4(2\omega + 1)(\omega + 1)}\right].$$

The error at one step is

$$\frac{\omega^4 h^5}{1440}(23\omega + 15)x^{\mathrm{V}}.$$


## VI  A SUMMARY STUDY OF THE GLOBAL METHODS.[1]

### 23. Generalities.

These methods consist of integrating once in the whole interval, then giving the successive improvements, each being extended over the whole interval. We put this study here, because we will consider these methods not as real integration methods, but as auxiliary means either to improve a result, or possibly to evaluate the errors.

These methods do not satisfy the first fundamental property of Chapter 1, paragraph 13. This has to be paid for essentially in the form of additional operations, rendering these methods not very competitive.

### 24.1  Picard's method.[2]

Picard's method consists of solving

$$x' = X(x, t), \qquad x(t_0) = x_0$$

by starting from an approximate solution $x_0(t)$ and by calculating

$$x_1(t) = x_0 + \int_{t_0}^{t} X(x_0(u), u)\,du.$$

One can begin again, i.e., iterate:

$$x_n(t) = x_0 + \int_{t_0}^{t} X(x_{n-1}(u), u)\,du.$$

[1]Fox and Goodwin, Clenshaw and Olver, Haussmann and Schwarzschild, Krilov, Warga [1, 2].

[2]Collatz [7], Krilov, Lombardi, Schelkunoff, Cernysenko, Picard [1, 2].

**24.2 Example.**

Let the equation be

$$y' = -y, \qquad y(0) = 1.$$

We start from $y_0(t) = 1$ and find

$$y_n(t) = 1 - \frac{t}{1} + \cdots + \frac{(-1)^n t^n}{n!}.$$

## 25. Investigation of numerical convergence.

Limiting ourselves to the preceding example, we see that the method converges whatever $t$ may be, but the convergence is numerically interesting only for $0 < t < 1$ (the values approach the limit from the very beginning). Let us study the general case of an unknown function, for which we would have

$$|y_2(t) - y_1(t)| \leqslant |y_1(t) - y_0(t)|$$

for all possible choices of $y_1(t)$ and $y_0(t)$. We can write

$$y_2(t) - y_1(t) = \int_{t_0}^{t} Y_y'(\xi, u)(y_1(u) - y_0(u))\, du.$$

The condition requires

$$\left| \int_{t_0}^{t} Y_y'(\xi, u)\, du \right| < 1.$$

This amounts to saying that the propagation parameter (Chapter 9, paragraph 15.1) lies between $e$ and $1/e$. The best conditions of application of this method are, therefore, those where the integration behaves almost like an approximate quadrature (propagation parameter is near 1).

In particular, a very small propagation parameter (i.e., a group of highly convergent integrals which is a favorable circumstance for good error propagation in the step methods) is not a favorable circumstance for the application of Picard's method.

## 26.1 Application of the method.

In order to evaluate the integral, one can use either a planimeter or an integrator. The direct application by means of analysis is, in general, excluded, because one rapidly arrives at integrals which cannot be expressed explicitly. Thus one can have recourse to an approximate expression by the approximate quadrature formulas. One would replace

$$x_{n+1}(t_p) = x_0 + \int_{t_0}^{t_p} X(x_n(u), u)\, du$$

by

$$x_{n+1}(t_p) = x_0 + h \sum_{i=p-\alpha_p}^{p+\beta_p} A_{p,i} X_n(t_i).$$

Moreover, one could use more and more precise formulas to improve the result.

### 26.2 Example.

Let $y' = ay$, $y(0) = 0$ whose analytic solution is $y(t) = 0$. One uses the formula:

$$y_{i+1, n+1} = y_{i, n+1} + \frac{h(Y_{i, n} + Y_{i+1, n})}{2} = y_{i, n+1} + \frac{ah(y_{i, n} + y_{i+1, n})}{2},$$

with $ah/2 = 0.1$, $n$ being the iteration cycle and $i$ being the subscript of the abscissa.

Here are two calculations corresponding to two different choices of the initial function:

| $n$ \ $i$ | 0 | 1 | 2 | 3 | 4 | 5 | 6 | 7 | 8 | 9 | 10 |
|---|---|---|---|---|---|---|---|---|---|---|---|
| 0 | 0 | 1 | 1 | 1 | 1 | 1 | 1 | 1 | 1 | 1 | 1 |
| 1 | 0 | 0.1 | 0.3 | 0.5 | 0.7 | 0.9 | 1.1 | 1.3 | 1.5 | 1.7 | 1.9 |
| 2 | 0 | 0.01 | 0.05 | 0.13 | 0.25 | 0.41 | 0.61 | 0.85 | 1.13 | 1.45 | 1.81 |
| 3 | 0 | 0.001 | 0.007 | 0.025 | 0.063 | 0.129 | 0.231 | 0.377 | 0.575 | 0.833 | 1.159 |
| 4 | 0 | 0.0001 | 0.0009 | 0.0041 | 0.0129 | 0.0321 | 0.0681 | 0.1289 | 0.2241 | 0.3649 | 0.5641 |

| $n$ \ $i$ | 0 | 1 | 2 | 3 | 4 | 5 | 6 | 7 | 8 | 9 | 10 |
|---|---|---|---|---|---|---|---|---|---|---|---|
| 0 | 0 | 0.1 | 0.2 | 0.3 | 0.4 | 0.5 | 0.6 | 0.7 | 0.8 | 0.9 | 1.0 |
| 1 | 0 | 0.01 | 0.04 | 0.09 | 0.16 | 0.25 | 0.36 | 0.49 | 0.64 | 0.81 | 1.0 |
| 2 | 0 | 0.001 | 0.006 | 0.019 | 0.044 | 0.085 | 0.146 | 0.231 | 0.344 | 0.489 | 0.67 |
| 3 | 0 | 0.0001 | 0.0008 | 0.0031 | 0.0094 | 0.0223 | 0.0454 | 0.0831 | 0.1406 | 0.2239 | 0.3398 |
| 4 | 0 | 0.00001 | 0.00010 | 0.00049 | 0.00174 | 0.00491 | 0.01168 | 0.02453 | 0.04690 | 0.08335 | 0.13729 |

As was asserted, one can state that the convergence is slower and slower as it moves away from the origin. It begins to grow worse near the values for which

$$\int_0^{nh} Y_y'\, du = 1,$$

i.e., for $n = 10$. The remedy is simple. It consists of cutting the interval of integration in two. If, in the case of the second initial function, one starts between 0.5 and 1, with $y(0.5) = 0$, one finds:

| $n$ \ $i$ | 5 | 6 | 7 | 8 | 9 | 10 |
|---|---|---|---|---|---|---|
| 0 | 0 | 0.6 | 0.7 | 0.8 | 0.9 | 1.0 |
| 1 | 0 | 0.0654 | 0.1419 | 0.2361 | 0.3497 | 0.4847 |
| 2 | 0 | 0.01194 | 0.0273 | 0.0537 | 0.0940 | 0.1520 |
| 3 | 0 | 0.0066 | 0.0100 | 0.0163 | 0.0274 | 0.0453 |
| 4 | 0 | 0.0061 | 0.0077 | 0.0101 | 0.0138 | 0.0197 |

*Remark.* One could improve the convergence a little by taking

$$y_{i+1, n+1} = y_{i, n+1} + \frac{ah(y_{i, n+1} + y_{i+1, n})}{2}.$$

### 27.1 Iterative improvement.

A possible use of the method consists of starting from a very close solution (for example, a result from a first approximate integration) and of improving this result by one iteration cycle. Naturally, it would be necessary to make use of a formula of a higher order than that of the first integration method. This improvement carries over into the global error (round-off error included) whereas the improvements based on other principles (for example, doubling the step) are weakened by the round-off error.

### 27.2 Example.

Let us return to the example of paragraph 26.2 with the initial values simulating a round-off error:

|   | 0 | 1 | 2 | 3 | 4 | 5 | 6 | 7 | 8 | 9 |
|---|---|---|---|---|---|---|---|---|---|---|
|   | 0 | 1 | 0 | −1 | 0 | 1 | 0 | −1 | 0 | 1 |
| 1 | 0 | 0.1 | 0.2 | 0.1 | 0 | 0.1 | 0.2 | 0.1 | 0 | 0.1 |
| 2 | 0 | 0.01 | 0.04 | 0.07 | 0.08 | 0.09 | 0.12 | 0.15 | 0.16 | 0.17 |
| 3 | 0 | 0.001 | 0.006 | 0.017 | 0.032 | 0.049 | 0.070 | 0.097 | 0.121 | 0.154 |
| 4 | 0 | 0.0001 | 0.0008 | 0.0031 | 0.0080 | 0.0161 | 0.0280 | 0.0447 | 0.0665 | 0.0940 |

One sees that the results of the first iteration cycle are periodic. On the other hand, those of the second cycle can lead to confusion, if one deviates too much from the starting point. The propagation parameter yields $1/e$ for $y_5$. Above that, the results of the second cycle pervert the judgment of the nature of the error concerning the initial data.

### 28. Relation with the step methods.

Let us return to the modification proposed at the end of paragraph 26.2. There we brought together the step methods, and we can well understand why the global methods are very costly: before the suggested modification one executes iterations on values which are far from the limit, which they must attain, and this costs time. Let us consider now a formula such as

$$x_{i+1} = x_i + \frac{h(13X_i + 13X_{i+1} - X_{i-1} X_{i+2})}{24}.$$

The application of such a formula by a difference method is very costly, because it requires first the calculation of provisional values of two steps for the value being calculated. But its use in the framework of a global method would be even more difficult, especially if it is a question of an integration in a long interval.

Finally, let us note that the procedures presented in Chapter 6, paragraphs 31 through 34 for the determination of starting values of a multistep method are nothing else than Picard's method applied to a very short interval, a favorable case.

### 29. Cotton's, or the residual, method.[1]

As always, let the system be $x' = X(x, t)$ and $x(t_0) = x_0$ and $z(t)$ be a function which yields an approximate solution. Relative to the function $z(t)$, one calls the function

$$q(t) = -z'(t) + X(z(t), t)$$

the *residual*.

The residual is zero for the exact solution. One can think that its size permits one to evaluate either the error, or to improve the solution. Set

$$u = x - z,$$
$$x' = X(x, t),$$
$$z' = X(z, t) - q(t),$$

whence:

$$u' = X(x, t) - X(z, t) + q(t) = J(\xi, t)u + q(t). \tag{1}$$

This system is analogous to that which we have met in the study of errors.

*Remark.* In general, $\xi$ is unknown, lying between $x$ and $z$, but for a linear system, $J$ is independent of $\xi$, and hence equation (1) permits one to determine $u(t)$ exactly.

### 30. Integrated residual.

In certain cases, there can be an interest in integrating the two members of (1), which gives

$$u(t) = \int_{t_0}^{t} J(\xi, v)u(v)\,dv + Q(t),$$

$$Q(t) = \int_{t_0}^{t} q(v)\,dv + u(t_0).$$

### 31.1 Iteration by the residual method.

Let the system be

$$x' = X(x, t), \qquad x(t_0) = x_0.$$

Let us give $x_0(t)$ arbitrary, with $x_0(t_0) = x_0$, and study the iteration

[1]Cotton [1, 2], Matthieu [2, 3], Sheldon, Zondek, and Friedmann, Uhlmann [2, 1].

$$x_{i+1}(t) = x_i(t) + z_i(t),$$

with

$$z_i'(t) = J(x_i(t), t) z_i(t) + q_i(t).$$

In passing to the $x_i$, we have

$$x_{i+1}' = X(x_i(t), t) + J(x_i, t)[x_{i+1}(t) - x_i(t)], \tag{1}$$

$$x_{i+1}(t_0) = x_0.$$

In comparison to Picard's method, we can establish the presence of an additional term.

### 31.2  Convergence of this iteration.

We can write

$$x'(t) = X(x, t) = X(x_i(t), t) + J(x_i(t), t)(x(t) - x_i(t))$$

$$+ \frac{1}{2!R} (\xi, \xi', t)[x(t) - x_i(t)][x(t) - x_i(t)],$$

or, subtracting from (1),

$$x_{i+1}'(t) - x'(t) = J(x_i, t)(x_{i+1} - x) - \frac{1}{2!} R(\xi, \xi', t)[x(t) - x_i(t)][x(t) - x_i(t)].$$

Finally, setting

$$x_{i+1}(t) - x(t) = v_{i+1}(t),$$

we arrive at

$$v_{i+1}' = J(x_i(t), t)v_{i+1} - \frac{R}{2}(\xi, \xi', t)v_i v_i.$$

Let $M(t, u)$ be the propagation matrix of this system. We can write

$$v_{i+1}(t) = -\frac{1}{2} \int_{t_0}^{t} M(t, u)R(\xi(u), \xi'(u), u)v_i(u)v_i(u) \, du,$$

whence

$$\{v_{i+1}(t)\} \leqslant K \max_{0 < u < t}^2 \{v_i(u)\} \max \int_{t_0}^{w} M(w, u)R(\xi(u), \xi'(u), u) \, du.$$

We see that, for this method, we have a quadratic convergence. In particular, the interval in which this iteration occurs, the numerical convergence ($\{v_{i+1}\} < \{v_i\}$ for all $i$) is all the faster as

$$\max_{0 < u < t} \{v_i\}$$

is smaller.

### 32.  Use of the residuals for the evaluation of the local errors.

We point out only the possibility of such an evaluation without giving an exact formula. Let us pass through the points $x_1$ obtained from a step method, a regular curve $z(t)$, and for this curve let us look for the residual

$$q(t) = -z'(t) + X(z(t), t).$$

To evaluate $z'(t)$, we can use an approximate differentiation formula of a higher order than that of the approximate integration formula, whose error we wish to study.

The results obtained by this method do not seem to be of as good a quality as those furnished by the methods of sections I and II.

## VII   ROUND-OFF ERROR IN THE APPROXIMATE INTEGRATION METHODS[1]

### 33. Generalities.

At each step, one commits a round-off error, which it is natural to compare with the truncation error. In this connection, we can distinguish three cases.

(a) The round-off error at one step is negligible compared to the truncation error. We do not concern ourselves with the round-off error. This way is conducive to wasting decimals, but it permits, in general, very good evaluations of the truncation error. It seems to be a reasonable compromise.

(b) The two errors are of the same order of magnitude. The round-off error behaves like noise (in the sense of the transmission theory), which masks in part the truncation error. In general, we can treat this error as a random quantity and consequently, apply to it statistical procedures. However, it will be necessary to recall that it is only a question of effort, which the facts can sometimes invalidate. Sometimes, one can establish curious situations. For example, let us return to the equation of Chapter 7, paragraph 15, with exactly the same method but with only six decimal places. We will find

| $t$ | $y_i$ | $y$ exact | $y_i$ to 8 decimal places |
|---|---|---|---|
| 0 | 1 | | |
| 0.1 | 0.999,833 | Exact values | |
| 0.2 | 0.998,667 | | |
| 0.3 | 0.995,504 | | |
| ... | ... | ... | ... |
| 0.4 | 0.989,356 | 0.989,356 | 0.989,355,76 |
| 0.5 | 0.979,253 | 0.979,253 | 0.979,252,40 |
| 0.6 | 0.964,258 | 0.964,258 | 0.964,256,60 |
| 0.7 | 0.943,483 | 0.943,484 | 0.943,480,89 |
| 0.8 | 0.916,112 | 0.916,113 | 0.916,108,42 |
| 0.9 | 0.881,422 | 0.881,423 | 0.881,416,93 |
| 1.0 | 0.838,811 | 0.838,812 | 0.838,804,93 |

One ascertains the curious phenomenon that the integration to six decimal places is exact except for a unit of the sixth order, whereas the integration to eight decimal places is, by far, not as good.

[1]Huskey, Henrici [4, 6, 8, 9].

(c) The round-off error is much more important than the truncation error. This situation is to be avoided. It can lead to completely aberrant results. Consider, for example,

$$y' = y, \quad h = 10^{-6}, \quad y(0) = 1,$$

where we calculate with five decimal places. Throughout the calculation, we will find

$$y = 1,$$

since the exact relation is

$$y_{i+1} = y_i + 10^{-6} y_i,$$

and since the second term is always suppressed by rounding.

### 34.1 Propagation of the round-off errors.

The investigation made in Chapter 9 is almost entirely applicable to the present problem. We have seen that the single-step methods and the Adams formulas lead to the same differential equation for the global error. This result permits us to treat simultaneously these two types of methods. Therefore, let the system in canonical form be

$$x' = X(x, t).$$

Equation (1) of paragraph 27, Chapter 9 is found to be replaced by

$$\zeta_{i+1} = M(t_{i+1}, t_i)\zeta_i + \epsilon_{i+1}, \tag{1}$$

where $\epsilon_{i+1}$ represents the round-off error committed in the evaluation of the $(i + 1)$st step, and $M(t, u)$ is the matrix solution of

$$M_t' = J \cdot M,$$

with $M(t_0, t_0) = I$.

Since $\zeta_0 = 0$, we deduce from (1)

$$M(t_0, t_{i+1})\zeta_{i+1} = \sum_{j=0}^{i+1} M(t_0, t_j)\epsilon_j,$$

from which we infer easily an upper bound of $\epsilon_i$, knowing an upper bound of the components of $\epsilon_j$ and of the elements of the matrix $M(t_i, t_j)$.

### 34.2 Statistical theory of the round-off errors.[1]

We assume that the $\epsilon_j$ are independent random variables with a mean of zero (which is not always exactly true) and a standard deviation $\sigma^2$. By neglecting higher order infinitesimals, we can write

$$\xi_{i+1} = (1 + hJ_i)\xi_i + \epsilon_i,$$

or, transposing, multiplying, taking the mean value, and neglecting terms of order $h^2$,

[1]Rademacher, Henrici [9], Gorog.

$$\overline{\xi_{i+1}\xi_{i+1}^*} = \sigma^2 I + \overline{\xi_i\xi_i^*} + hJ_i\overline{\xi_i\xi_i^*} + h\overline{\xi_i\xi_i^* J_i^*}.$$

The symbol * denotes the transpose, and the bar indicates the mean value. $I$ is the unit matrix. If we set

$$R_i = \overline{\xi_i\xi_i^*},$$

we see that

$$R_{i+1} = \sigma^2 I + R_i + hJ_i R_i + hR_i J_i^*.$$

This can be considered as an approximate integration formula for the matrix differential system.

$$R' = \frac{\sigma^2}{h} I + JR + RJ^*.$$

This differential system is of order $n^2$, which reduces the possibility of its use considerably.

## VIII   GENERAL REMARKS ON THE APPROXIMATE INTEGRATION METHODS

After this long exposition of methods, it is now necessary for us to come to a conclusion.

### 35. Multistep or single-step method.

In Chapter 9, paragraph 36, we have shown that, with equal amount of work and a comparable precision, the single-step methods of the R. K. type are competitive with the multistep methods. The first ones offer uncontestable advantages:

—modification of the length of the step is more flexible (it can take place at each step).

—principally, the calculation of starting values is needless.

This last advantage is often decisive, especially when there occur points of discontinuity in the course of the calculation. Nevertheless, the modification of the length of the step implies the evaluation of the error per step. For the RK method, we have given procedures of error evaluation, but they entail an additional amount of calculation, or make use of neighboring points. On the other hand, in the multistep methods, the calculation of the differences or Milne's procedure furnishes an evaluation of the error per step. Finally, there are cases where a method of order 4 is insufficient and leads to taking an excessively short step. We have tried to show how one can construct formulas of orders higher than 4 which are prompted by the Runge-Kutta principle.

### 36. Actual choice of a method.

By all means, the actual choice of a method for a given problem will depend on a large number of factors, the most important ones of which are perhaps those we just examined. It is certain that considerations such as the programming time and the execution time, the existence of certain programs, the number of cases to be treated, the employed personnel, and so on can sometimes play a determining role.

Generally, the goal of theoretical work cannot be to give rules of operation applicable to all situations, but only to furnish original scientific information which can orient the operation.

### 37. Remark on the choice of the order.

In all of this book, we have strived to establish methods of as high an order as possible. One should not believe that, in passing from one method to another of higher order, one increases the precision automatically.

Let us take an actual example. Consider the improved tangent method (Chapter 3, paragraph 1.1) and the classic Runge-Kutta method (Chapter 3, paragraph 5.1) for one and the same first order equation. It suffices to compare the errors per step. In order to make the comparison at the same

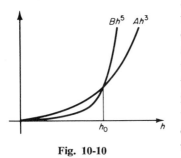

amount of work, one can take a step $h$ for the first, and a step $2h$ for the second. The error at an interval $2h$ is for the first $Ah^3$, and for the second $Bh^5$. The two representative curves of the variations of these quantities have in all cases relative shape indicated in Fig. 10-10. One sees that, for $h < h_0$, it is the higher order method which is more precise. On the other hand, for $h > h_0$, one has to prefer the method of a lesser order.

**Fig. 10-10**

Actually, the precision corresponding to the step $h_0$ will often be very poor, but it is not difficult to construct an example where it suffices.

Likewise, let us recall that the infinitesimal order is not the only criterion which one could use for measuring the quality of a method, although this is undoubtedly the most convenient one. The use of other criteria leads, without doubt, to other integration methods.

### 38. Change of system.

We have set forth methods requiring the approximate integration of a system. But, in general, it is possible to replace one system by another by change of function or variable. It may be interesting to transform a system before submitting it to a numerical integration method in order to establish the best conditions from the point of view of:

—simplicity of calculations.

—precision.

Consider the equation

$$y' = \frac{y}{\cos^2 t}, \qquad y(0) = 1.$$

By setting $\tan t = u$ one can integrate it directly. This gives $y' = y$. The transformation is advantageous from the viewpoint of simplicity, because it avoids calculating $\cos t$, $\cos^2 t$, and dividing by this quantity.

Likewise, it is advantageous from the viewpoint of precision. The Cauchy-Lipschitz method with ten steps in the interval $(0, \pi/4)$ gives for the errors:

$214 \times 10^{-3}$   with the original form,
$124 \times 10^{-3}$   with the simplified form.

## Problems

1. What are the actual and calculated errors when one is applying (a) the improved tangent method, (b) Euler's method, (c) Runge-Kutta classic to the differential equations

$$y' = \frac{y}{x} - y^2, \qquad y(1) = 1, \qquad h = 0.2 \qquad (1 \leqslant x \leqslant 2)$$

and

$$y'' + y + y^2 = x, \qquad y(0) = 1, \qquad y'(0) = 0, \qquad h = 0.1 \qquad (0 \leqslant x \leqslant 1)$$

Which method gives the least calculated error?

2. Evaluate the quadrature error in Milne's method for the above two problems.

3. Do the same for Adams' method.

4. In the above two problems, under what conditions would it be desirable to double the step size? to halve the step size?

5. Calculate the residual (Cotton's method) for the above two problems.

# BIBLIOGRAPHY

**Abbreviations of names of journals or of organizations.**

| | |
|---|---|
| A.C.M., | Association for Computing Machinery |
| A.M.S., | American Mathematical Society |
| C.R.A.S., | Comptes rendus de l'Académie des Sciences (Paris) |
| I.B.M., | International Business Machines |
| J.M.P., | Journal of Mathematics and Physics |
| M.T.A.C., | Mathematical Tables and other Aids in Computation |
| N.B.S., | National Bureau of Standards |
| S.I.A.M., | Society for Industrial and Applied Mathematics |
| Z.A.M.M., | Zeitschrift für Angewandte Mathematik und Mechanik |
| Z.A.M.P., | Zeitschrift für Angewandte Mathematik und Physik |

S. ABIAN and A.B. BROWN [1], On the solution of simultaneous first order implicit differential equations. *A.M.S. Notices*, **5** (1958), p. 660 (Résumé).

S. ABIAN and A.B. BROWN [2], On the solution of an *n*th order implicit differential equation. *A.M.S. Notices*, **5** (1958), p. 774 (Résumé).

S. ABIAN and A.B. BROWN [3], On the solution of simultaneous implicit equations. *A.M.S. Notices*, **5** (1958), p. 786 (Résumé).

ADAMS (see BASHFORTH).

J. ALBRECHT, Beiträge zum Runge-Kutta-Verfahren. *ZAMM*, **35** (1955), pp. 100–110.

R. ALONSO, A starting method for the three points Adams predictor corrector method. *Journal A.C.M.*, **7** (1960), pp. 176–180.

F. L. ALT, *Electronic digital computer*. Academic Press, New York (1958), 336 pages.

M. ALTMAN, Iterative methods for the numerical solutions of ordinary differential equations. *Symposium, Rome* (1960), Birkhauser, Basel, pp. 174–176.

W. H. ANDERSON, The solution of simultaneous ordinary differential equations using a general purpose digital computer. *Comm. A.C.M.*, **3** (1960), pp. 355–360.

W. H. ANDERSON, J. R. JOHNSON, Numerical integration of differential equations on the 704 EDPM. *Communic Electron*, **27** (1956), pp. 569–574.

N. H. ANDERSON, R. B. BALL, and J. R. VOSS, A numerical method for solving control differential equations on digital computers. *Journal A.C.M.*, **7** (1960), pp. 61–68.

R. ANSORGE and W. TORNIG, Zur Stabilität des Nyströmschen Verfahrens, *ZAMM*, **40** (1960), pp. 568–570.

H. A. ANTOSIEWICZ, Lyapunov-like functions and approximate solutions of ordinary differential equations. *Symposium, Rome* (1960), Birkhauser, Basel, pp. 265–268.

E. APARO, Sulla resoluzione numerica delle equazioni integrali di Volterra de seconda specie. *Rendic. Accad. Lincei*, VIII, **26** (1959) pp. 183–188.

G. A. ARTEMOV, On a modification of Chaplygin's method for systems of differential equations of the first order. *Dokl. Akad. Nauk. SSSR*, **101** (1955), pp. 197–200.

N. V. AZBELEV [1], On an approximate solution of differential equations based on Chaplygin's method. *Dokl. Akad. Nauk. SSSR*, **83** (1952), pp. 517–519.

N. V. AZBELEV [2], On the restrictions of the application of Chaplygin's theorem. *Dokl. Akad. Nauk. SSSR*, **89** (1953), pp. 589–591.

N. V. AZBELEV [3], A sufficient condition for the applicability of Chaplygin's method. *Dokl. Akad. Nauk. SSSR*, **99** (1954), pp. 493–494.

N. V. AZBELEV [4], On the extension of Chaplygin's method beyond the validity of the theorem on differential inequalities. *Dokl. Akad. Nauk. SSSR*, **102** (1955), pp. 429–430.

B. N. BABKIN [1], Approximate solution of differential equations of arbitrary order by successive approximations method based on Chaplygin's theorem on differential inequalities. *Dokl. Akad. Nauk. SSSR*, **59** (1948), pp. 419–422.

B. N. BABKIN [2], On a modification of Chaplygin's method for approximate integration. *Dokl. Akad. Nauk. SSSR*, **67** (1949), pp. 213–216.

B. N. BABKIN [3], On the approximate solution by Chaplygin's method, of first order ordinary differential equations which are not solved for the derivative. *Prikl. Mat. Meh. SSSR*, **17** (1953), pp. 634–638.

B. N. BABKIN [4], Approximate integration of systems of ordinary first order differential equations by Chaplygin's method. *Isv. Akad. Nauk. SSSR*, Ser. Mat. **18** (1954), pp. 477–484.

BAGGOTT (see LEVY).

N. S. BAHVALOV [1], On the estimate of the error in numerical integration of differential equations by the Adams extrapolation method. *Dokl. Akad. Nauk. SSSR*, **104** (1955), pp. 683–686.

N. S. BAHVALOV [2], A few remarks concerning numerical integration of differential equations by the method of finite differences. *Dokl. Akad. Nauk. SSSR*, **104** (1955), pp. 805–808.

V. A. BAILEY and J. M. SOMERVILLE, The graphical solution of ordinary differential equations. *Phil. Mag.*, VII, **26** (1938), pp. 1–31.

BALL (see ANDERSON).

A. BARD, Recherche des formules du type Runge-Kutta, comportant une dérivée suivante. Thesis, Grenoble (1961).

A. BARD, F. CESCHINO, J. KUNTZMANN, and P. LAURENT, Formules de base de la méthode de Runge-Kutta. *Chiffres*, **4** (1961), pp. 31–37.

E. H. BAREISS, The error estimation in an approximate solution of an ordinary second-order differential equation (Résumé). *Bull. Amer. Math. Soc.*, **63** (1957), p. 13.

BARON (see SALVADORI).

F. BASHFORTH and J. C. ADAMS, *An attempt to test the theories of capillary action.* Cambridge University Press, 1883.

BATEMAN (see BENNETT).

H. A. BAUER, Graphische Integration der ausserballistischen Hauptgleichung mit Ermittlung der Geschwindlichkeitsrisses und der Geschosbahn. *Math. Natur-wiss., Unterricht* (1943), pp. 45–55.

W. F. BAUER [1], Milne's method for the numerical solution of ordinary differential equations. Carr Scott-Notes on digital computers and date processors. University of Michigan (1956), 4 pages.

W. F. BAUER [2], The Monte Carlo method. *Journal S.I.A.M.* (1958), pp. 438–451.

E. BECK, Zwei Anwendungen der Obreschkoffschen Formel. *ZAMM*, **30** (1950), pp. 84–93.

A. A. BENNETT, W. E. MILNE, and H. BATEMAN, *Numerical integration of differential equations.* Dover Publication (1956), 108 pages.

M. BERTOLINO, Procédés de l'encadrement des solutions des équations différenti-elles. *Bull. Soc. Math. et Phys.*, Serbie, **9** (1957), pp. 261–269.

W. G. BICKLEY [1], A simple method for the numerical solution of differential equations. *Phil. Mag.*, **13** (1932), pp. 1006–1014.

W. G. BICKLEY [2], Difference and associated operators with some applications. *J.M.P.*, **27** (1948), pp. 183–192.

W. G. BICKLEY and J. MacNAMEE, Matrix and other direct methods for the solution of systems of linear difference equations. *Phil. Trans. Roy. Soc.*, London, **A 252** (1959), pp. 70–131.

L. Bieberbach, On the remainder of the Runge-Kutta formula in the theory of ordinary differential equations. *ZAMP*, **2** (1951), pp. 233–248.

V. Blaess, Zur angenäherten Lösung gewöhnlicher Differentialgleichungen. *V.D. I.Z.*, **81** (1937), pp. 587–596.

C. Blanc [1], Evaluations Stochastiques d'erreurs, I—École Polytechnique de l'Université de Lausanne (1953), 28 pages.

C. Blanc [2], Sur les formules d'intégration approchée d'équations différentielles. *Arch. Math.*, **5** (1954), pp. 301–308.

Ch. Blanc and W. Liniger, Stochastische Fehlerauswertung bei numerischen Methoden. *ZAMM*, **35** (1955), pp. 121–130.

G. Blanch, On the numerical solution of equations involving differential operators with constant coefficients. *MTAC*, **6** (1952), pp. 219–223.

E. K. Blum [1], On the Runge-Kutta fourth order method. *Bull. Amer. Math. Soc.*, **63** (1957), p. 386 (Résumé).

E. K. Blum [2], A modification of the Runge-Kutta fourth-order method. *Math. of Comp.*, **16** (1962), pp. 176–187.

L. V. Bocek, The numerical integration of equations in a complex region. *Vycisl. Mat. Vycisl. Tehn.*, **2** (1955), pp. 94–96.

N. A. Bohan, An attempt at numerical integration on punched card machines of the equations of motion of minor planets for a given system of initial conditions. *Akad. Nauk SSSR Bull. Inst. Teoret Astro*, **5** (1952), pp. 203–211.

P. S. Bondarenko [1], New method of numerical integration of ordinary differential equations. *Ukrain. Mat. Z.*, **12** (1960), pp. 118–131.

P. S. Bondarenko [2], The stability of calculation algorithms. *Dopovidi Akad. Nauk. Ukr.* (1961), pp. 153–157.

G. Boole, *The calculus of finite differences*, 4th edition. Chelsea, 1957, 336 pages.

A. D. Booth [1], Basforth-Adams Method for the numerical solution of differential equations. *Nature*, **173** (1954), pp. 635–636.

A. D. Booth [2], *Numerical methods*. Butterworths Scientific Publications, London (1955), 195 pages.

M. Borkmann, Ueber einige Ergänzungen zum Blaesschen Verfahren. *Die Technik*, **8** (1953), pp. 475–480.

N. V. Boulton, Forward integration of simultaneous linear differential equations. *Ordnance Board Applied Ballistics Dep. Report* No. 39.

M. C. Breiter, Study of parameters in a differential equation related to blast. *Ballistic Res. Labo. Aberdeen Proving Ground Memo.*, Rep. No. 822 (1954), 13 pp.

T. F. Bridgland, A note on numerical integrating operators. *Journal S.I.A.M.*, **6** (1958), pp. 240–256.

P. Brock and F. J. Murray [1], Project Cyclone-Reeves Instrument Corporation:

Planning and error analysis for the numerical solution of a test system of differential equations on the IBM Sequence calculator. *Special devices center, Reeves Instrument Corporation.*

P. BROCK and F. J. MURRAY [2], The use of exponential sums in step by step integration. *MTAC*, **6** (1952), pp. 63–78.

P. BROCK and F. J. MURRAY [3], The use of exponential sums in step by step integration II. *MTAC*, **6** (1952), pp. 138–150.

M. L. BRODSKII, Asymptotic estimation of the errors in numerical integration of systems of ordinary differential equations by the difference methods. *Dokl. Akad. Nauk. SSSR*, **93** (1953), pp. 599–602.

D. BROUWER, On the accumulation of errors in numerical integration. *Astron. Journ.*, **46** (1937), pp. 149–153.

J. H. BROWN, Solution of differential equations. *Carr-Scott notes on digital computers and data processors*, Michigan, 1956.

J. H. BROWN (see ABIAN).

I. S. BRUK, A procedure for solving ordinary differential equations. *Dokl. Akad. Nauk. SSSR*, **53** (1946), pp. 523–526.

R. A. BUCKINGHAM, *Numerical methods.* Pitman, London, 1957, 597 pages.

H. BÜCKNER, Uber eine Näherungslösung der gewönhlichen linearen Differentialgleichungen 1ᵉʳ Ordnung. *ZAMM*, **22** (1942), pp. 143–152.

B. M. BUDAK and A. D. GORBUNOV [1], Convergence of certain difference procedures for the equations $y' = f(x, y)$ and $y'(x) = f(x, y(x)), y(x - \theta(x))$. *Vestnik Moskov. Univ. Ser. Mat. Meh. Astronom. Fiz. Him.* (1958), pp. 23–32.

B. M. BUDAK and A. D. GORBUNOV [2], Stability of the calculation procedures used in the solution of the Cauchy problem for the equation $y' = f(x, y)$ by a difference method at several points. *Dokl. Akad. Nauk. SSSR*, **124** (1959), pp. 1191–1194.

B. M. BUDAK and A. D. GORBUNOV [3], Difference formulas at several points for the solution of the Cauchy problem for $y' = f(x, y)$. *Dokl. Akad. Nauk. SSSR*, **140** (1961), pp. 291–295.

E. BUKOVICS [1], Eine Verbesserung und Verallgemeinerung des Verfahrens von Blaess zur numerischen Integration gewöhnlicher Differentialgleichungen. *Ost. Ing. Arch.*, **4** (1950), pp. 338–349.

E. BUKOVICS [2], Beiträge zur numerischen Integration, I. Der Fehler beim Blaess schen Verfahren zur numerischen Integration gewöhnlicher Differentialgleichungen $n$-ter Ordnung. *Monatsh. Math.*, **57** (1953), pp. 217–245.

E. BUKOVICS [3], Beiträge zur numerischen Integration II, III. Der Fehler beim Runge-Kutta Verfahren zur numerischen Integration gewöhnlicher Differentialgleichungen $n$-ter Ordnung. *Monatsh. Math.* **57** (1954), pp. 333–350; **58** (1954), pp. 258–265.

D. H. CALL and R. F. REEVES, Error estimation in Runge-Kutta procedures. *Comm. A.C.M.*, **1** (1958), pp. 7–8.

V. CAPRA [1], Valutazione degli errori nella integrazione numerica dei sistemi di equazioni differenziali ordinarie. *Atti. Accad. Sci. Torino. Cl. Sci. Fis. Mat. Nat.*, **91** (1957), pp. 188–203.

V. CAPRA [2], Nuove formule per l'integrazione numerica delle equazioni differenziali ordinarie del 1° et del 2° ordine. *Univ. Torino. Rend. Sem. Mat.*, **16** (1956–57), pp. 301–359.

CARNYI (see VLASOV).

J. W. CARR, Errors bounds for the Runge-Kutta single-step integration process. *Journal A.C.M.*, **5** (1958), pp. 39–44.

A. E. CARTER and D. H. SADLER, The application of the National accounting machine to the solution of first order differential equations. *Quart. J. Mech. Appl. Math.*, **1** (1948), pp. 433–441.

L. CASTAGNETTO, Sur l'intégration numérique de l'équation de stabilité. *C.R.A.S.*, **246** (1958), pp. 255–257.

A. CAUCHY, *Oeuvres*, 2nd series, Vol. 11.

C.E.C.E., Report describing the problems solved by the IRSIA-FNRS-Computer in April-May 1957, *Progress Report. Comité d'études et d'exploitation des calculateurs électroniques* (*Belgique*).

E. A. ČERNYŠENKO, On a method of approximate solution of the Cauchy problem for ordinary differential equations. *Ukrain. Mat. Z.*, **10** (1958), pp. 89–100.

F. CESCHINO [1], Critère d'utilisation du procédé de Runge-Kutta. *C.R.A.S.*, **238** (1954), pp. 986–988.

F. CESCHINO [2], L'intégration approchée des équations différentielles. *C.R.A.S.*, **243** (1956), pp. 1478–1479.

F. CESCHINO [3], Sur une formule de rang 5. *Chiffres*, **2** (1959), pp. 39–42.

F. CESCHINO [4], L'emploi des formules de prédiction-correction. 1° *Congrès de l'AFCAL*, Gauthier-Villars, Paris, (1961), pp. 37–41.

F. CESCHINO [5], Modification de la longueur du pas dans l'intégration numérique par les méthodes à pas liés. *Chiffres*, **2** (1961), pp. 101–106.

F. CESCHINO [6], Une méthode de mise en œuvre des formules d'Obrechkoff pour l'intégration des équations différentielles. *Chiffres*, **2** (1961), pp. 49–54.

F. CESCHINO [7], Evaluation de l'erreur par pas dans les problèmes différentiels. *Chiffres*, **5** (1962).

F. CESCHINO (see BARD).

F. CESCHINO and J. KUNTZMANN [1], Impossibilité d'un certain type de formule d'intégration approchée à pas liés. *Chiffres*, **1** (1958), pp. 95–101.

F. CESCHINO and J. KUNTZMANN [2], Faut-il passer à la forme canonique dans les problèmes différentiels de conditions initiales. *Congrès international sur le traitement de l'information,* Paris, (1959), pp. 33–36.

F. CESCHINO and J. KUNTZMANN [3], Deux remarques sur l'erreur dans la résolution approchée des problèmes de conditions initiales. *Chiffres,* **2** (1959), pp. 249–252.

N. G. CETAEV, On the estimation of approximate integration. *Prikl. Math. Meh.,* **21** (1957), pp. 419–421.

F. G. CHADAJA [1], On the error in the numerical integration of ordinary differential equations by the finite difference method. *Trav. Inst. Math. Tbilissi,* **11** (1942), pp. 97–108.

F. G. CHADAJA [2], On the problem of numerical integration of ordinary differential equations. *Bull. Acad. Sci. Georg. SSSR,* **2** (1941), pp. 601–608.

K. T. CHANG, On the numerical solution of simultaneous linear differential equations. *Journal, S.I.A.M,* **7** (1959), pp. 468–472.

V. A. CHECHIK, Approximate method for the solution of systems of singular differential equations. *Dokl. Akad. Nauk. SSSR.,* **110** (1956), pp. 517–520.

C. W. CLENSHAW [1], The numerical solution of linear differential equations in Chebyshev series. *Proc. Camb. Phil. Soc.,* **53** (1957), pp. 134–149.

C. W. CLENSHAW [2], The numerical solution of ordinary differential equations in Chebyshev series. *Symposium Rome* (1960), Birkhauser, Basel, pp. 222–227.

C. W. CLENSHAW and A. R. CURTISS, A method for numerical integration on an automatic computer. *Num. Math.,* **2** (1960), pp. 197–205.

C. W. CLENSHAW and F. W. OLVER, Solution of differential equation by recurrence relations. *MTAC,* **5** (1951), pp. 34–39.

C. J. COHEN and E. C. HUBBARD, An algorithm applicable to numerical integration of orbits in multiple revolution steps. *Astrom. J.,* **65** (1960), pp. 454–6.

G. I. COHN and B. SALTZBERG, Solution of nonlinear differential equations by the reversion method through the first thirteen terms. *J.A.P.,* **24** (1953), pp. 180–186.

L. COLLATZ [1], Lösung gewisser Differentialgleichungen mit dem harmonischen Analysator. *Ber. Math. Tagung Tübingen* (1946), pp. 60–61.

L. COLLATZ [2], Natürliche Schrittweite bei numerische Integration von Differentialgleichungenssystemen. *ZAMM,* 22 (1942), pp. 216–225.

L. COLLATZ [3], Differenzenverfahren zur numerischen Integration von gewöhnlichen Differentialgleichungen *n*-ter Ordnung. *ZAMM,* **29** (1949), pp. 199–209.

L. COLLATZ [4], Uber die Instabilität beim Verfahren der zentralen Differenzen für Differentialgleichungen zweiter Ordnung. *ZAMP,* **4** (1953), pp. 153–154.

L. COLLATZ [5], Einige Anwendungen funktionalanalytischer Methoden in der praktischen Analysis. *ZAMP,* **4** (1953), pp. 327–357.

L. COLLATZ [6], *Numerische Behandlung von Differentialgleichungen.* Springer-

Verlag, Berlin-Gottingen-Heidelberg, 1st ed., 1951; 2nd ed., 1955; 3rd ed. (English translation), 1960.

L. COLLATZ [7], Einige funktional analytische Methoden bei der numerischen Behandlung von Differentialgleichungen. *ZAMM*, **38** (1958), pp. 264–267.

L. COLLATZ [8], Fixed point theorems and monotone operators for initial value problems. *Colloque du centre international provisoire de calcul*, Rome (1959), pp. 56–63.

L. COLLATZ and R. ZURMÜHL [1] Beiträge zu den Interpolations-verfahren der numerichen Integration von Differentialgleichungen 1 und 2 Ordnung. *ZAMM*, **22** (1942), pp. 42–55.

L. COLLATZ and R. ZURMÜHL [2], Zur Genauigkeit verschiedener Integrations-Verfahren bei gewöhnlichen Differentialgleichungen. *Ing. Arch.*, **13** (1942), pp. 34–36.

S. D. CONTE and R. F. REEVES, A Kutta third order procedure for solving differential equations requiring minimum-storage. *Journal A.C.M.*, **3** (1956), pp. 22–25.

P. COOPERMAN, A new method for the approximate solution of differential equations. *May Meeting of the Allegheny Mountain section A.M.S.* (1959) (Résumé).

E. COTTON [1], Sur l'intégration approchée des équations différentielles. *Acta Math.*, **31** (1908), pp. 107–126.

E. COTTON [2], Sur l'intégration approchée des équations différentielles. *Bull. Soc. Math. France*, **36** (1908), pp. 225–246.

P. H. COWELL and A. C. D. CROMMELIN [1], Investigation of the Greenwich observations 1909. Motion of Halley's Comet from 1759 to 1910, Edinburgh, 1910.

P. H. COWELL and A. C. D. CROMMELIN [2], The orbit of Jupiter's eighth satellite. *Monthly, No.* **68** (1958), pp. 576–581.

CRAGGS (see MITCHELL).

C. P. CRAMER, La mise en pratique de la méthode S.A. Kasakov d'intégration numérique de certaines équations différentielles ordinaires. *ONERA, Traduction Tech.* 1128 (1948).

R. L. CRANE and R. J. LAMBERT, Stability of a generalized corrector formula. *Journal ACM*, **9** (1962), pp. 104–107.

CROMMELIN (see COWELL).

M. CUENOD, *Méthode de calcul a l'aide de suites*. Feissly Edit., Lausanne (1955), 75 pages.

J. H. CURTISS, Sampling methods applied to differential and integral equations. *Proc. Sem. Scient. Comput. I.B.M.* (1949), pp. 87–109.

A. R. CURTISS (see CLENSHAW).

G. DAHLQUIST [1], Fehlerabschätzungen bei Differenzen-methoden zur numerischen

Integration gewöhnlicher Differentialgleichungen. *ZAMM*, **31** (1951), pp. 239–240.

G. DAHLQUIST [2], Convergence and stability in the numerical integration of ordinary differential equations. *Math. Skand*, **4** (1956), pp. 33–53.

G. DAHLQUIST [3], Stability and error bounds in the numerical integration of ordinary differential equations. *Transac. Roy. Inst. Techn.*, Stockholm, **130** (1959), 86 pages.

D. DAINELLI, Sull'integrazione numerica delle equazioni differenziali ordinarie. *Univ. Roma Ist. Naz. Alta. Mat.* **5** (1948), pp. 393–405.

L. S. DEDERICK, Firing tables. *Proc. first Symp. Annal. Harvard Univ.*, XVI (1947), pp. 194–199.

DEIDO (see NORIMATSU).

S. C. R. DENNIS [1], Finite differences associated with second order differential equations. *Quart. J. Mech. Appl. Math.*, **13** (1960), pp. 453–457.

S. C. R. DENNIS [2], The numerical integration of ordinary differential equations possessing exponential type solutions. *Proc. Cambr. Phil.*, **56** (1960), pp. 240–246.

DODIER (see VALIRON).

G. DUFFING, Zur numerischen Integration gewöhnlicher Differentialgleichungen 1$^{er}$ und 2$^{er}$ ordnung. *Forschungs. Gem. Ing. Wesen*, **224** (1920), pp. 29–50.

W. J. DUNCAN [1], Assessment of errors in approximate solution of differential equations. *Quart. J. Mech. Appl. Math.*, **1** (1948), pp. 470–476.

W. J. DUNCAN [2], Technique of the step by step integration of ordinary differential equations. *Phil. Mag.*, **39** (1948), pp. 493–509.

L. D. EARNEST, Kutta integration with error control. *12th nation meeting. A.C.M.*, Houston, June 1957 (Résumé).

F. EDELMAN, An interpretive subroutine for the solution of systems of first order ordinary differential equations on the 650. *I.B.M. Tech. Newsletter*, **13** (1957), pp. 52–72.

H. ELTERMANN, Fehlerabschätzung bei näherungsweiser Lösung von Systemen von Differentialgleichungen erster Ordnung. *M.Z.*, **62** (1955), pp. 469–501.

L. EULER, *Institutiones calculi integralis*. Oeuvres complètes, Berlin, (1913), vol. 11, pp. 424–427; vol. 12, pp. 271–274.

V.M. FALKNER, A method of numerical solution of differential equations. *Phil. Mag.*, **21** (1936), p. 621–640.

E. FEHLBERG [1], Eine Methode zur Fehlerverkleinerung beim Runge-Kutta Verfahren. *ZAMM*, **38** (1958), p. 421–426.

E. FEHLBERG [2], Neue genauere Runge-Kutta Formeln für Differentialgleichungen zweiter Ordnung. *ZAMM*, **40** (1960), p. 252–258.

E. Fehlberg [3], Neue genauere Runge-Kutta Formeln für Differentialgleichungen *n*-ter Ordnung. *ZAMM*, **40** (1960), p. 449–455.

E. Fehlberg [4], Numerisch stabile Interpolationsformeln mit günstiger Fehlerfortpflanzung für Differentialgleichungen erster und zweiter Ordnung. *ZAMM*, **41** (1961), p. 101–110.

L. Feinstein and M. Schwarzschild, Automatic integration of linear second order differential equations by means of punched card machines. *Rev. Sci. Inst.*, **12** (1941), pp. 405–408.

F. Florinsky, Uber die Methode von Kowell. *Appl. Math. Mec.*, **2** (1934), pp. 91–100.

S. Flügge, Zur numerischen und graphischen Integration von Schwingungsgleichungen. *Z. Physik*, **133** (1952), pp. 449–450.

C. V. D. Forrington, Extentions of the predictor-corrector method for the solution of systems of ordinary differential equations. *Computer J.*, **4** (1961), pp. 80–84.

L. Fox [1], Relaxation and step by step methods. *MTAC*, **5** (1951), pp. 92–95.

L. Fox [2], The use of large intervals in finite difference equations. *MTAC*, **7** (1953), pp. 14–18.

L. Fox [3], A note on the numerical integration of first order differential equations. *Quart. J. Mech. Appl. Math.*, **7** (1954), pp. 367–378.

L. Fox [4], Chebyshev methods for ordinary differential equations. *Computer J.*, **4** (1962), pp. 318–331.

L. Fox [5], *Numerical solution of ordinary and partial differential equations*. Pergamon Press (1962), 509 pages.

L. Fox and E. T. Goodwin, Some new methods for the numerical integration of ordinary differential equations. *Proc. Camb. Phil. Soc.*, **45** (1949), pp. 373–388.

L. Fox and A. R. Mitchell, Boundary-value techniques for the numerical solution of initial-value problems in ordinary differential equations. *Quart. J. Mech. Appl. Math.*, **10** (1957), pp. 232–243.

M. Franck, Eine neue Methode graphischer Integration der Differentialgleichungen. *Math. Sborn.*, **40** (1933), pp. 129–143.

T. Frey [1], One improvement of the Runge-Kutta-Nyström method. *Period. Polytech. Electr. Eng. Hongr.*, **2** (1958), pp. 141–165.

T. Frey [2], Anwendung der Momente der Integralkurven zur numerischen Lösung von Differentialgleichungen. *Magyar Tud. Akad. Alkalm. Mat. Inst. Közl.*, **2** (1953), pp. 395–414.

C. H. Frick and J. E. Mulligan, A set of predictor and corrector formulas for the numerical solution of ordinary differential equations. Spring meeting of the Maryland-District of Columbia-Virginia Section 1956. *Mathematical Association of America.*

A. FRICKE, Uber die Fehlerabschätzung des Adamschen Verfahren zur Integration gewöhnlicher Differentialgleichungen 1$^{er}$ Ordnung. *ZAMM*, **29** (1949), pp. 165–178.

FRIEDMAN (see SHELDON).

E. FROBERG, On the solution of ordinary differential equations with digital computing machines. *Kungl. Fys. Sallsk. Lund. For.*, **20** (1950), pp. 136–152.

C. FROESE, An evaluation of Runge-Kutta type methods for higher order differential equations. *J.A.C.M.*, **8** (1961), pp. 637–644.

P. FUNK, Ueber Duffings Methode zur numerischen Integration von gewöhnlichen Differentialgleichungen. *ZAMM*, **7** (1927), pp. 410–411.

D. GAIER, Uber die Konvergenz des Adamschen Extrapolationsverfahrens. *ZAMM.*, **36** (1956), p. 230.

B. A. GALLER and D. P. ROZENBERG, A generalization of a theorem of Carr on error bounds for Runge-Kutta procedures. *Journal A.C.M.*, **7** (1960), pp. 57–60.

M. GARNIER, Calcul des tables et abaques de tir (méthode G.H.M.). *Memorial de l'Artillerie Française*, **8** (1929), pp. 5–266.

W. GAUTSCHI [1], Uber die zeichnerischen Ungenauigkeiten und die zweckmässige Bemessung der Schrittlange beim graphischen Integrationsverfahren von Meissner. *Verh. Natur. Ges., Basel*, **65** (1954), pp. 49–66.

W. GAUTSCHI [2], Uber den Fehler des Runge-Kutta-Verfahrens für die numerische Integration gewöhnlicher Differentialgleichungen $n$-ter ordnung. *ZAMP*, **6** (1955), pp. 456–461.

W. GAUTSCHI [3], Numerical integration of ordinary differential equations based on trigonometric polynomials. *Num. Math*, **3** (1961), pp. 381–397.

M. K. GAVURIN, On a method of numerical integration of linear, homogeneous differential equations adapted to mechanical calculation. *Trudy Steklov*, **28** (1949), pp. 152–156.

G. GENTINI, Alcune formole notevali per il calcole delle equazione differenziale. *Ric. Ingeni*, **6** (1938), pp. 34–36.

F. GENUYS, Rapport général sur le traitement numérique des équations différentielles. *Symposium, Rome* (1960), Birkhauser, Basel, pp. 89–103.

S. GILL, A process for the step by step integration of differential equations in an automatic digital computing machine. *Proc. Camb. Phil. Soc.*, **47** (1951), pp. 96–108.

GODWIN (see FOX).

N. A. GOL'COV, On the utilization of a functional series for deducing formulae involved in various numerical methods of solving ordinary differential equations. *Dokl. Akad. Nauk. SSSR.*, **120** (1958), pp. 450–453.

GORBUNOV (see BUDAK).

S. GORN, The automatic analysis and control of computing errors. *Journal S.I. A.M.*, **2** (1954), pp. 69–81.

E. GOROG, Etude statistique de l'erreur de calcul dans les sommes de nombres écrits en virgule flottante. *Chiffres*, **4** (1961), pp. 69–86.

E. M. GRABBE, S. RAMO and D. E. WOOLDRIGE, *Handbook of automation, computation and control*, John Wiley, New York, 1958 (vol. 1, ch. 14).

C. F. GRANDWELL, The solution of differential equations on an electronic digital computer. *Engineer*, **196** (1953), pp. 36–39.

R. GRAVADOS, A method of integrating the equations of motion of a body. 8^{me} *Congrès international d'astronautique*, Lisbon (1957).

W. GRAVES, A method for the step by step integration of differential equations on MIDAC. *Carr. Scott. Notes on digital Computers* (1956), 9 pages.

H. J. GRAY, Propagation of truncation errors in the numerical solution of ordinary differential equations by repeated closures. *Journal A.C.M.*, **2** (1955), pp. 5–17.

H. GRAY and S. A. SCHELKUNOFF, The approximate solutions of linear differential equations. *Bell-System Techn. Journ.*, **27** (1948), pp. 350–364.

R. T. GREGORY, A method for deriving numerical differentiation formulas. *Amer. Math. Mont.*, **64** (1957), pp. 79–82.

E. GROSSWALD, Transformations useful in numerical integration methods. *Journal S.I.A.M.*, **7** (1959), pp. 76–84.

H. GRÜNSKY, Eine Methode zur Lösung von Anfangswertproblemen bei gewöhnlichen und partiellen linearen Differentialgleichungen zweiter Ordnung. *ZAMM*, **34** (1954), pp. 291–292.

A. GUILLOU and B. LAGO, Domaine de stabilité associé aux formules d'intégration numérique d'équations différentielles, à pas séparés et à pas liés. Recherche de formules à grand rayon de stabilité. *Premier Congrès de l'AFCAL*, Gauthier-Villars, Paris, 1961, pp. 43–56.

K. HAIN and F. HERTWECK, Numerical integration of ordinary differential equations by difference methods with automatic determination of steplength. *Symposium, Rome* (1960), Birkhauser, Basel, pp. 122–128.

G. HAMEL, Zur Fehler Abschätzung bei gewöhnlichen Differentialgleichungen ersten Ordnung. *ZAMM*, **29** (1949), pp. 337–341.

P. C. HAMMER and J. W. HOLLINGSWORTH [1], Numerical treatment of differential equations, I. *Chicago Meeting A.M.S.* (1954), (Résumé).

P. C. HAMMER and J. W. HOLLINGSWORTH [2], Numerical treatment of differential equations, II. *Chicago Meeting A.M.S.* (1954), (Résumé).

P. C. HAMMER and J. W. HOLLINGSWORTH [3], Trapezoidal Methods of approximating solutions of differential equations. *MTAC*, **9** (1955), pp. 92–96.

R. W. HAMMING, Stable predictor-corrector methods for ordinary differential equations. *Journal A.C.M.*, **6** (1959), pp. 37–47.

D. R. Hartree [1], A method for the numerical integration of first order differential equations. *Proc. Camb. Phil. Soc.*, **46** (1950), pp. 523–524.

D. R. Hartree [2], *Numerical Analysis*. Oxford Clarendon Press, 1952, 287 pages.

L. F. Hausmann and M. Schwarzschild, Automatic integration of linear sixth order differential equations by means of punched-card machines. *Rev. of Sc. Instr.*, **18** (1947), pp. 877–883.

M. V. Hayes, Numerical solutions of differential equations using automatic computers. Thesis, Cambridge, Massachussets, 1950.

L. Hellerman, A computer analytic method for solving differential equations. *Proceedings of the Eastern Joint Computer Conference. IRE*, No. 16, Dec. 1959, pp. 238–244.

P. Henrici [1], Symmetric Runge-Kutta methods for integrating ordinary differential equations of the first order. *Bulletin AMS*, **63** (1957), p. 389 (Résumé).

P. Henrici [2], On the error of a method of Hammer and Hollingsworth for integrating ordinary differential equations. *Bulletin AMS*, **63** (1957), p. 389 (Résumé).

P. Henrici [3], Methods for integrating ordinary differential equations based on gaussian quadrature. *Bulletin AMS*, **63** (1957), p. 390 (Résumé).

P. Henrici [4], Theoretical and experimental studies on the accumulation of error in the numerical solution of initial value problems for systems of ordinary differential equations. *Congrès international sur le traitement de l'information* (Paris, 1959), pp. 36–44.

P. Henrici [5], Error and numerical stability of two three step methods of integrating $y' = f(x, y)$ (Résumé). *A.M.S. Notices*, **5** (1958), p. 55.

P. Henrici [6], A unified theory of propagated error and numerical stability for some methods of integrating ordinary differential equations (Résumé). *A. M.S. Notices*, **5** (1958), p. 55.

P. Henrici [7], The numerical integration of certain differential equations with missing first derivative (Résumé). *A.M.S. Notices*, **5** (1958), p. 56.

P. Henrici [8], The propagation of round-off error in the numerical solution of initial value problems involving ordinary differential equations of the second order. *Symposium. Rome.* (1960). Birkhauser, Basel, pp. 275–291.

P. Henrici [9], *Discrete variable methods in ordinary differential equations*, Wiley (1962), 407 pages.

P. Herget [1], Integration of the differential equation. $d^2P/dr^2 = PF(r)$ using the type 601 multiplying Punch. *Proc. Sc. Comp. Forum IBM*, 1948, pp. 39–41.

P. Herget [2], Numerical integration with punched cards. *Astr. J.*, **52** (1946), pp. 115–117.

S. Herrick, Step by step integration of $x'' = f(x, y, z, t)$ without a corrector. *MT-AC*, **5** (1951), pp. 61–67.

HERTWECK (see HAIN).

K. HEUN, Neue Methode zur approximativen Integration der Differentialgleichungen einer Variablen. *Z. Math. Phys.*, **45** (1900), pp. 23–38.

HOLLINGSWORTH (see HAMMER).

J. T. HORNER and M. ROBINSON, Numerical solution of ordinary differential equations. *Symposium in the aircraft industry, IBM* (1957).

A. S. HOUSEHOLDER [1], *Principles of numerical analysis*, McGraw-Hill, 1953, 274 pages.

A. S. HOUSEHOLDER [2], Truncation error in the partial difference representations. *A.C.M. Meeting*, Houston, 1957.

HUBBARD (see COHEN).

T. E. HULL and W. A. LUXEMBURG, Numerical methods and existence theorems for ordinary differential equations. *Num. Math.*, **2** (1960), pp. 30–41.

T. E. HULL and A. C. R. NEWBERY [1], Error bounds for a family of three points integration procedures. *Journal S.I.A.M.*, **7** (1959), pp. 402–412.

T. E. HULL and A. C. R. NEWBERY [2], Integration procedures which minimize propagated errors. *S.I.A.M. Journal*, **9** (1961), pp. 31–47.

H. D. HUSKEY, On the precision of a certain procedure of numerical integration. *J. Res. N.B.S.*, **42** (1949), pp. 57–62.

A. HUTA [1], Une amélioration de la méthode de Runge-Kutta-Nyström pour la résolution numérique des équations différentielles du premier ordre. *Acta. Fac. Nat. Univ. Comenian Math.*, **1** (1956), pp. 201–224.

A. HUTA [2], Contribution à la formule de sixième ordre dans la méthode de Runge-Kutta-Nyström. *Acta. Fac. Nat. Univ. Comenian. Math.*, **2** (1957), pp. 21–24.

E. L. INCE, *Ordinary Differential equations*. Dover (1926).

R. INZINGER, Zur graphischen Integration linearer Differentialgleichungen. *Ost Ing. Arch.*, **1** (1947), pp. 410–420.

D. V. IONESCU [1], A generalization of a property occurring in the Runge-Kutta method for numerical integration of differential equations. *Acad. R. P. Romine. Bul. Sti. Sect. Sti. Mat. Fiz.*, **6** (1954), pp. 229–241.

D. V. IONESCU [2], Generalization of a property which occurs in the Runge-Kutta method for numerical integration of differential equations. *Acad. R. P. Romine. Bull. Sti. Sect. Sti. Mat. Fiz.*, **8** (1956), pp. 67–100.

J. JACKSON, Note on the numerical integration of $d^2x/dt^2 = f(x, t)$. *Monthly Notice of the Royal Astronomial Soc.*, **84** (1924), pp. 602–606.

L. S. JACOBSEN, On a general method of solving second order ordinary differential equations by phase displacements. *J. Appli. Mech.*, **19** (1952), pp. 543–553.

W. H. JOHNSON, Numerical solution of two simultaneous second order differential equations. *IBM Industrial Computation Seminar* (1950), pp. 71–73.

JOHNSON (see ANDERSON).

A. L. JOUKOV, On the convergence of the solution of a difference equation towards the solution of a differential equation. *Dokl. Akad. Nauk. SSSR*, 117 (1957), pp. 174–176.

G. H. KEITEL, An extension of Milne's three point method. *Journal A.C.M.*, 3 (1956), pp. 212–222.

KELLEY (see SHANE).

G. KJELLBERG, Quelques problèmes traités avec B.A.R.K. *Les machines à calculer et la pensée humaine.* Congrès Paris (1953), pp. 319–328.

A. N. KOLMOGOROV, A few remarks on the problem of numerical integration of differential equations by finite differences methods. *Izv. Akad. Nauk. SSSR*, 104 (1955), pp. 805–809.

KÖNIG (see RUNGE).

Z. KOPAL, *Numerical analysis with emphasis on the application of numerical techniques to problems of infinitesimal calculus in a single variable.* Chapman and Hall, 1955, 556 pages.

A. KORGANOFF, Sur des formules d'intégration numérique des équations différentielles donnant une approximation d'ordre élevé. *Chiffres*, 1 (1958), pp. 171–180.

A. N. KRILOFF, Sur l'intégration numérique approchée des équations différentielles. *Mémorial de l'Artillerie Française*, 6 (1927), pp. 353–423.

O. P. KRAMER, An application of the method of S. A. Kazakov to the numerical integration of certain ordinary differential equations. *Bull. Acad. Sci. URSS, Cl. Sci. Tech.* (1947), pp. 609–644.

F. KRUCKEBERG, Zur numerischen Integration und Fehlerfassung bei Anfangswertaufgaben gewöhnlicher Differentialgleichungen. Thesis, Bonn (1961).

F. KRUCKBERGER and H. UNGER, On the numerical integration of ordinary differential equations and the determination of error bounds. *Symposium, Rome* (1960), pp. 369–379.

Y. H. KU, A method for solving third and higher order non linear differential equations. *J. Franklin Inst.*, 1953, p. 229–244.

K. S. KUNZ, *Numerical analysis*, McGraw-Hill, New York (1957), 381 pages.

J. KUNTZMANN [1], Remarques sur la méthode de Runge-Kutta. *C.R.A.S.*, 242 (1956), pp. 2221–2223.

J. KUNTZMANN [2], Deux formules optimales du type de Runge-Kutta. *Chiffres*, 2 (1959), pp. 21–26.

J. KUNTZMANN [3], Evaluation de l'erreur sur un pas dans les méthodes à pas séparés. *Chiffres*, 2 (1959), pp. 97–102.

J. KUNTZMANN [4], *Méthodes numériques. Interpolation-Dérivation.* Dunod, 1960.

J. KUNTZMANN [5], Neuere Entwickelungen der Methode von Runge und Kutta, *ZAMM*, **41** (1961), pp. 28–31.

J. KUNTZMANN [6], Panorama des méthodes de résolution numérique approchée des problèmes différentiels de conditions initiales. 3° *Centenaire de la Mort de B. Pascal*, Clermont Ferrand (1962).

J. KUNTZMANN [7], Nouvelle méthode pour l'intégration approchée des équations différentielles. *Congrès de Munich* (1962).

J. KUNTZMANN (see F. CESCHINO; see BARD).

W. KUTTA, Beiträge zur näherungsweisen Integration totaler Differentialgleichungen. *Zeitschrifft Math und Physik*, **46** (1901), pp. 435–453.

LAGO (see GUILLOU).

LAMBERT (see CRAWE).

C. N. LANCE, *Numerical methods for high speed computers*. Iliffe and Sons. London, 1960.

C. N. LANCE and M. H. ROGERS, The numerical solution of the differential equations governing the motion of viscous fluid between two rotating discs. *Symposium, Rome* (1960) Birkhauser, Basel, pp. 213–221.

C. LANCZOS, Solution of ordinary differential equations by trigonometric interpolation. *Symposium, Rome* (1960), Birkhauser, Basel, pp. 22–32.

F. LANGER, *Proceedings of a symposium on numerical approximation*. University of Wisconsin Press (1959), 426 pages.

P. J. LAURENT [1], Méthode du type de Runge-Kutta pour des systèmes différentiels de formes particulières. Thesis, Grenoble, 1960.

P. J. LAURENT [2], Méthodes spéciales du type de Runge-Kutta. *Premier Congrès AFCAL*, Gauthier-Villars, 1961, pp. 27–36.

LAURENT (see BARD).

R. J. LEMELIN, Elementary numerical solutions to ordinary differential equation. *Carr-Scott Notes in digital Computers and data processors*. University of Michigan, 1956, p. 3.

H. F. LESH, The method of automatic interruption. 15*th A.C.M. National Conférence*, 1960.

H. LEVY [1], The numerical solution of a certain class of differential equations. *Proc. London Math. Soc.*, **24** (1926), pp. 459–470.

H. LEVY [2], A numerical study of differential equations. *Journal of London Math. Soc.*, **7** (1932), p. 305.

H. LEVY and E. A. BAGGOTT, *Numerical solution of differential equations*. Dover, New York (1950), 238 pages.

A. LINDBERGER, Integration of second order linear differential equations on the type 602 Calculating Punch. *Proceedings Scientific Computation Forum IBM*, 1948, pp. 34–38.

E. Lindelöf, Remarques sur l'intégration numérique des équations différentielles ordinaires. *Acta. Soc. Sci. Fenn.*, A 2 (1938), pp. 3–21.

W. Liniger, Zur Stabilität der numerischen Integrationsmethoden für Differentialgleichungen. Thesis, Lausanne, 1957, 95 pages.

W. Liniger (see C. Blanc).

J. P. Lombardi, Application of the Picard-Lindelöf iteration method to the solution of differential equations. *Univ. Nat. Eva. Peron. Publi. Fac. Ci. Fisico-mat. Serie Tercera Publi. Esp.*, 43 (1953), pp. 117–136.

M. V. Lomonosov, Some remarks on the numerical integration of ordinary differential equations by finite difference methods. *Dokl. Akad. Nauk. SSSR*, 6 (1955), pp. 805–809.

M. Lotkin [1], On the accuracy of Runge-Kutta's method. *MTAC*, 5 (1951), pp. 129–133.

M. Lotkin [2], A new integrating procedure of high accuracy. *J.M.P.*, 31 (1952), pp. 29–34.

M. Lotkin [3], Some problems solvable on computing machines. *Comm. Pure Appl. Math.*, 7 (1954), pp. 149–158.

M. Lotkin [4], The propagation of error in numerical integrations. *Proc. Amer. Math. Soc.*, 5 (1954), pp. 869–887.

M. Lotkin [5], On the improvement of accuracy in integration. *Quart. Appl. Math*, 13 (1955), pp. 47–54.

M. Lotkin [6], The propagation of error in numerical integrations. *Aberdeen Proving Ground Report* 875 (1953), p. 34.

M. Lotkin [7], A note on the midpoint method of integration. *J.A.C.M.*, 3 (1956), pp. 208–211.

M. Lotkin and H. N. Browne, On the accuracy of the adjoint method of differential corrections. *Amer. Math. Monthly*, 63 (1953), pp. 97–105.

W. S. Loud, On the long-run error in the numerical solution of certain differential equations. *J.M.P.*, 28 (1949), pp. 45–49.

P. O. Löwdin, On the numerical integration of ordinary differential equations of the first order. *Quart. Appl. Math.*, 10 (1952), pp. 97–111.

C. M. Lozinskii [1], The interval of existence of a solution of a system of ordinary differential equations. *Dokl. Akad. Nauk. SSSR*, 94 (1954), pp. 17–19.

C. M. Lozinskii [2], Evaluation of the error committed in the approximate solution of a system of differential equations. *Dokl. Akad. Nauk. SSSR*, 92 (1953), pp. 225–228.

C. M. Lozinskii [3], On equations in variations. *Dokl. Akad. Nauk. SSSR*, 93 (1953), pp. 621–624.

C. M. Lozinskii [4], On the approximate solutions of systems of ordinary differential equations. *Dokl. Akad. Nauk. SSSR*, 97 (1954), pp. 29–32.

LUXEMBOURG (see HULL).

M. N. LUZIN, On Chaplygin's method of approximate integration. *Uspehi Math. Nauk.*, **6** (1951), pp. 3–27.

MACNAMEE (see BICKLEY).

D. MACE and L. H. THOMAS, *An extrapolation formula for stepping the calculation of the orbit of an artificial satellite several revolutions ahead at a time.* Service Bureau Corporation and Watson Scientific Computing Laboratory, New York, 162 pages.

K. MAGNUS, Uber ein Verfahren nur Berechnung nichtlinearer Schwingungs-und Regelungs-Systeme. *V.D.I. Forschungsheft*, Nr. 451 (1961), pp. 1–32.

G. J. MAKINSON and A. YOUNG, The stability of solutions of differential and integral equations. *Symposium, Rome* (1960), Birkhauser, Basel, pp. 499–509.

W. F. MANNING and J. MILLMAN, Note on numerical integration. *Phys. review*, **53** (1938), p. 673.

MARCHANT [1], Milne method of step by step integration of ordinary differential equations when starting values are known. *Marchant Methods MM. 216, Mathematics* (1942), pp. 1–10.

MARCHANT [2], Milne method of step by step double integration of second order differential equations in which first derivatives are absent. *Marchant methods MM. 216 A, Mathematics* (1943), pp. 1–6.

MARCHANT [3], Starting values for Milne method integration of ordinary differential equations of first order or of second order when first derivatives are absent. The method of Taylor's series. *Marchant methods MM. 261, Basic Math.*, 1943, pp. 1–4.

MARCHANT [4], Starting values for Milne method integration of ordinary differential equations of the first order. The method of Milne. *Marchant Methods MM. 260, Basic Math.*, 1944, pp. 1–11.

D. W. MARTIN, Runge-Kutta methods for integrating differential equations on high speed digital computers. *Comput. Journ.*, **1** (1958), pp. 118–123.

J. L. MASSERA, Formules pour les différences finies avec application à l'intégration approchée des équations différentielles du premier ordre. *Publi. Inst. Mat. Univ. Mac. Litoral*, **4** (1943), pp. 99–166.

P. MATHIEU [1], Uber das Extrapolationsverfahren von Adams zur angenäherten Lösung gewöhnlicher Differentialgleichungen. *Elemente der Math.*, **5** (1950), pp. 25–31.

P. MATHIEU [2], Uber die Fehlerabschätzung beim Extrapolationsverfahren von Adams (I). Gleichungen erster Ordnung. *ZAMM*, **31** (1951), pp. 356–370.

P. MATHIEU [3], Uber die Fehlerabschätzung beim Extrapolationsverfahren von Adams. *ZAMM*, **32** (1952), p. 235.

P. MATHIEU [4], Uber die Fehlerabschätzung beim Extrapolationsverfahren von

Adams (II). Gleichungen zweiter und höherer Ordnung. *ZAMM*, **33** (1953), pp. 26–41.

N. METROPOLIS and S. ULAM, The Monte Carlo method. *J. Amer. Stat. Assoc.*, **44** (1949), pp. 335–341.

SCH. E. MIKELADZE [1], On the integration of differential equations by difference methods. *Bull. Acad. Sci. URSS, Sci. Math.* (1939), pp. 627–642.

SCH. E. MIKELADZE [2], Generalization of a method of numerical integration of differential equations by means of quadrature formulae. *Trav. Inst. Math. Tbilissi*, **7** (1940), pp. 46–63.

SCH. E. MIKELADZE [3], New formulae for approximate integration, of differential equations. *Dokl. Akad. Nauk. SSSR*, **61** (1948), pp. 789–790.

SCH. E. MIKELADZE [4], Numerical integration. *Usp. Math. Nauk.*, **3** (1948), pp. 3–88.

SCH. E. MIKELADZE [5], Numerical integration of differential equations in the complex plane. *Soobsc. Akad. Nauk. Gruzin SSSR*, **17** (1956), pp. 97–102.

SCH. E. MIKELADZE [6], A general method for numerical solution of differential equations. *Soobsc. Akad. Nauk. Gruzin SSSR*, **22** (1959), pp. 513–518.

MILLMAN (see MANNING).

W. E. MILNE [1], Numerical integration of ordinary differential equations. *Math. Monthly*, **33** (1926), pp. 455–460.

W. E. MILNE [2], A note on the numerical integration of differential equations. *Journal of Res. N.B.S.*, **43** (1949), pp. 537–542.

W. E. MILNE [3], Note on the numerical integration of differential equations. *Amer. Math. Monthly*, **48** (1941), pp. 52–53.

W. E. MILNE [4], Note on the Runge-Kutta Method. *Journal of Res. N.B.S.*, **44** (1950), pp. 549–550.

W. E. MILNE [5], On the numerical integration of certain differential equations. *Amer. Math. Monthly*, **44** (1933), pp. 322–327.

W. E. MILNE [6], *Numerical solution of differential equations.* John Wiley and Sons, New York; Chapman and Hall, London (1953), 275 pages.

MILNE (see BENNETT).

W. E. MILNE and R. R. REYNOLDS [1], Stability of a numerical solution of differential equations. *Journal A.C.M.* **6** (1959), pp. 196–203.

W. E. MILNE and R. R. REYNOLDS [2], Stability of a numerical solution of differential equations. *Journal A.C.M.*, **7** (1960), pp. 46–56.

W. E. MILNE and R. R. REYNOLDS [3], Fifth-order methods for the numerical solution of ordinary differential equations. *Journal ACM*, **9** (1962), pp. 64–70.

H. MINEUR, *Techniques de Calcul numérique.* Librairie Polytechnique Ch. Béranger, Paris (1952), 605 pages.

R. von Mises, Zur numerischen Integration von Differentialgleichungen. *ZAMM*, **10** (1930), pp. 81–92.

Mitchell (see Fox).

A. R. Mitchell and J. W. Craggs, Stability of difference relations in the solution of ordinary differential equations. *MTAC*, **7** (1953), pp. 127–129.

E. Mohr, Uber das Verfahren von Adams zur Integration gewöhnlicher Differentialgleichungen. *Math. Nach.*, **5** (1951), pp. 209–218.

H. Molitz [1], Uber einige Lösungsmethoden für gewöhnliche Differentialgleichungen. *Bericht*, **29** (1946), DEFA-LRSL.

H. Molitz [2], La résolution numérique des équations différentielles d'après la méthode de Runge-Kutta. *Aktennotiz*, **18** (1947), DEFA-LRSL.

H. Morel, Evaluation de l'erreur sur un pas dans la méthode de Runge-Kutta. *C.R.A. S.*, **243** (1956), pp. 1999–2002.

S. Moriguti, Theory of numerical convergence of iterative processes with application to differential equations. *Symposium, Rome* (1960), Birkhauser, Basel, pp. 423–432.

D. Morrison, Optimal mesh size in the numerical integration of an ordinary differential equation. *Journal ACM*, **9** (1962), pp. 98–103.

Morrison (see Stoller).

F. R. Moulton. *Differential equations*. Macmillan, New York, 1930.

I. S. Muhin [1], On the accumulation of errors in the numerical integration of differential equations. *Prikl. Mat. Meh.*, **16** (1952), pp. 753–755.

I. S. Muhin [2], Application of the Markov-Hermite interpolation polynomials to the integration of ordinary differential equations. *Prikl. Math. Mech.*, **16** (1952), pp. 231–238.

Mulligan (see Frick).

F. J. Murray, Planning and error considerations for the numerical solution of a system of differential equations on a sequence calculator. *MTAC*, **4** (1950). pp. 133–144.

Murray (see Brock).

E. Mussel, La méthode des approximations successives de M. Picard et ses applications possibles en balistique. *Mémorial de l'Artillerie Française*, **1** (1922), pp. 217–224.

National Bureau of Standards, *Monte Carlo Method*, U.S. Dep. of Commerce Applied Math Ser., **12** (1951).

National Physical Laboratory, *Modern computing methods*. National Physical Laboratory, Her Majesty's Stationary Office (1957), 129 pages.

G. Neidhofer, Intégration approchée des équations différentielles lorsque la dérivée d'ordre le plus élevé ne figure que dans un terme correctif. *Chiffres*, **2** (1959), pp. 43–53.

NEWBERRY (see HULL).

H. P. NIELSEN, Uber die Restglieder einiger Formeln für die mechanische Quadratur. *Arkiv. für Math. Astr. fysik*, **4** (1908), pp. 1–12.

A. NORDSIECK, On numerical integration of ordinary differential equations. *Math. of Computation*, **16** (1962), pp. 22–49.

T. NORIMATSU and T. DEIDO, Circle test on Runge-Kutta integration method. *15th A.C.M. National Conference* (1960).

A. NOWAKOWSKI, Zur numerischen Integration von Differentialgleichungen mit der Rechenmaschinen. *ZAMM*, **13** (1933), pp. 299–322.

J. B. NUGEYRE, Un procédé mixte (Runge-Kutta, pas liés) d'intégration des systèmes différentiels du type $x'' = X(x, t)$. *Chiffres*, **4** (1961), pp. 55–68.

B. V. NUMEROV [1], A method of extrapolation of perturbations. *Mon. Nat. Roy. Astr.*, **84** (1924), pp. 592–601.

B. V. NUMEROV [2], Note on the numerical integration of $y'' = f(x, y)$. *Astron. Nachricht*, **230** (1927), pp. 359–364.

B. V. NUMEROV [3], The extrapolation method to the numerical integration of linear differential equations of the second order. *Bull. Acad. Sc. URSS*, **1** (1932), pp. 1–8.

E. J. NYSTRÖM, Uber die numerische Integration von Differentialgleichungen. *Acta. Soc. Sc. Fennicae*, **50** (1925), pp. 1–55.

N. OBRESCHKOFF [1], Neue Quadraturformeln. *Abh. Preuss. Akad. Wiss. Math. Nat. Kl.* 4 (1940), pp. 1–20.

N. OBRESCHKOFF [2], Sur les quadratures mécaniques. *Spi. Bulg. Akad., Nauk.*, **65** (1942), pp. 191–289.

OLVER (see CLENSHAW).

H. OULES [1], Une méthode de résolution numérique de l'équation intégrale du type de Volterra. *Chiffres*, **3** (1960), pp. 137–142.

H. OULES [2], Sur l'intégration numérique des équations intégrales du type de Volterra. *Symposium, Rome* (1960), Birkhauser, Basel, pp. 117–121.

A. PAPOULIS, On the accumulation of errors in the numerical solution of differential equations. *J.A.P.*, **23** (1952), p. 173–176.

E. PFLANZ [1], Uber die Bildung finiter Ausdrücke für die Lösung linearer Differentialgleichungen. *ZAMM*, **17** (1937), pp. 296–300.

E. PFLANZ [2], Bemerkungen über die Methode von G. Duffing zur Integration von Differentialgleichungen. *ZAMM*, **28** (1948), pp. 167–172.

H. T. H. PIAGGIO, On the numerical integration of differential equations. *Phil. Mag.*, **37** (1919), pp. 596–600.

E. PICARD [1], Sur l'application des méthodes d'approximations successives à l'étude de certaines équations différentielles ordinaires. *J. Math, Pures, Appl.*, **9** (1893), pp. 217–271.

E. Picard [2], *Traité d'analyse*. Gauthier-Villars, Vol. II, Chap. XI, 3rd ed. 1925.

Posch (see Sauer).

P. Pouzet [1], Méthode d'intégration numérique de l'équation intégrale de Volterra de seconde espèce. *C.R.A.S.*, **250** (1960), pp. 3101–3102.

P. Pouzet [2], Intégration numérique des équations intégro-différentielles du type de Volterra. *C.R.A.S.*, **250** (1960), pp. 3269–3270.

P. Pouzet [3], Méthode d'intégration numérique des équations intégrales et in-tégro-différentielles du type de Volterra de seconde espèce. Formules de Runge-Kutta. *Symposium, Rome* (1960), Birkhauser, Basel, pp. 362–368.

P. Pouzet [4], Etude en vue de leur approximation numérique, des solutions d'é-quations intégrales et intégrodifférentielles du type de Volterra pour des problèmes de conditions initiales. Thesis, Strasbourg (1962).

V. S. Pugachov [1], Problem of exterior ballistics of bombs. *Appl. Math. Mec.*, **6** (1942), pp. 281–286.

V. S. Pugachov [2], On the approximate solution of the general problem of ex-terior ballistics. *Appl. Math. Mec.*, **5** (1941), pp. 263–266.

W. Quade [1], Grundsätzliches zur numerischen Integration von gewöhnlichen Differentialgleichungen. *ZAMM*, **30** (1950), pp. 276–278.

W. Quade [2], Numerische Integration von gewöhnlichen Differentialgleichungen durch Interpolation nach Hermite. *ZAMM*, **37** (1957), pp. 161–169.

W. Quade [3], Uber die Stabilität numerischer Methoden zur Integration gewöhn-licher Differentialgleichungen erster Ordnung. *ZAMM*, **39** (1959), pp. 117–135.

W. Quade [4], Numerische Integration von Differentialgleichungen bei Approxi-mation durch trigonometrische Ausdrücke. *ZAMM*, **31** (1951), pp. 237–238.

P. M. Quinlan, Curve fitting and integral curves for non linear differential equa-tions. A generalised step-function approach. *Technical note no.* **5,** University Coll. Cork (1958), 37 pages.

F. Rabinovitch, Sur une nouvelle méthode d'intégration approchée des équations différentielles du second ordre. *Ann. Radioélec.*, **1** (1945), pp. 134–151.

F. Rabinovitch, The use of subroutines on SEAC for numerical integration of differential equations and for Gaussian quadrature. *Proc. ACM Meeting*, Toronto, 1952.

H. A. Rademacher, On the accumulation of errors in processes of integration on high speed calculating machines. *Proc. First Symp. Ann. Harvard*, **16** (1947), pp. 176–187.

J. R. M. Radok [1], Approximate solution of differential equations by exponential extrapolation. *Polytechnic Inst. of Brooklyn*, N.Y. (1958), pp. 1–15.

J. R. M. Radok [2], Method of functional extrapolation for the numerical integra-tion of differential equations. *Journal S.I.A.M.*, **7** (1959), pp. 425–431.

A. Ralston, Some theoretical and computational matters relating to predictor-corrector methods of numerical integration. *Computer Journal*, **4**, (1961), pp. 64–67.

A. RALSTON and H. S. WILF, *Mathematical methods for Digital Computers*. John Wiley, New York (1960), 293 pages.

RAMO (see GRABBE).

H. L. REED, Numerical integration of oscillatory systems. *Ballistic Research Laboratories Aberdeen Proving Ground* (1955), no. 957, 15 pages.

REEVES (see CALL; see CONTE).

E. REMES, Some approximate formulae for the numerical integration of differential equations. *Phil. Mag.*, **7** (1928), pp. 392–400.

RENO (see M. SHANE).

REYNOLDS (see MILNE).

REZNIKOVKII (see SCIGOLEV).

J. R. RICE, Split Runge Kutta method. *J. Res. N.B.S.*, **64** (1960), pp. 151–170.

C. H. RICHARDSON [1], *An introduction to the calculus of finite differences*. Van Nostrand, New York, 1954, 142 pages.

C. H. RICHARDSON [2], The deferred approach to the limit. *Phil. Trans. Roy. Soc.*, London, **266** *A* (1927), pp. 299–361.

W. RICHTER [1], Estimation de l'erreur commise dans la méthode de W.E. Milne pour l'intégration d'un système de *n* équations différentielles du premier ordre. Thesis, Neuchâtel, 1952, 43 pages.

W. RICHTER [2], Sur l'erreur commise dans la méthode d'intégration de Milne. *C. R. A. S.*, **233** (1951), pp. 1342–1344.

H. H. ROBERTSON, Some new formulae for the numerical integration of ordinary differential equations. *Congrès de l'UNESCO, Paris* (1959), pp. 106–108.

ROBINSON (see HORNER).

ROGERS (see LANCE).

J. B. ROSEN, Stability and bounds for nonlinear systems of difference and differential equations. *J. Math. Anal. and Appl*, **2** (1961), pp. 370–393.

ROZENBERG (see GALLER).

C. RUNGE [1], Uber die numerische Auflösung von Differentialgleichungen. *Math. Annalen*, **46** (1895), pp. 167–178.

C. RUNGE [2], Uber die numerische Auflösung totaler Differentialgleichungen. *Nachr. Gesel. Wiss.*, Göttingen (1905), pp. 252–257.

C. RUNGE and H. KÖNIG, *Vorlesungen über numerisches Rechnen*. Springer (1924), 572 pages.

C. RUNGE and F. WILLERS, Numerische und graphische Integration gewöhnlicher und partieller Differentialgleichungen. *Enzyklopädie der Math. Wiss.*, II *C* **2**, pp. 141–159.

H. RUTISHAUSER [1], Uber die Instabilität von Methoden zur Integration gewöhnlicher Differentialgleichungen. *ZAMP*, 3 (1952), pp. 65–74.

H. RUTISHAUSER [2], Bemerkungen zur numerischen Integration gewöhnlicher Differentialgleichungen *n*-ter Ordnung. *ZAMP*, 6 (1955), pp. 497–498.

H. RUTISHAUSER [3], Bemerkungen zur numerischen Integration differentialer Gleichungen *n*-ter Ordnung. *Num. Math.*, 2 (1960), pp. 263–279.

S. SABLIET, Méthodes mathématiques utilisées pour résoudre numériquement les intégrales et les systèmes d'équations différentielles à l'aide des ordinateurs électroniques. *Rev. gén. Sci. pures appl.*, 46 (1957), pp. 223–227.

L. SACHNOFF, Integration of simultaneous differential equations using multiple stepsizes. *15th ACM National Conference* (1960).

SADLER (see CARTER).

SALTZBERG (see COHN).

M. G. SALVADORI, Extrapolation formulas in linear difference operators. *Proc. of the 1st U.S. Nat. Cong. of Applied Mechanics*, Chicago (1951), pp. 15–18.

M. G. SALVADORI and M. L. BARON, *Numerical methods in engineering*, 2nd ed. Prentice-Hall, Englewood Cliffs, N. J., 1961, 258 pages.

H. E. SALZER [1], Coefficients for numerical integration with central differences. *J.M.P.*, 22 (1943), pp. 115–135.

H. E. SALZER [2], Table of coefficients for double quadrature without difference for integrating second order differential equations. *J.M.P.*, 24 (1945), pp. 135–140.

H. E. SALZER [3], Coefficients for repeated integration with central differences. *J.M.P.*, 28 (1949), pp. 54–61.

H. E. SALZER [4], Formulas for numerical integration of 1st et 2nd order differential equations in the complex plane. *J.M.P.*, 29 (1950), pp. 207–216.

H. E. SALZER [5], Osculatory extrapolation and a new method for the numerical integration of differential equations. *Jour. Franklin Inst.*, 262 (1956), pp. 111–119.

H. E. SALZER [6], Numerical integration of $y'' = \Phi(x, y, y')$ using osculatory interpolation. *Journ. Franklin Inst.*, 263 (1957), pp. 401–409.

H. E. SALZER [7], Trigonometric interpolation and predictor-corrector formulas for numerical integration. *Meeting A.M.S.*, Pasadena (1960).

H. E. SALZER [8], Multiple quadrature with central differences on one line. *Math. of Comp.*, 16 (1962), pp. 244–248.

SAMARSKII (see TIHONOV).

H. von SANDEN, *Praxis der Differentialgleichungen*. Walter de Gruyter, Berlin, 1955, 114 pages.

D. SARAFYAN, A general method for the approximate solution of ordinary differential equations of first order. *67th Meeting A.M.S.*, Washington (1961).

R. SAUER and M. POSCH, Anwendungen des Adamsschen Integrationsverfahrens in der Ballistik. *Ing. Arch.*, **12** (1941), pp. 158–168.

J. B. SCARBOROUGH, *Numerical mathematical analysis.* 2nd ed. Oxford University Press, 1950, 511 pages.

E. SCHECHTER [1], Sur l'erreur du procédé d'intégration numérique de Runge-Kutta. *Acad. R.P. Rom. Fil. Chy. Stud. Cerc. Mat.*, **8** (1957), pp. 115–124.

E. SCHECHTER [2], De la délimitation des erreurs dans certains procédés d'intégration numérique des équations différentielles. *Acad. R.P. Romine*, **9** (1958), pp. 115–124.

E. SCHECHTER [3], De la délimitation des erreurs dans certains procédés d'intégration numérique des équations différentielles. *Acc. R.P. Roman Fil Cluj Stud. Cerc. Math.*, **9** (1958), pp. 343–350.

S. A. SCHELKUNOFF, Solution of linear and slightly nonlinear differential equations. *Quart. Appl. Math.*, **3** (1946), pp. 348–355.

SCHELKUNOFF (see GRAY).

J. SCHRÖDER [1], Neue Fehlerabschätzungen für verschiedene Iterationsverfahren, *ZAMM*, **36** (1956), pp. 168–181.

J. SCHRÖDER [2], Funktionalanalytische Herleitung von Fehlerabschätzungen und ihre praktische Durchführung auf Rechenanlagen. *ZAMM*, **40** (1960).

J. SCHRÖDER [3], Fehlerabschätzungen mit Rechenanlagen bei gewöhnlichen Differentialgleichungen erster Ordnung. *Num. Math.*, **3** (1961), pp. 39–61.

J. SCHRÖDER [4], Verbesserung einer Fehlerabschätzung für gewöhnliche Differentialgleichungen erster Ordnung. *Num. Math.*, **3** (1961), pp. 125–130.

G. SCHULZ [1], Interpolationsverfahren zur numerischen Integration gewöhnlicher Differentialgleichungen. *ZAMM*, **12** (1932), pp. 44–59.

G. SCHULZ [2], Fehlerabschätzungen für den Störmerschen Integrationsverfahren. *ZAMM*, **14** (1934), pp. 224–234.

B. M. SCIGOLEV and P. T. REZNIKOVKII, On the application of the Runge-Kutta method to the numerical solution of the equation of celestial mechanics. *Moscov. Gos. Univ. Soobsc. Astr.*, **92** (1953), pp. 3–22.

SCHWARZSCHILD (see HAUSMANN; see FEINSTEIN).

P. SCONZO, Formule di estrapolazione per l'integrazione numerica delle equazioni differenziali ordinarie. *Boll. Un. Math. Ital.*, **3** (1954), pp. 391–399.

G. SEEGMULLER, Error analysis for the numerical solution of certain differential equations in gasdynamics, *Symposium, Rome* (1960), Birkhauser, Basel, pp. 312–319.

F. SERVAIS, Sur l'estimation des erreurs dans l'intégration numérique des équations différentielles linéaires du second ordre. *Ann. Soc. Sci. Bruxelles*, **70** (1956), p. 5–8.

E. J. SHANE, J. L. KELLEY, and F. V. RENO, *Exterior Ballistics*. Univ. Denver Press (1953), 834 pages.

J. W. SHELDON, B. ZONDEK, and M. FRIEDMAN, On the time-step to be used for the computation of orbits by numerical integration. *MTAC*, **11** (1957), pp. 181–189.

SHELDON (see ZONDEK).

G. L. SHUE, Simplified numerical integration. A successive approximation difference-table method for the solution of differential equations. *Aircraft Engrg.*, **26** (1954), pp. 89–94.

M. SIMOKAWA, Nomographic solutions of ordinary differential equations of the first and second order. *Mem. Fac. Techn. Kanazawa Univ.*, 1953, pp. 1–13.

Y. SIRET, Principe des méthodes de Runge-Kutta à pas liés. Thesis, Grenoble (1962).

M. A. SKALKINA, On the preservation of asymptotic stability in the passage from the differential equations to the corresponding difference equations. *Dokl. Akad. Nauk. SSSR*, **104** (1955), pp. 505–508.

A. SLIBAR, Graphic-numerical integration of a system of simultaneous ordinary non linear differential equations of the second order. *Ost. Ing. Arch.*, **10** (1956), pp. 288–291.

S. N. SLUGIN, A modification of the abstract analogue to Chaplygin's method. *Dokl. Akad. Nauk. SSSR*, **120** (1958), pp. 256–259.

M. A. SNEIDER, Applicatione sui calcolatori elettronici 650 IBM (1620. IBM). *Symposium, Rome* (1960), Birkhauser, Basel, pp. 351–354.

SOMERVILLE (see BAILEY).

T. H. SOUTHARD and E. C. YOWELL, An alternative "predictor-corrector" process. *MTAC*, **6** (1952), pp. 253–254.

J. F. STEFFENSEN, On numerical integration of differential equations. *Skand. Aktuar. Tid.*, **5** (1922), pp. 20–36.

T. E. STERNE, The accuracy of numerical solutions of ordinary differential equations. *MTAC*, **7** (1953), pp. 159–164.

K. STOHLER, Eine Vereinfachung bei der numerischen Integration gewöhnlicher Differentialgleichungen. *ZAMM*, **23** (1943), pp. 120–122.

L. STOLLER and D. MORRISON, A method for the numerical integration of ordinary differential equations. *MTAC*, **12** (1958), pp. 269–272.

C. STÖRMER [1], Sur les trajectories des corpuscules électrisés. *Arch. Sci. Phys. Nat. Geneve*, **24** (1907), pp. 5–18, 113–158, 211–247.

C. STÖRMER [2], Méthode d'intégration numérique des équations différentielles ordinaires. *Congrès International des Mathématiciens*. Strasbourg (1921), pp. 243–257.

M. R. SURA-BURA, Estimation of errors in the numerical integration of ordinary differential equations. *Prikl. Mat. Mekh.*, **16** (1952), pp. 575–588.

J. TAMARKINE, Sur la méthode de Störmer pour l'intégration approchée des équations différentielles ordinaires. *M.Z.*, **16** (1923), pp. 214–219.

L. H. THOMAS (see D. MACE).

A. N. TIHONOV and A. A. SAMARSKII, On the finite difference schemes for equations with discontinuous coefficients. *Dokl. Akad. Nauk. SSSR*, **108** (1956), pp. 393–396.

J. TODD [1], Solution of differential equations by recurrence relations. *MTAC*, **4** (1950), pp. 39–44.

J. TODD [2], Experiments in the solution of differential equations by Monte Carlo methods. *J. Wash. Acad. Sci.*, **44** (1954), pp. 377–381.

S. S. TOKTALAEVA, Formulae with ordinates for the approximate integration of ordinary first order differential equations. *Vichi. Math.*, **5** (1959), pp. 3–57.

W. TOLLMIEN [1], Uber die Fehlerabschätzung beim Adamsschen Verfahren zur Integration gewöhnlicher Differentialgleichungen. *ZAMM*, **18** (1938), pp. 83–90.

W. TOLLMIEN [2], Bemerkung zur Fehlerabschätzung beim Adamsschen Interpolationsverfahren. *ZAMM*, **33** (1953), pp. 151–155.

W. TORNIG, Zur Konvergenz der Differenzenschemaverfahren. *ZAMM*, **40** (1960), pp. 423–424.

W. TORNIG (see ANSORGE).

TSUSHIMA (see URABE).

F. J. TURTON [1], The errors in the numerical solution of differential equations. *Phil. Mag.*, **28** (1939), pp. 359–363.

F. J. TURTON [2], Two notes on the numerical solution of differential equations. *Phil. Mag.*, **28** (1939), pp. 381–384.

ULAM (see METROPOLIS).

W. UHLMANN [1], Fehlerabschätzungen bei Anfangswertaufgaben gewöhnlicher Differentialgleichungssysteme. I. Ordung. *ZAMM*, **37** (1957), pp. 88–99.

W. UHLMANN [2], Fehlerabschätzungen bei Anfangswertaufgaben 1$^{er}$ gewöhnlichen Differentialgleichungen höherer Ordnung. *ZAMM*, **37** (1957), pp. 99–111.

H. UNGER, Zur numerischen Behandlung von Anfangswertproblemen bei gewöhnlichen linearen Differentialgleichungen 2$^{ter}$ Ordnung. *ZAMM*, **25-27** (1947), pp. 135–136.

UNGER (see KRUCKBERGER).

M. URABE, Theory of errors in numerical integration of ordinary differential equations. *J. Sci. Hirosh. Univ.*, A **125** (1961), pp. 3–62.

M. URABE and T. TSUSHIMA, On numerical integration of ordinary differential equations. *J. Sc. Hirosh. Univ. Ser. A*, **17** (1953), pp. 193–219.

M. URABE and H. YANAGIHARA, On numerical integration of the differential equation $y^{(n)} = f(x, y)$. *J. Sc. Hirosh. Univ. Ser. A*, **18** (1954), pp. 55–76.

M. Valiron and H. Dodier, Calcul des trajectories curvilignes par arcs et des altérations d'après les méthodes américaines. *Mémorial de l'Artillerie Française*, **6** (1927), pp. 425–525.

O. Vejvoda [1], Evaluation d'erreur de la formule de Runge-Kutta. *Apl. Mat.*, **2** (1957), pp. 1–23.

O. Vejvoda [2], Die Fehlerabschätzung der Runge-Kutta Formel. *Nachrichten der Oster. Math. Gesel.*, **47/48** (1957) p. 86.

L. Vietoris [1], Der Richtungsfehler einer durch das Adamssche Interpolationsverfahren gewonnenen Näherungslösung einer Gleichung $y' = f(x, y)$. *Oster. Akad. Wiss. Math. Nat. Kl.*, S.B., IIa, **162** (1953), pp. 157–167.

L. Vietoris [2], Der Richtungsfehler einer durch das Adamssche Interpolationsverfahren gewonnenen Näherungslösung eines Systems von Gleichungen $y'_k = f_k(x, y_1, y_2, \dots, y_m)$. *Oster. Akad. Wiss. Math. Nat. Kl.*, S.B. IIa, **162** (1953), pp. 293–299.

I. O. Vlasov and I. A. Carnyi, On a method of numerical integration of ordinary differential equations. *Akad. Nauk. SSSR. Inzenernyi Sbornik*, **8** (1950), pp. 181–186.

R. de Vogelaere [1], On a new method to solve in the large some nonlinear differential equations using high speed digital computers. *Nachrichtentech. Fachber.*, **4** (1956), pp. 184–185.

R. de Vogelaere [2], A method for the numerical integration of differential equations of second order without explicit first derivatives. *Journal Res. N.B.S.*, **54** (1955), pp. 119–125.

R. de Vogelaere [3], On a paper of Gaunt concerned with the start of numerical solutions of differential equations. *ZAMM*, **8** (1957), pp. 151–156.

Y. U. Vorobev, A method of numerical integration of a class of equations of mathematical physics and its application to problems of electron optics. *Akad. SSSR Zurnal Tech. Fiz.*, **22** (1952), pp. 1166–1173.

L. M. Vorobev, Application of Chaplygin's approximate integration method to a certain class of ordinary nonlinear second order differential equations. *Uspehi Math. Nauk.* (N.S.), **11** (1956), pp. 181–185.

E. V. Voronovskaya, On a modification of Chaplygin's method for first order differential equations. *Prikl. Mat. Meh.*, **19** (1955), pp. 121–126.

Voss (see Anderson).

D. D. Wall, Note on predictor-corrector formulas. *MTAC*, **10** (1956), p. 167.

J. Warga [1], On a class of iterative procedures for solving normal systems of ordinary differential equations. *J.M.P.*, **31** (1953), p. 223–243.

J. Warga [2], A note on the paper "On a class of iterative procedures for solving normal systems of ordinary differential equations." *J.M.P.*, **32** (1954), p. 315.

J. Weissinger [1], Eine Fehlerabschätzung für die Verfahren von Adams und Störmer. *ZAMM*, **32** (1952), pp. 62–67.

J. WEISSINGER [2], Numerische Integration impliziter Differentialgleichungen. *ZAMM*, **33** (1953), pp. 63–65.

J. WEISSINGER [3], Eine verschärfte Fehlerabschätzung zum Extrapolationsverfahren von Adams. *ZAMM*, **30** (1950), pp. 356–363.

D. J. WHEELER, Note on Runge-Kutta method of integrating ordinary differential equations. *Computer Journal*, **2** (1959), p. 23.

H. S. WILF [1], An open formula for the numerical integration of first order differential equations. *MTAC*, **11** (1957), pp. 201–203.

H. S. WILF [2], An open formula for the numerical integration of first order differential equations II. *MTAC*, **12** (1958), pp. 55–58.

H. S. WILF [3], A necessary and sufficient condition for locally stable numerical integration. *AMS. Notices*, 1959, p. 187 (Résumé).

H. S. WILF [4], A stability criterion for numerical integration. *Journal ACM*, **6** (1959), pp. 363–366.

H. S. WILF [5], Maximally stable numerical integration. *Journal SIAM*, **8** (1960), pp. 537–540.

WILF (see RALSTON).

M. V. WILKES [1], A method of solving second order simultaneous linear differential equations using the Mallock machine. *Proc. Camb. Phil. Soc.*, **36** (1940), pp. 204–208.

M. V. WILKES [2], A note on the use of automatic adjustment of strip width in quadrature. *Nachrichtentech. Fachber. Dtsch.* **4** (1956), pp. 182–183.

WILLERS (see RUNGE).

K. P. WILLIAMS, The numerical integration of $x''(t) = G(x)$. *MTAC*, **8** (1954), pp. 121–122.

E. M. WILSON, A note on the numerical integration of differential equations. *Quart. J. Mech. Appl. Math.*, **2** (1949), pp. 208–211.

E. A. WINN, A matrix method for the numerical solution of linear differential equations with variable coefficients. *J. Roy. Aero. Soc.*, **61** (1957), pp. 133–134.

H. S. WOLANSKI, Numerical solution of second order non linear simultaneous differential equations. *Proc. Comput. Seminar IBM* (1951), pp. 98–104.

J. R. WOMERSLEY, Scientific computing in Great Britain. *MTAC*, **15** (1946), pp. 110–117.

WOOLRIDGE (see GRABBE).

YANAGIHARA (see URABE).

R. L. YOUNG, Report on experiments in approximating the solution of a differential equation. *Journal A.C.M.*, **3** (1956), pp. 26–28.

YOWELL (see SOUTHARD).

K. V. ZADIRAKA [1], Solution by Chaplygin's method of second order linear differential equations with variable coefficients. *Dopod. Akad. Nauk. Ukrain.* (1951), pp. 163–170.

K. V. ZADIRAKA [2], The approximate integration by Chaplygin's method of second order linear differential equations with variable coefficients. *Ukrain. Math. Zurn.*, **4** (1952), pp. 299–311.

T. ZECH, Anschauliches zur Picarditeration bei Differentialgleichungen. *ZAMM*, **17** (1937), pp. 341–352.

P. W. ZETTLER-SEIDEL, Improved Adams method of numerical integration of differential equation. *International Congress of Math.*, Cambridge, Mass., (1950), p. 666.

A. I. ZHUKOV, On the convergence of the solution of a difference equation towards the solution of a differential equation. *Dokl. Akad. Nauk. SSSR*, **117** (1957), pp. 174–176.

A. ZILLER, Méthodes de différentiation et d'intégration numériques; applications. *Publi. scient. et Techn. Min. de l'Air. Note Technique 50* (1955), 150 pages.

ZONDEK (see SHELDON).

B. ZONDEK and J. W. SHELDON, On the error propagation in Adam's extrapolation method. *MTAC*, **13** (1959), pp. 52–55.

R. ZURMÜHL [1], Zur numerischen Integration gewöhnlicher Differentialgleichungen zweiter und höherer Ordnung. *ZAMM*, **20** (1940), pp. 104–116.

R. ZURMÜHL [2], Runge-Kutta Verfahren zur numerischen Integration von Differentialgleichungen *n*-ter Ordnung. *ZAMM*, **28** (1948), pp. 173–182.

R. ZURMÜHL [3], Runge-Kutta Verfahren unter Verwendung höherer Ableitungen, *ZAMM*, **32** (1952), pp. 153–154.

R. ZURMÜHL (see COLLATZ).

# INDEX